California

Discovery EDUCATION | SCIENCE TECHBOOK

The Living Earth

To obtain permission(s) or for inquiries, submit a request to:
Discovery Education, Inc.
4350 Congress Street, Suite 700
Charlotte, NC 28209
800-323-9084
Education_Info@DiscoveryEd.com

ISBN 13: 978-1-68220-649-2

Printed in the United States of America.

3 4 5 6 7 8 9 10 WEB 23 22 21 20 19   B

Acknowledgments
Acknowledgment is given to photographers, artists, and agents for permission to feature their copyrighted material.

Cover and inside cover art: paffy / Shutterstock.com

Table of Contents

Dear Student,

You are about to experience science like you never have before! In this class, you'll be using California Science Techbook™—a comprehensive science program developed by the educators and designers at Discovery Education. Science Techbook is full of Explorations, videos, Hands-On Activities, digital tools, reading passages, animations, and more. These resources will help you learn scientific concepts and procedures, and apply them to the world around you. California Science Techbook allows you to work at your own pace and investigate questions you may have related to science. You'll even be able to monitor your progress in real time using the Student Learning Dashboard.

The Student Edition accompanies the digital Science Techbook. You have access to Science Techbook's core text—the key ideas and details about each scientific concept—even when you do not have access to a device or the Internet. You can use this resource to explore important ideas, make connections to the digital content, and develop your own scientific understanding.

This Student Edition is organized by concept and includes the following:

- OVERVIEW: What's it all about? Lesson Questions, Lesson Objectives, and key vocabulary will help you prepare for each science concept.

- ENGAGE: What do you already know about the topic? Follow a link to uncover your prior knowledge about each concept.

- EXPLORE: What are the main ideas in the concept? The Explore pages include core text and images to help you answer each of the concept's Lesson Questions. Use evidence to write a scientific explanation and answer questions to check for understanding.

- STEM IN ACTION: How is science used in the real world and in STEM careers? Read more in this section to find out how the knowledge you're building applies to real-world situations—both today and in the future.

Throughout this Student Edition, you'll find QR codes that take you to the corresponding online section of Science Techbook for that concept. To use the QR codes, you will need a QR reader. Readers are available for almost any device. The reader will scan the code and direct you to the correct page or resource in Science Techbook.

Enjoy this deep dive into the exciting world of science!

Sincerely,

The Discovery Education Science Team

Dear Parent/Guardian,

This year, your student will be using California Science Techbook™, a comprehensive science program developed by the educators and designers at Discovery Education. Science Techbook is an innovative program that offers engaging, real-world problems to help your student master key scientific concepts and procedures. In class, students experience dynamic content, Explorations, videos, digital tools, and game-like activities that inspire and motivate scientific learning and curiosity.

This Student Edition allows students to explore the core Techbook content when the Internet is not available. Students are encouraged to use this resource to read about key ideas, seek connections, think about scientific questions, and develop their own scientific understanding.

This Student Edition is organized by concept and includes the following:

- OVERVIEW: Students preview a concept's Lesson Questions, Lesson Objectives, and key vocabulary to help them make connections to the science content.

- ENGAGE: Students answer questions to activate their prior knowledge of a concept's essential ideas, and begin making connections to the Explain Question.

- EXPLORE: Students deepen their understanding of the concept by exploring the core text related to each Lesson Question. Online, students have access to additional resources, Hands-On Activities, and interactives. They will also complete scientific explanations and answer questions to check for understanding.

- STEM IN ACTION: Students connect the skills and knowledge they are building in each concept with real-world applications. Online, they can explore related videos and resources, and complete additional activities.

Within this resource, you'll find QR codes that take you and your student to a corresponding section of Science Techbook. Once in Techbook, students will have access to the Core Interactive Text of each concept, as well as thousands of resources and activities that build deep conceptual scientific understanding. Additionally, tools and features such as the Interactive Glossary and text-to-speech functionality allow Science Techbook to target learning for students of a variety of abilities. To use the QR codes, you'll need a QR reader. Readers are available for phones, tablets, laptops, desktops, and virtually any device in between.

We encourage you to support your student in using California Science Techbook. Together, may you and your student enjoy a fantastic year of science!

Sincerely,

The Discovery Education Science Team

Earth's Spheres

LESSON OVERVIEW

Lesson Question

■ What are the major components of the Earth system?

Lesson Objective

By the end of the lesson, you should be able to:

■ understand the major components of Earth as a system.

Key Vocabulary

Which terms do you already know?

☐ asthenosphere
☐ atmosphere
☐ biosphere
☐ continental crust
☐ core
☐ crust
☐ cryosphere
☐ freshwater
☐ gabbro
☐ geosphere
☐ greenhouse gas
☐ groundwater
☐ glacier
☐ hydrosphere
☐ lithosphere
☐ magnetic field
☐ mantle
☐ oceanic crust
☐ solar wind

dlc.com/ca10008s

Exploring Earth's Spheres

dlc.com/ca10009s

Modern homes come equipped with many systems—heating, cooling, electrical, water, and sewer. Each system contributes to the comfort, health, and convenience of a home's occupants. What happens when different parts of a system are impacted by severe weather conditions?

SYSTEM DISRUPTION

Home systems interact in a kitchen, where electricity, gas, and water systems all contribute to convenient meal preparation and dishwashing. This kitchen was flooded by Hurricane Sandy. What happens when home systems are disrupted by Earth's systems?

EXPLAIN QUESTION

How do Earth's spheres interact as systems, both within each sphere and among other spheres?

What Are the Major Components of the Earth System?

Many Spheres

Earth can be divided into various spheres that describe the planet's land, water, air, and life. The **geosphere** describes the solid exterior and interior of the planet. The **hydrosphere** consists of all the water on the planet's surface, including the oceans, lakes, ice, and rivers, as well as the moisture in the air. The **atmosphere** consists of the "ocean" of air that surrounds the surface of the planet. A fourth sphere, the **biosphere**, consists of all life on Earth.

The spheres of Earth are all interdependent. This means that they support one another. Energy and mass move among the various spheres in an attempt to establish and maintain states of equilibrium. The carbon cycle is an example of the interaction between the spheres. The biosphere is heavily dependent on the presence of carbon to support and sustain life. At the same time, much of the geosphere is composed of carbonate rocks and minerals that accumulate in the oceans (hydrosphere). Other cycles, which operate similar to the carbon cycle, include the water cycle, the nitrogen cycle, and the phosphate cycle. Energy is distributed around Earth continuously when heat is transferred between the atmosphere, the hydrosphere, the geosphere, and the biosphere under the influence of the global circulation system.

SPHERES WITHIN SPHERES

Earth has layers, from its core to its outer atmosphere. How do these layers overlap and interact?

The Geosphere

The geosphere consists of Earth's **core**, **mantle**, and **crust**. The core is divided into two sections. The solid inner core has a radius of 1,200 km. The liquid outer core, which is 2,250 km thick, surrounds the inner core. At 2,900 km, the mantle is the thickest region of the planet. The mantle is divided into three sections—the mesosphere, the **asthenosphere**, and the rigid, upper mantle directly beneath the crust. The upper mantle and the crust together are referred to as the **lithosphere**.

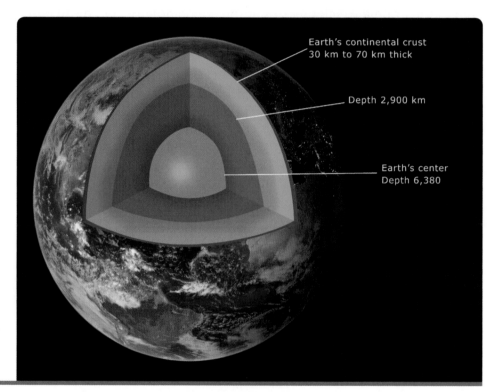

Earth's continental crust
30 km to 70 km thick

Depth 2,900 km

Earth's center
Depth 6,380

GEOSPHERE

The geosphere describes the rocks and minerals that make up Earth's core, mantle, and crust. How does the geosphere change at different depths?

The solid exterior of the planet is called the *crust*. It is composed of rocks and minerals dominated by eight elements: oxygen (46.6 percent), silicon (27.72 percent), aluminum (8.13 percent), iron (5.00 percent), calcium (3.63 percent), sodium (2.83 percent), potassium (2.70 percent), and magnesium (2.09 percent). Earth's crust is classified as **oceanic crust** or **continental crust** based on each one's composition of rocks and minerals. The composition of oceanic crust is primarily iron and magnesium silicate minerals. It is 4–6 km thick but very dense. Conversely, continental crust is 30–70 km thick and composed primarily of aluminum silicate minerals. Because oceanic crust is denser, it sinks beneath continental crust at locations where they come together. The crust and the uppermost part of the mantle form the lithosphere, which moves across the planet's surface in large sections called plates.

Geothermal Gradient

The temperature of Earth's interior is not constant. The geothermal gradient describes how temperature increases with depth beneath Earth's surface. This steady increase is caused by the release of residual heat from when the planet formed. For every kilometer in Earth's crustal interior, the temperature increases by 25°C. Temperatures in Earth's mantle and core level off. The core is thought to be about 5,000°C.

With this information, scientists performed a number of laboratory experiments to determine the temperature and pressure conditions necessary to produce the rock fragments brought to Earth's surface during volcanic eruptions. These experiments suggested that Earth's interior is an environment of intense pressure and temperature. They also discovered that the chemical composition of the rock on the outer surface of Earth differs significantly from the composition of materials found deep within the planet.

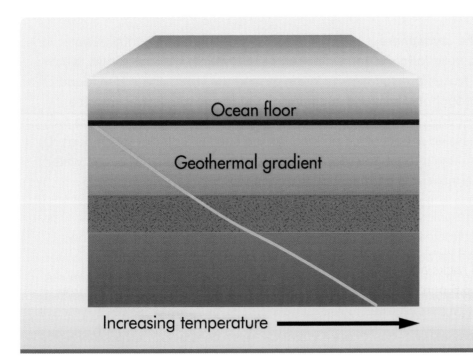

THE GEOTHERMAL GRADIENT

As depth increases beneath Earth's surface, temperature increases over a predictable gradient until it reaches a certain level. How would the thermal gradient affect miners in deep mines?

The Hydrosphere

Seventy percent of the planet's surface is covered with water. The hydrosphere includes all water in the Earth system. Ninety-seven percent of water on Earth is found in the oceans. The remaining liquid water is found in lakes, rivers, and **groundwater**. Water also exists in the form of ice on Earth's surface and in the atmosphere.

Water is classified by its percentage of dissolved solids. **Freshwater** is characterized by low concentrations of dissolved solids. Freshwater is typically less than 0.5 parts per thousand (ppt). Saltwater is classified by higher concentrations of dissolved solids. Brackish water contains 0.5–30 ppt dissolved solids. Saline water, commonly called saltwater, contains 30–50 ppt dissolved solids. Brine contains more than 50 ppt dissolved solids. The ocean has an average salinity of 35 ppt. The salinity of water changes constantly as it passes through different stages of the hydrologic, or water, cycle.

The Cryosphere

The **cryosphere** is the part of the hydrosphere that contains water in its solid form. Frozen water comes in a variety of forms. Snow, which is frozen precipitation, is found around the world. Ice is also found throughout the world in the form of **glaciers**, ice shelves, sea ice, icebergs, and permafrost. These features vary in scale. Glaciers are massive sheets of ice on land. An ice shelf is a glacier that moves off land into a body of water. Sea ice forms from frozen ocean water. Permafrost is permanently frozen land.

The poles contain most of the frozen water on Earth. The Arctic Ocean is situated over the North Pole. It is covered by sea ice that grows and recedes with the seasons. Permafrost, glaciers, and snow cover the northern regions of the North American and Eurasian continents, along with Greenland and Iceland. Antarctica lies over the South Pole. Glaciers cover the continent and extend as sea ice into the surrounding seas and oceans. Frozen water can also be found in regions of high elevation, such as Mount Kilimanjaro in Africa.

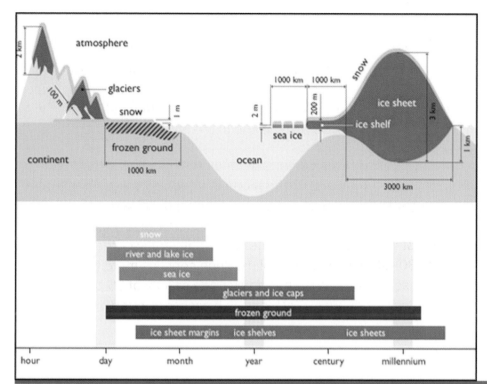

CRYOSPHERE

The cryosphere is part of the hydrosphere. Why is ice in the cryosphere found in so many regions around the world on so many different timescales?

Saltwater

Saltwater accounts for 97 percent of water on the planet. Most of this water is found in the ocean. Almost all elements in the periodic table can be found in ocean water. However, the elements are not found at the same concentration. This concentration is determined by a balance between the supply of ions (charged particles) from land and the removal of ions from the ocean. Organisms, sediment, and hydrothermal vent systems add to or remove elements from the ocean. The six most abundant ions in ocean water are called *major constituents*. They are the chloride ion (Cl^-), sodium ion (Na^+), sulfate ion (SO_4^{2-}), magnesium ion (Mg^{2+}), calcium ion (Ca^{2+}), and potassium ion (K^+).

The minor constituents in the ocean are dissolved salts that range in concentration from 1 to 100 parts per million. As the following table shows, these major and minor constituents account for more than 99 percent of all dissolved ions in the ocean. The concentration of the minor constituents is low because these ions are removed from the ocean more quickly than they are supplied.

Chemical Ion	Percent of Salinity Dissolved Solids in Ocean Water
Chloride	55.03
Sodium	30.59
Sulfate	7.68
Magnesium	3.68
Calcium	1.18
Potassium	1.11
Carbon (in the form of bicarbonate)	0.41
Bromide	0.19
Borate	0.08
Strontium	0.04
Fluoride	0.003

The remaining ions can be found in concentrations lower than 1 part per million. The number of trace ions is too numerous to list but includes nitrate (NO_3^-), lithium (Li^+), rubidium (Rb^+), phosphate (PO_4^{3-}), and iodine (I^-), Concentrations of trace ions are low in ocean water because the ions are removed from solution by chemical reactions and biological processes.

Freshwater

The remaining 3 percent of water on the planet's surface is fresh. However, about 69 percent of freshwater is trapped in glaciers and ice sheets in Antarctica and Greenland. Around 30 percent is groundwater. Approximately 1 percent of Earth's freshwater is surface water found in streams, lakes, ponds, ice, and snow.

Streams and rivers begin at headwaters and flow to lower elevations, ending at the mouth. Small rivers and streams may join to become larger rivers. A stream or river often empties into a lake, bay, sea, or ocean. The water in a river or stream may change as it flows from the headwater to the mouth. Temperature may increase, oxygen levels may decrease, and clarity may be reduced.

Ponds and lakes range in size from a few square meters to thousands of square kilometers. The characteristics of the water vary depending on the depth and shape of the water body.

Groundwater is water found in the spaces between sediments and rock underground. The water begins as rain, snow, or ice that permeates the soil and seeps into the permeable rock. The water collects in a saturated zone beneath a boundary called the *water table*. An aquifer is the rock unit through which the groundwater flows. An aquifer is typically gravel, sand, sandstone, or fractured or permeable rock.

The Atmosphere

The atmosphere consists of a gaseous mixture of air that surrounds the surface of the planet. Volcanoes released many of the gases that make up the atmosphere. Nitrogen dominates the mixture because it does not react with minerals and rocks at Earth's surface. The concentration of nitrogen has increased slowly through time. It now makes up 78 percent of all gases in the atmosphere. The next most abundant gas in the atmosphere is oxygen, which has stabilized at 21 percent. The oxygen in the atmosphere is a product of photosynthetic organisms.

The remaining gases are found in the atmosphere in trace amounts. Several of the trace gases have a tremendous impact on the planet. Carbon dioxide, water vapor, methane, sulfur dioxide, ozone, and nitrogen oxides are **greenhouse gases**. Greenhouse gases absorb long-wavelength radiation from Earth's surface that is heated by the sun. The higher the concentration of greenhouse gases in the atmosphere, the more heat is kept close to the planet's surface. If the atmosphere did not absorb this long-wavelength radiation, the planet would still heat up during the day. However, the heat would be lost to the upper atmosphere at night. The rapid transition in temperature during this 24-hour cycle would affect the ability of life to survive on the planet's surface.

Atmospheric Gases

The following table lists the concentrations of the gases that make up Earth's atmosphere:

Gas	Chemical Composition	Concentration (%)
Nitrogen	N_2	78.08
Oxygen	O_2	20.95
Water vapor	H_2O	Less than 0.4
Argon	Ar	0.93
Carbon dioxide	CO_2	0.038
Neon	Ne	0.00182
Ozone	O_3	0.0008
Helium	He	0.00052
Methane	CH_4	0.00017
Krypton	Kr	0.00011
Nitrogen oxides	NO, NO_2	0.00003
Sulfur dioxide	SO_2	Less than 0.00003

The Biosphere

The biosphere consists of those parts of the planet where life exists. It forms a narrow layer ranging from approximately 11 km beneath the ocean's surface to 9 km in the air, from the equator to the polar ice caps. Thus, the biosphere consists of parts of the geosphere, hydrosphere, and atmosphere.

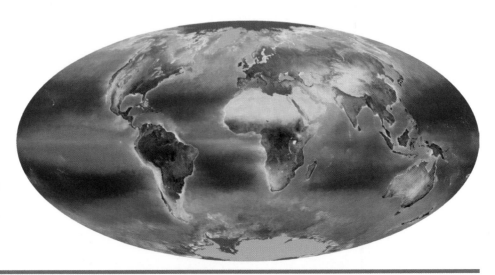

LIFE ON EARTH

This image depicts the relative amounts of life on Earth. Greens represent land life; blues represent marine life. What factors account for the variable abundance of life?

Why does life exist where it does on Earth? The most important factors are the existence of liquid water and the flow of energy. Earth's atmosphere allows enough solar radiation to reach the planet's surface to maintain an average global temperature of approximately 15°C. With less solar radiation, Earth could become too cold for life (as Mars has); with more solar radiation, the planet could become too hot (like Venus).

In terms of energy, Earth is an open system—the planet is continually gaining and losing energy. In terms of matter, however, Earth is considered a closed system. While organisms live, they absorb nutrients from their environments; when they die and decompose, the matter that makes up their bodies returns to the environment. In this way, the biosphere is continually replenished to make way for new life. A huge diversity of organisms, linked by food webs and other relationships, are involved in this process. The maintenance of a healthy biosphere, therefore, requires the careful stewardship of high levels of biological diversity.

Earth's Magnetic Field

Earth is exposed to material ejected from the sun's surface. This material moves like wind through space. The interaction between charged particles in the **solar wind** and Earth's **magnetic field** produces a barrier of space around the planet that deflects most of the charged particles ejected from the sun. This barrier is called the magnetosphere. The bow shock describes the frontal blast of the ions as they approach Earth. The charged particles are heated, which slows them as they deflect around Earth. As the ions pass the planet, the *magnetosphere* expands to 1,000 times Earth's radius, producing the magnetotail.

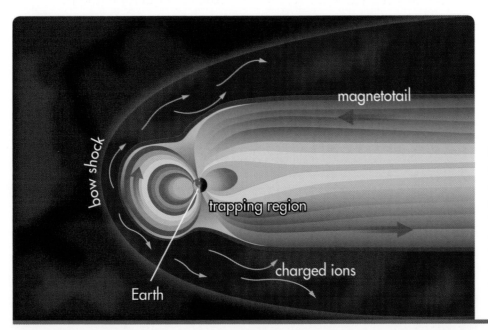

magnetotail

bow shock

trapping region

Earth

charged ions

EARTH'S MAGNETOSPHERE

Charged ions ride the solar wind to Earth, where they are heated and deflected around the planet to create the magnetosphere. How does the magnetosphere protect life on Earth?

Forming the Magnetic Field

Earth behaves like a dipole magnet, which is similar to a common bar magnet. Scientists think the planet's magnetic field is produced by Earth's core. The molten iron and nickel in the core circulates as the planet rotates. This circulation produces a magnetic field with poles near the planet's North and South Poles. Magnetic field lines can help us visualize this magnetic field. They indicate the strength and direction of the magnetic field.

Currently, the magnetic field lines exit the magnetic South Pole and travel around the planet, where they enter at the magnetic North Pole. Because the magnetic field lines enter at the magnetic North Pole, the arrow on a compass points to the north.

EARTH'S MAGNETIC FIELD

In this diagram of Earth's magnetic field, the magnetic field lines exit at the South Pole and enter at the North Pole. Why are the magnetic poles slightly different from Earth's geographic poles?

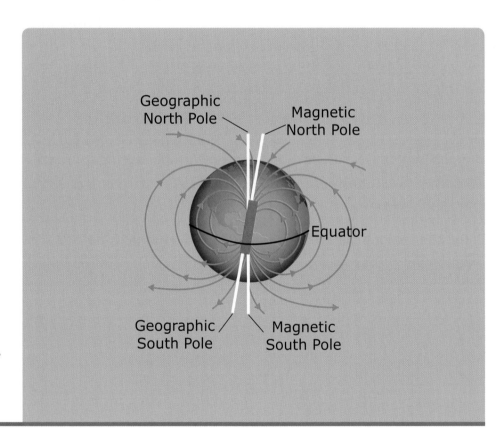

Solar Wind

The solar wind consists of charged particles (ions) ejected from the sun's upper atmosphere. These particles flow away from the sun at about 400 km/s (but can vary in speed from 300 to 800 km/s). Earth's magnetic field deflects the ions around the planet like water deflected around the bow of a ship. The shape and size of the magnetic field is defined by the strength and speed of the solar wind. The magnetic field protects the planet from the high energy–charged particles carried in the solar wind. This protection allowed life on Earth to develop and survive. A small amount of the charged particles in the solar wind become trapped in Earth's magnetic field. These particles form the Van Allen belt 6,400 km above Earth's surface.

Consider the Explain Question

How do Earth's spheres interact as systems, both within each sphere and with other spheres?

Your answer to this question will become the claim for your scientific explanation.

dlc.com/ca10010s

Check Your Understanding

Go online to check your understanding of this concept's key ideas.

dlc.com/ca10011s

STEM in Action

Applying Earth's Spheres

Periodically, Earth's magnetic field flips. The current magnetic field is characterized by magnetic field lines exiting the magnetic South Pole and entering at the magnetic North Pole. This is described as a normal episode, or Normal. At other times in Earth's past, the magnetic field lines exited at the magnetic North Pole and entered at the magnetic South Pole. These are described as reversed episodes, or Reversals. If you were standing in the woods during a reversal, the compass arrow would follow the magnetic field lines and point toward the magnetic South Pole.

MAGNETIC POLE REVERSAL

Earth's magnetic field is constantly changing. What will change about the behavior of a compass during the next reversal?

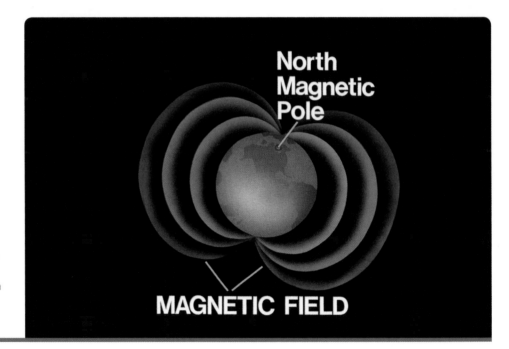

North Magnetic Pole

MAGNETIC FIELD

Scientists still cannot fully explain why Earth's magnetic field flips, but many think it has something to do with rotation in Earth's core. The reversal does not happen rapidly. A given episode commonly lasts hundreds of thousands of years, though some episodes in Earth's past have lasted millions of years.

Reversals occur periodically through time. As lava erupts onto the planet's surface, including on the ocean floor, particles of iron in the lava align with the existing magnetic field. The iron particles are locked into place when the lava cools below the Curie point (770°C). The iron particles can be reset only if the rock is heated above the Curie point. If this happens, the iron particles will align with the existing magnetic field. Geologists study the magnetic field in iron-rich igneous rock, such as basalt and **gabbro**, to decipher how the field changed in the past and to predict how, and when, it will change in the future.

Magnetic Reversals

Data for the last 10 million
years of the Cenozoic era

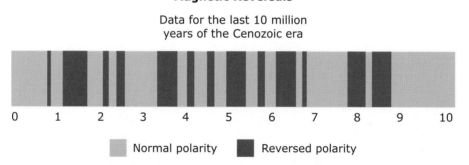

Normal polarity   Reversed polarity

PATTERN OF MAGNETIC REVERSALS

How does the striped pattern of magnetic reversals in igneous rock around ocean ridges support the theory of plate tectonics?

STEM and Earth's Spheres

The interaction of Earth's spheres was especially evident in the Gulf of Mexico in 2010. The explosion of a Deepwater Horizon oil drilling platform killed 11 workers. The failed well eventually released an estimated 4.2 million barrels of oil into the ocean. The oil formed long plumes below the surface, giant slicks on the ocean surface, and kilometers of soiled beaches and marshland. The atmosphere was filled with evaporated hydrocarbons, causing headaches, nausea, and other symptoms of illness among nearby residents and workers. Every part of the biosphere was affected, from the largest dolphins and sea turtles to the tiniest bacteria, and plants and animals of every size in between.

Teams of engineers scrambled to design and deploy a method to cap the well. They tried multiple methods before the leak was contained. Meanwhile, scientists from every relevant specialty rushed to the scene. They took measurements, assessed the situation, and made predictions about both short- and long-term effects of the disaster on the ocean, land, atmosphere, and living things. Samantha Joye, a marine scientist with the University of Georgia, was among those who brought a team to investigate the events as they unfolded.

OIL SLICK

What are the long-term effects of the Deepwater Horizon oil spill on Earth's hydrosphere and biosphere?

OIL-COVERED PELICAN
This pelican is trying to dry off the oil on his body. How do the interactions of Earth's spheres affect the spread of oil after a deep-water leak?

In the years since the Deepwater Horizon spill, scientists continue to monitor conditions on land, in the water, and on the ocean floor. Population surveys suggest optimism for some species, such as some fish and shellfish. The dolphin population has not yet recovered. Biodiversity has suffered at depth, as well. After the spill, dispersants were spread by airplane to break up the oil on the ocean surface. The smaller oil drops sank, settling on the ocean floor in large patches. Samantha Joye's research group uses robots to collect and analyze samples from the ocean floor to determine the extent of the area that is contaminated.

The contributions of scientists such as Dr. Joye, and the engineers who design the equipment they use, provide information that is crucial to understanding the effect of an oil spill. Their findings can be used to inform policymakers who make decisions that may help to prevent oil spills—or to most effectively clean up a spill when it does occur.

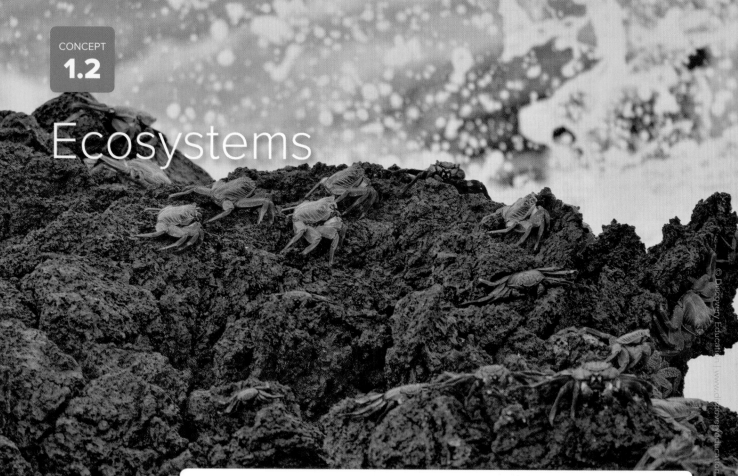

Ecosystems

dlc.com/ca10012s

LESSON OVERVIEW

Lesson Questions

- What are the characteristics of a population, a community, and an ecosystem?
- How do organisms interact within a community?
- How is an ecosystem established?
- What are the unique characteristics of water communities?
- What external factors influence ecosystems? How do species, populations, communities, and entire ecosystems respond to these external factors?

Key Vocabulary

Which terms do you already know?

- [ ] abiotic
- [ ] age pyramid
- [ ] biodiversity
- [ ] biosphere
- [ ] biotic
- [ ] carbon
- [ ] carnivore
- [ ] carrying capacity
- [ ] commensalism
- [ ] community
- [ ] competition
- [ ] decomposer
- [ ] density-dependent factors
- [ ] density-independent factors
- [ ] detritivore
- [ ] detritus
- [ ] ecosystem
- [ ] energy pyramid

Lesson Objectives

By the end of the lesson,
you should be able to:

- Compare a population, a
  community, and an ecosystem.
- Evaluate the interactions
  between organisms in
  ecosystems according to the
  stable or changing conditions.
- Summarize the process
  through which an ecosystem is
  established.
- Identify patterns in the
  characteristics of water
  communities.
- Evaluate the impacts of human
  activities on the environment
  and biodiversity and design a
  solution.
- Explain the cycling of matter and
  flow of energy among organisms
  in an ecosystem using
  mathematical representations.

Key Vocabulary continued

- ☐ exotic species
- ☐ exponential growth
- ☐ food chain
- ☐ food web
- ☐ herbivore
- ☐ heterotroph
- ☐ keystone species
- ☐ logistic growth
- ☐ mutualism
- ☐ niche
- ☐ omnivore
- ☐ parasitism
- ☐ pioneer species
- ☐ population
- ☐ predation
- ☐ predator
- ☐ prey
- ☐ primary consumer
- ☐ primary succession
- ☐ scavenger
- ☐ secondary consumer
- ☐ secondary succession
- ☐ species
- ☐ succession
- ☐ survivorship curve
- ☐ tertiary consumer
- ☐ trophic level
- ☐ water

Exploring Ecosystems

dlc.com/ca10013s

How many types of organisms can you observe living in your home? As well as people and pets, remember to count the plant species and any insects or arachnids you might see. What about the ones you cannot see?

© Discovery Education | www.discoveryeducation.com • Image: JUAN GARTNER / Science Photo Library / Getty Images

DUST MITES

Most of the organisms that live in your home can only be seen under a microscope. Some live in your carpets and on your walls. Where do you think these live?

EXPLAIN QUESTION

What components are necessary for the function of a successful ecosystem?

What Are the Characteristics of a Population, a Community, and an Ecosystem?

Populations

All of the organisms of the same **species**, occupying a certain area, make up a **population**. The area where a population lives is its habitat. For example, white-tailed deer live in forest habitats. Moray eels live in saltwater habitats. All populations are affected by **abiotic** factors, like weather and **water** resources. They are also affected by **biotic** factors, like available food sources and human activities.

The measurable characteristics of a population, or population demographics, include density, distribution, and size. Population density is the number of individuals per unit area. For example, suppose a forest that is 50 square kilometers contains 3,000 white-tailed deer. The population density for deer in this forest would be 60 deer per square kilometer. Of course, most square kilometers in the forest would not contain exactly 60 deer—some sections would contain fewer, and others would contain more.

Density often varies greatly among species living in the same area—the forest described above may contain only a few foxes per square kilometer and hundreds of red oak trees. Ecologists may be able to simply count individuals in a population to determine its density. Or, they may have to make a random count in a sample area to calculate an estimated density.

When describing a population's distribution, scientists often use three general terms. Individuals in a population are most commonly distributed in a clumped pattern. The diagram of a clumped distribution shows three groups of organisms within the overall population. Other times, distribution may look random without any particular pattern. Rarely do individuals display a nearly uniform distribution. In the diagram of a nearly uniform distribution, individuals within the population are spread relatively evenly throughout the habitat. As with density, a population's distribution varies with time, usually in response to environmental changes.

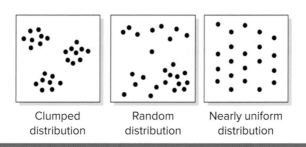

Clumped distribution | Random distribution | Nearly uniform distribution

POPULATION DISTRIBUTION TYPES

Distribution may be nearly uniform, random, or clumped. Which organisms would display these types of population distribution?

The size, or growth rate, of any population changes when one or more of the following changes: birth rate, death rate, or rate of individuals joining the population (immigration) or leaving the population (emigration). If a population experiences equivalent immigration and emigration, and its birth rate exceeds its death rate, the population will grow.

Communities

All the populations of organisms living together in an environment make up a **community**. Several factors affect the structure of a community. These factors include climate, topography, available resources throughout the year, adaptive traits of organisms in the community, overall population size, and interactions among different species within the community. These interactions make up the community's structure. Communities change and develop over time. Some communities will reach a stable state to become a climax community. Different climax communities develop under different environmental conditions. Biologists classify climax communities into groups based on their similarities and differences. These groups are called *biomes*. Examples of biomes are temperate forest and coral reefs.

CORAL REEF

Different populations of different fish species live together and form a coral reef community in a reef ecosystem. What other things in this picture are part of the reef ecosystem?

Ecosystems

Organisms interacting with one another and with their physical surroundings make up an **ecosystem**. The abiotic factors of an ecosystem are the nonliving components, including water, climate, and soil. The biotic factors are the living components and include all of the plants, animals, and other organisms. All ecosystems are open systems with inputs, transfers, and outputs of energy and nutrients.

Ecosystems have no fixed size. An ecosystem can be as small as a temporary puddle or as large as a lake or forest. Different ecosystems contain different species. Some ecosystems have very few species, whereas others have many species. The number of species in an ecosystem is one way to measure its **biodiversity**. A healthy ecosystem has stable species diversity and is better able to recover after serious damage by human action or natural disaster.

Within an ecosystem, each species has its own preferred place to live, called its *habitat*. For example, a mallard duck may live in a pond habitat. Each species also performs a number of roles within the ecosystem. These roles, combined with the organism's habitat, are called its ecological **niche**. Different species occupy different niches. If a niche becomes available or a new niche forms, an organism will eventually evolve to fill it. The rule is that no species occupies exactly the same niche as another. If they try to occupy the same niche, they will compete for the same resources. Eventually, the better-adapted species will push the other species to extinction.

We are learning about new species every day, and we are just figuring out the roles they play in the natural world. By studying and maintaining biodiversity, we help keep our planet healthy.

SCIENTISTS MONITORING AN ECOSYSTEM

What measurements do you think these scientists are taking?

How Do Organisms Interact within a Community?

Species Interactions

Even the simplest communities consist of species that interact with one another. Five main types of species interactions are summarized in the chart. Long-term species interactions can result in co-evolution—the change in one species that results in a change in another species.

Interaction	Description	Example
competition	A relationship in which two or more individuals or species compete for the same resource	Three different species of mice compete for food in a woodland community.
predation	A relationship in which one species, the predator, hunts another species, the prey	Great horned owls are predators of cottontail rabbits.
parasitism	A relationship in which one species (a parasite) benefits at the expense of the other species (a host)	A tapeworm lives in the intestines of a dog, absorbing nutrients from the dog's digestive system.
commensalism	A relationship that directly benefits one species but does not greatly affect the other, if at all	Maple trees provide a nesting place for blue jays, but the trees are unaffected by the blue jays.
mutualism	A relationship that directly benefits both species	Clownfish use sea anemone for shelter, and the clownfish lure food for the sea anemone.

Interactions within a Species: Group Behavior

Individual organisms within a community interact in ecologically significant ways with other species, but they also display specialized behaviors with other members of their species. These behaviors include flocking, shoaling, herding, hunting, migrating, swarming, mating, and rearing offspring. Behaviors that involve interactions between members of the same species are called *intraspecific behaviors*.

Intraspecific behaviors can greatly increase the chances of survival and reproductive success for the individuals that engage in them. Schooling is an example of beneficial group behavior. When fish school, they form a large group that interacts as a unit to forage, move, and avoid **predators**. Many species of fish that school are small or lack defenses that would protect individual members from predators—schooling reduces the chance of individual **predation**. Sardines are notable for their schooling behavior. While a single sardine would soon be eaten, a group of several hundred sardines appears to be large and is visually confusing to predators. In addition, large numbers of fish swimming together are more likely to detect predators. If a school of fish is attacked, there is a selfish advantage for individual members because other fish are likely to be eaten in place of them.

SCHOOL OF FISH

These tropical fish swim in a school. How does this behavior benefit all the fish in the school?

Other intraspecific behaviors involve complex social interactions to improve the group members' likelihood of survival. These types of behaviors usually require complex communication and decision-making processes. For example, meerkats form tightly knit "gangs" in which each individual plays a role in promoting the group's welfare and survival. Group members communicate using complex sounds, gestures, and smells. They use this communication system to organize tasks within the gang. Some meerkats serve as guards and alert the group to danger. Others tend to and protect their young, forage for food, or construct new tunnels in their underground dens. The harsh desert environment makes it unlikely that a single meerkat could carry out all of these tasks, yet these group behaviors enable meerkats to thrive and reproduce.

A tenet of evolutionary theory is that **competition** among individuals plays a significant role in natural selection. If this is the case, how does cooperation evolve? In many instances, cooperation can be identified in groups of individuals that are closely related. Cooperation is seen at its most extreme in social insects. When a worker bee stings while defending its hive, its internal organs are ripped out of its body, and it dies. However, all bees in a hive are very closely related—worker bees are all non-reproductive sisters—so the genes carried by the dead worker are shared by other bees in the hive. In this way, a hive of bees can be considered a type of super-organism that competes with other hives and carries its genes onto future generations. Individuals are closely related, like extended families, in many other animal groups. These animals have evolved cooperation because if they cooperate, the genes each individual carries, and have in common with their kin, are more likely to be passed to the next generation.

SOCIAL INSECTS

In a colony of yellow jackets, the insects are either sisters or half sisters. Why does this impact the way they behave?

Feeding Relationships

Organisms need energy in order to survive and perform life functions. Different organisms obtain energy in different ways. Producers convert light energy into chemical energy to produce biomass from inorganic resources. Plants are the most evident producer in terrestrial ecosystems. Algae and some types of prokaryotes are also producers.

Consumers obtain energy by eating other organisms. Any organism that eats only producers is called a **primary consumer**. One example is an **herbivore**, which is an animal that eats only plants. **Secondary consumers** obtain some or most of their energy by consuming primary consumers. Secondary consumers include **omnivores**, which eat plants and other consumers, or **carnivores**, which eat only consumers. **Tertiary consumers** obtain energy by eating secondary consumers. All tertiary consumers are carnivorous. Each level of producers and consumers is a **trophic level**. It is not uncommon for an organism to occupy more than one trophic level, depending on what it eats. Trophic levels, particularly those of parasites, may continue above the tertiary consumer levels. The flow of energy in an ecosystem passes from one trophic level to another in a single direction.

Some organisms obtain energy by breaking down dead plant and animal matter. **Detritivores** consume **detritus**—dead organic matter or organic wastes. Earthworms, millipedes, and fiddler crabs are examples of detritivores. **Scavengers** are a type of detritivore that specializes in eating the remains of dead animals. Vultures are an example of a scavenger. **Decomposers**, which include fungi and certain prokaryotes, break down and absorb nutrients from dead organic matter or organic wastes. Decomposers support the functioning of an ecosystem because they cycle important nutrients like **carbon** and nitrogen back into soil, air, and water.

Food Chains and Food Webs

A **food chain** is a linear representation of the directional flow of energy from one organism to another organism in an ecosystem. Food chains illustrate the basic relationships between organisms in a community. Communities typically consist of much more complex relationships than a food chain because organisms may obtain energy from different trophic levels. A **food web** provides a more accurate view of the flow of energy in a community because it includes connections between food chains.

The different levels in a food chain or web are called *trophic levels*. Producers are on the first trophic level, primary consumers are on the second trophic level, and so on, up the food chain. Some organisms may occupy more than one trophic level, such as bears, which are omnivores. Some energy is lost each time it is transferred along a food chain from one trophic level to the next. This is because organisms use energy for their life processes, such as moving or reproducing. Between one level of a food chain and the next, only about 10 percent of the energy is passed along. So, for example, a squirrel may eat 1,000 calories of acorns but the number of calories available to the squirrel's predator, a red-tailed hawk, would only be around 100 calories or less. The actual amount will vary, but the net result is that there is more energy available at lower trophic levels than higher ones. This energy difference is one reason why there are more squirrels than hawks and more gazelles than lions.

Human agriculture is most efficient at providing food when it focuses on the lower trophic levels. If we eat grain, then we obtain more energy than we would if we ate grain-fed cattle. In fact, we could feed about 10 times as many people. Most agricultural food chains involve either eating producers at the lowest trophic level—such as eating grain directly—or eating primary consumers just one trophic level higher—such as eating herbivores. Wild food chains from which we get food may be longer. For example, many of the fish we eat are carnivores on the third or fourth trophic level of a freshwater or marine ecosystem. As the world's population gets larger, food in many areas will be in short supply. Harvesting at the producer level will enable the planet to support a large, stable population. Perhaps in the future most people will choose to be vegetarians.

How Is an Ecosystem Established?

Succession

Ecosystems are dynamic; the environment plus the communities of organisms within an ecosystem are always changing. Some changes are hardly noticeable. For example, a lake may dry up slowly over hundreds of years and eventually become grassland. An observer would probably not notice the small, day-to-day changes in the lake. Other changes are drastic, such as those caused by natural disasters. A volcanic eruption may destroy an entire ecosystem, including all soil microorganisms, plants, and animals, leaving nothing but bare rock in a matter of hours. In either case, as ecosystems change, communities are replaced over time by new communities during a process called **succession**.

Scientists have identified two types of succession. **Primary succession** occurs when communities form on a surface that was previously unoccupied by organisms. On land, the mechanical and chemical weathering activities of soil fungi and bacteria break down rock and release inorganic nutrients. In this way, they start to build soil. Early communities of the photosynthetic lichens and mosses can grow on bare rock. These organisms further weather the surface of the rock. These first species to colonize an area are called **pioneer species**. Large animals are scarce or not present because there is little food for them to eat.

Eventually soil is established that includes organic material from dead and decomposed pioneer organisms. Wind-blown seeds are introduced. In some environments this will result in the growth of a meadow with grasses and wildflowers. The plants are food for animals like rodents, birds, and insects. Later stages of succession result from competition for resources, replacing meadow with shrubs and bushes. These changes attract different species of animals that prefer these habitats. Eventually the shrubs and bushes are replaced with young trees, forming a forest. The process will continue. The species in the forest may change until a stable community is formed. This type of community is called a *climax community*.

A major disaster, such as a volcanic eruption, may revert an ecosystem to the start of primary succession. Less severe disturbances, such as falling trees, a fire, or flood, would result in a **secondary succession**. Provided the soil had not been destroyed entirely, many plants could still grow from seeds or seedlings present in the ecosystem before the disturbance. Secondary succession after a forest fire may start with grasses and herbs, which are rapidly replaced by pines, and then possibly hardwood trees, such as oak and maple.

ECOLOGICAL SUCCESSION

This plant is growing in a lava field. Why is this an example of primary succession?

During succession, communities grow and replace one another until a climax community forms. A climax community has a relatively stable species composition. **Keystone species** are often established in climax communities. A keystone species is one that has relatively low abundance but greatly influences community structure. For example, a species of sea stars living in the Pacific Ocean consumes large amounts of mussels. This feeding relationship, in turn, keeps the population of mussels in check and opens the habitat to numerous other species to live in the community. If the sea star population were to decrease, the mussel population would likely increase. As the mussels occupy more space and consume more resources, the populations of other species in the community would likely decrease. The sea star is, therefore, considered a keystone species because it maintains the stability of the ecosystem.

Natural or human activities sometimes lead to the introduction of an **exotic species** to an ecosystem. Although they are non-native to the area, exotic species may become an established part of the community if they are pre-adapted to the new environment. Sometimes they occupy vacant niches and spread very rapidly. Sometimes exotic species are harmless to an ecosystem. Many exotic species, however, cause damage to ecosystems. They may negatively affect native species by increasing competition for resources, by overfeeding on native **prey** species, or by overpopulating, because they have no natural predators. For this reason, they are commonly referred to as *invasive species*.

INVASIVE BURMESE PYTHONS

These once tropical pythons are an invasive species in the Florida Everglades, where they predate on many native species. How could climate change increase the numbers and spread of invasive species?

What Are the Unique Characteristics of Water Communities?

Freshwater, Marine, and Estuarine Ecosystems

Ecosystems in water are called *aquatic ecosystems*. These ecosystems may be freshwater or marine, depending on salinity levels. Freshwater ecosystems cover a small percentage of Earth's surface. They have very low salinity and form in rivers, lakes, ponds, streams, and wetlands. Marine ecosystems cover about three-fourths of Earth's surface and contain moderate to high levels of salinity. They form in oceans and include ecosystems as varied as coral reefs and the open ocean. Where marine and freshwater ecosystems meet, in the estuaries of rivers, for example, another ecosystem forms. These estuarine ecosystems are characterized by changing levels of salinity and may include species from the ocean, from rivers, and those found only in estuarine conditions.

As with terrestrial communities, water communities are affected by changes to their environment. For example, aquatic organisms are adapted to a range of temperatures in which they live. If temperatures change too much, organisms unable to adapt will not survive.

Terrestrial communities depend on aquatic ecosystems for vital resources, like food, oxygen, and drinking water. For example, marine algae provide much of Earth's oxygen supply and take in large amounts of carbon dioxide from the atmosphere. Fish and crustaceans provide coastal regions with much of their food supply and support the local economy.

What External Factors Influence Ecosystems? How Do Species, Populations, Communities, and Entire Ecosystems Respond to These External Factors?

Succession may lead ecosystems to develop climax communities. Even climax communities are disrupted by external factors. External factors that influence ecosystems are called *disturbances*. Examples include forest fire, pollution, or other human activities, such as conversion of land to agricultural or urban use. When this happens the process of succession is interrupted or the climax community is destroyed.

The organisms within a disrupted community will respond to change. This may result in a change in the number of individuals in a population. Some species may die off in that ecosystem. Others may move to similar undisturbed areas. Some species are more sensitive than others to environmental change. These species are useful indicator species. They can be used to warn scientists that change is taking place. For example, some species are particularly sensitive to certain types of pollution. Their disappearance or reduction in numbers can tell scientists the impact of the pollution.

FOREST FIRE

Forest fires can devastate natural communities and ecosystems. However, they are a natural part of many ecosystems. How can a forest fire lead to an increase, rather than a loss, of species diversity?

Changing global climate results in ecosystem disturbance. Animals and plants responding to a warming climate may move their range—extending it to areas that were previously too cold for them. Animals may change their behavior, migrating to warmer areas earlier and leaving later. They may also lengthen their breeding seasons. Others may have the reverse problem. For example, polar bears prey on seals out on the Arctic sea ice. The bears have had to turn to other food sources as warmer temperatures have reduced the extent of ice.

Some disturbances have severe negative consequences, whereas others actually improve the health of the environment and increase species diversity. A mature forest represents a climax community. It is self-sustaining unless a disturbance occurs. Consider just the plants. Large trees are the dominant plant species. The large canopy blocks most of the light from reaching the understory and forest floor, so smaller plants, young trees, and shrubs are unable to thrive. The forest floor is smothered with years of accumulated dead wood, branches, leaves, and cones, which provide abundant fuel for a fire. A forest fire would quickly burn this material plus the mature trees. This scenario seems like an extreme disturbance, but the forest can quickly rebound. The soil hasn't been washed away or sealed in a layer of lava. Instead, the burned organic matter enriches the soil and opens up space for seeds to germinate and root in the ground. In fact, the cones of some pine trees actually require the heat of a burn to release their seeds. The burned canopy no longer blocks sunlight from reaching the forest floor. Without competition from the mature tree canopy that was once above, new seedlings and saplings can grow into young forest plants to replace those destroyed by fire. Fire enabled new life for the forest by the process of secondary succession.

Consider the Explain Question

What components are necessary for the function of a successful ecosystem?

Go online to complete the scientific explanation.

dlc.com/ca10014s

Check Your Understanding

What factors or events would need to occur for a lake environment to evolve into a grassland?

dlc.com/ca10015s

STEM in Action

Applying Ecosystems

Science has demonstrated that ecosystems can be quite robust as different species adapt to survive changing conditions. However, adaptations can take time, and that is something many ecosystems do not have when a sudden change occurs. Human activity can have rapid and lasting effects on an ecosystem. Our activities not only affect numbers of populations, but they also have the potential to wipe out entire species. We humans exist inside nature; we need the other organisms in our own ecosystem just as they all need each other. Human activity affects the balance within many ecosystems, even the ones we are not ourselves living in. For example, clear-cutting (the widespread and total removal of trees) is the most economical method for harvesting trees, and yet it removes all of several species from an ecosystem. The tree species removed provided shelter, food, and nutrients to other organisms in the ecosystem. The complete removal of such important members will cause instant damage to the other organisms in the ecosystem. Over time, the area may recover, but forestry companies often replant fast-growing, single-species forests in place of the ones they took. This means the biodiversity of the ecosystem is lost, and the original ecosystem may never be able to recover. A new ecosystem will eventually develop in its place, but it is often unlikely that the same types of organisms will be able to thrive in the new ecosystem.

CROP MONOCULTURES

Humans often grow plants, like these trees, in monocultures containing just one planted species. How do such practices impact biodiversity?

PLASTIC IN THE OCEANS

Plastics do not biodegrade quickly. As a result, they have become a major pollutant. How might plastics in the ocean impact marine organisms?

Understanding how the organic and inorganic materials found in an ecosystem are interdependent on each other is vital in recognizing how humans may be affecting an ecosystem and our first step in designing ways to lessen the damage we inflict on the natural world. Governments are beginning to recognize the importance of placing regulations on companies to hold them responsible for their effect on ecosystems. New environmental laws are encouraging selection cutting, where only trees of a certain size and quality are removed from the ecosystem, which allows smaller trees to continue to grow. Advancements in technology mean we can design more efficient machines that release less-harmful chemicals into the environment. Technology can also help us find solutions to make up for the damage we have already caused. Many researchers are working on a method to remove the vast amount of plastic collecting in the North Pacific Ocean garbage patch. Placing a monetary penalty on companies to hold them accountable for accidental or deliberate damage to ecosystems is another way to encourage safer, cleaner practices.

CLEAR-CUT LOGGING

Clear-cutting destroys ecosystems. What kind of impact will clear-cutting have on the rest of the community?

STEM and Bioremediation

The scientific study of ecosystems has brought much valuable data that has helped spearhead changes to laws and regulations. Companies profiting from the extraction of natural resources are often subject to regulations to prevent them from damaging the environment. Water, forests, minerals, and aquatic organisms are important natural resources for human survival. Unfortunately, these laws are not universal, and many of them have not been in place long enough to reverse the damage already inflicted on different ecosystems.

Rising out of growing concerns that humans have irreversibly damaged part of the planet, some ecologists have begun exploring novel ways to clean up pollutants. Biologists have already identified the ways that some organisms can clean up their own environment. Sewer systems can pollute water ecosystems through accidental chemical or nutrient runoff during floods or heavy rainstorms. Mussels and clams can remove harmful bacteria from the water, filtering 2 liters of water a day. Adding additional bivalve shellfish to an aquatic ecosystem can help clear the harmful bacteria using the process of bioremediation.

Phytoremediation derives from the Greek word for plant (*phyto*) and the Latin word for restoring balance (*remidium*). It is a method that specifically uses the properties of natural organisms to remove harmful material from an ecosystem. Biologists are now combining bioremedial concepts with engineering techniques to apply what they know about plant physiology and create feasible ways to clean water. Understanding that the mycelium part of fungi has the ability to absorb bacteria and break down chemicals in the soil, scientists created dams from sacks of mushrooms. These are placed across streams to encourage water to run over the mushrooms, allowing them to remove bacteria and absorb and filter harmful chemicals from petroleum by-products, such as oils and pesticides. Not all mushrooms have the ability to safely clean water. Some mushrooms are harmful to humans. Poisonous mushrooms are not safe to eat, and some are not even safe for humans to touch.

In addition, researchers continue to find other organisms that will prove useful at phytoremediation. Several plants are now recognized for their ability to remove toxins from the soil, and scientists are at work researching plants that are the most efficient at toxin removal. Studies on sunflowers show that they have a promising ability to remove radioactive elements from the soil. Sunflowers planted around the site of the Chernobyl nuclear power plant accident have demonstrated they can take up radioactive elements in their roots and store it without damage to their own structure. In this case, the radioactive toxin has not disappeared but instead has been merely removed from the soil and stored in the plant. The sunflowers need to be harvested and disposed of safely, but they isolate and make it easy to remove previously harmful material that was otherwise difficult and dangerous to remove. Similarly, tobacco plants have been altered to remove the chemicals from explosives, and several strains of mustard plants are useful at removing metals such as lead.

SUNFLOWER PHYTOREMEDIATION

Sunflowers are effective at removing radioactive materials from the soil. How might this remediation method be beneficial to humans?

Describing Populations

dlc.com/ca10016s

LESSON OVERVIEW

Lesson Questions

- What are the factors of population demographics?
- What is the difference between density-dependent and density-independent factors?
- What are the differences between exponential and logistical growth?
- How is population growth affected by carrying capacity?
- How are age structures created?
- What are the differences between type I, type II, and type III survivorship curves?

Key Vocabulary

Which terms do you already know?

- [ ] age pyramid
- [ ] carrying capacity
- [ ] community
- [ ] competition
- [ ] density-dependent factors
- [ ] density-independent factors
- [ ] ecosystem
- [ ] exponential growth
- [ ] logistic growth
- [ ] population
- [ ] population demographics
- [ ] population density
- [ ] renewable resource
- [ ] species
- [ ] survivorship curve

Lesson Objectives

By the end of the lesson, you should be able to:

- Analyze population demographics, including size, density, and distribution.
- Differentiate between density-dependent and density-independent factors.
- Distinguish between exponential and logistic growth.
- Identify patterns related to mathematical representations of the carrying capacity, K, of a population.
- Construct an age structure diagram for a population.
- Distinguish among type I, II, and III survivorship curves.

Declining Animal Populations

dlc.com/ca10017s

All over Earth, many animal populations are in decline. What factors do you think impact how large or small their populations are? How do environmental factors influence animal populations?

NUTS FOR SQUIRRELS

What factors impact squirrel populations?

EXPLAIN QUESTION

❙ **Explain the factors that impact squirrel populations.**

What Are the Factors of Population Demographics?

Populations

Ecologists study various levels of organization of the natural world. Defining these levels of organization helps clarify the scope of the ecologists' studies. An **ecosystem** includes all the living and nonliving components of the environment in a specified area. A **community** refers to a collection of interacting **species** or populations in an ecosystem. A population is a group of individuals of a species within a community. A species is defined as a group of interbreeding organisms that can produce fertile offspring.

Population ecology focuses on all the members of a given species living in a given location. Studying populations gives ecologists information about the population size, density, and distribution of organisms.

Population Size and Density

The size of a population can be used to determine both the health of the given population as well as the health of the ecosystem. Changes in population size can be caused by natural or human-caused ecological and environmental processes. Determining the cause of an observed population fluctuation requires long-term studies of normal population fluctuations.

The size of a population varies with births, deaths, immigration, and emigration. The rate of increase of a population (r) is affected by factors such as the average number of offspring, the average life span, the age at which organisms reproduce, and survival of the young. Multiplying r by the current population size (N) is used to calculate the rate of a population's growth (G). The equation can be written as $G = rN$.

Growing populations have a positive r value, hence G is also positive. Declining populations have a negative r value, hence G is negative. The value of r also changes based on the timeframe used in the calculation. Seasonal and other short-term changes in population size are common and natural. These can be due to fluctuations in temperature, disease cycles, food availability, and other factors. Long-term trends in populations indicate larger-scale ecosystem changes.

Population size is only one factor to consider when studying a population. Population density is the number of individuals per unit area or volume. In human populations, urban areas have higher population densities than rural areas. Similarly, population densities vary based on the available resources in an area. Increased population density makes finding a mate easier but increases **competition** for resources.

In cases where the population size is relatively small (such as on an island), population density can be measured directly. For larger populations, density must be estimated using sampling techniques. Sampling techniques vary based on the organism and location being studied. For example, counting the individual insects on a given tree and multiplying by the number of trees in the area will provide an estimate of the population density of a given insect population.

Population Distribution

Describing population distributions provides information about environmental and social factors affecting the population. Clumped distribution is common in situations where resources are unequally dispersed. Plants and other organisms may show clumped distribution around water sources or areas of increased nutrient concentration. Clumped distribution can also result from positive interactions between individuals. Clumped distributions, such as those seen in fish, can protect individuals in the group from predation and make it easier for individuals to find mates.

SCHOOL OF FISH

Populations of fish are often clumped into schools. How could clumped distribution due to schooling behavior benefit individual fish?

© Discovery Education | www.discoveryeducation.com • Image: Massimiliano Finzi / Shutterstock

Uniform distribution results from negative interactions between individuals. In areas with a relatively even distribution of resources, plants with fewer competitors in their immediate vicinity have increased access to resources. These plants may produce chemicals to inhibit the growth of other plants. This produces a uniform distribution, as the plants do not grow well when they are too close to each other. Animals generally achieve uniform distribution through territorial behaviors rather than chemical inhibition.

CALIFORNIA POPPIES

Populations of flowers in fields are often uniformly distributed. What explains the uniform distribution of flowers in a field?

Random distribution is less common in the natural world. This occurs when the relationship between individuals is neither positive nor negative. Individuals are independent of each other and resources are sufficient throughout the environment.

Population Demographics

Population ecologists study population size, density, and distribution to gain an understanding of the health of the population as well as how individuals in the population interact with each other and their surroundings. Demographics are statistical data that represent these factors. Scientists use census data to characterize the demographics of human populations. These data can then be used to make political and policy decisions. Ecologists can use population demographics to develop action plans for conservation.

What Is the Difference between Density-Dependent and Density-Independent Factors?

Density-Dependent Factors

Population demographics vary due to both **density-dependent factors** and **density-independent factors**. Density-dependent factors affect populations more as the population density increases. Competition for resources becomes more intense as density increases. Resource availability is an example of a density-dependent factor.

Infectious diseases are diseases that can spread from one host to another. Infectious diseases are a density-dependent factor. An increase in density increases the rate of host interactions, which in turn hastens the spread of the disease. This axiom supports health professionals' recommendations that people with infectious diseases—such as the flu—stay home and avoid interactions with other people.

Predation is also a density-dependent factor. Higher numbers of prey result in increases in the predator population. Higher predator numbers increase the predation rate. Higher numbers of prey can change predator behavior. Many predators prefer to hunt more abundant prey. As a particular prey population becomes less abundant, predators choose a different prey population (if available). Decreases in the number of prey will also decrease predator numbers. Decline in predators releases the predation stress on the prey population and their numbers increase again. These cyclic fluctuations in population sizes of predator and the prey result in the so-called predator–prey relationship and the co-evolution of predators and prey.

Density-dependent factors are generally biotic, or living, components. Resource availability is one notable exception as these resources can either be biotic, such as prey numbers, or abiotic, such as availability of water.

Density-Independent Factors

Density-independent factors are often abiotic. By definition, they do not vary with population density. Severe weather events such as fires and floods affect large and small populations regardless of population size. Human activities such as the release of pollutants and habitat destruction can also affect populations independent of density. Non-infectious diseases are an example of a biotic density-independent factor. Non-infectious diseases such as cancer, which are not spread from individual to individual, have similar rates in high- and low-density populations.

What Are the Differences between Exponential and Logistical Growth?

Exponential Population Growth

Exponential growth of a population occurs when the growth rate is density-independent and constant. Exponential growth causes a population to increase rapidly over time. The increase in population size can be seen as a J-shaped curve on a graph. The steep slope is due to the continually increasing population. As an example, imagine a population of bacteria that reproduces by each cell dividing once per hour, so that the population doubles every hour. The table below shows the number of bacterial cells over a period of time, starting with a single cell.

Time	Number of Cells
1 hour	2
2 hours	4
3 hours	8
4 hours	16
5 hours	32
6 hours	64
7 hours	128
8 hours	256
9 hours	512
10 hours	1,024

EXPONENTIAL GROWTH

This table shows the exponential growth of a group of cells that double during a specific time period. What circumstances are necessary for this theoretical pattern to occur in a natural setting?

Populations growing in ideal conditions and without limitations will initially show exponential growth. Invasive species are an ecological problem in part because they undergo exponential growth. When these organisms are first brought to a new environment, they often do not have natural predators or parasites. They can grow unchecked if the new environment is favorable. These organisms will increase in number very quickly. Invasive organisms tend to take over unoccupied niches or out-compete native organisms. This can drive native organisms to extinction.

Many species rely on exponential growth as their main reproductive strategy. These organisms are referred to as *r*-selected. The *r* refers to rate of increase because this strategy relies on producing many offspring. In general, *r*-selected species are adapted to unstable habitats. Fungi are *r*-selected. Decomposers grow when a tree or other organism dies. They cannot plan for a new food source and will eventually exhaust a given source. As a result, fungi grow quickly and reproduce large numbers of spores before the food source is exhausted. In general, *r*-selected organisms tend to be small, grow quickly, produce large numbers of offspring, and provide very little parental care to offspring.

DECOMPOSERS

This decomposing log in the forest is covered with fungi. What makes fungi an *r*-selected species?

Logistical Population Growth

Populations tend to grow exponentially until they are regulated by lack of resources or other factors. Once the population size nears the ecosystem's **carrying capacity**, the rate of increase will slow. The carrying capacity is the largest population size that can be supported by the ecosystem. Logistical growth is density-dependent because the density of the population is limiting its growth.

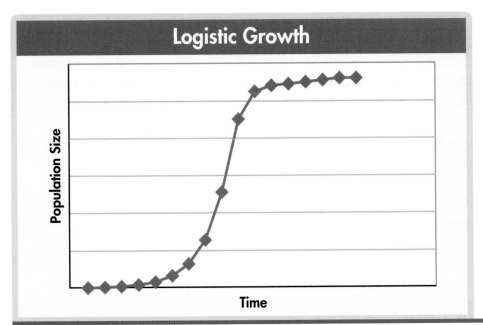

LOGISTICAL GROWTH

Populations show logistic growth as the population nears the ecosystem's carrying capacity. What is the name given to the shape of a logistic growth curve?

Some species use logistical growth as a reproductive strategy. These organisms are called *K*-selected. *K* is the abbreviation for carrying capacity. *K*-selected organisms are adapted to stable environments. Their population sizes tend to remain near the carrying capacity of the environment. These populations are generally regulated by density-dependent factors such as predator–prey interactions and resource availability. *K*-selected organisms tend to be larger, grow slowly, produce fewer offspring, provide parental care to offspring, and are adapted to stable environments.

Species that produce fewer offspring tend to provide more parental care. Each individual organism has a finite energy supply and cannot allocate energy to both high reproductive rates and extensive parental care of each offspring. These reproductive strategies apply to plants as well as to animals. In plants, parental care can be defined as energy allocation to the seeds. Plants that produce large seeds with abundant nutrient storage tend to produce fewer seeds overall.

How Is Population Growth Affected by Carrying Capacity?

Carrying Capacity

The carrying capacity (K) of a habitat is the largest population size that can be supported in an ecosystem over a period of time. Many factors, including water, light, nutrients, and space, influence an ecosystem's carrying capacity. In theory, a population will grow exponentially until it is using all of its available resources. At this point, the population should stabilize at the carrying capacity. At carrying capacity, death rate equals birth rate. This rarely occurs in nature because disease, predation, and density-independent factors, such as an extremely cold winter, usually intervene.

If you know calculus, the carrying capacity can be used to determine the logistical growth curve for a population. If a population size (N) is below the carrying capacity, it will grow at a rate that is proportional to $(K - N)/K$. This information can be used to generate a **logistic growth** equation:

$$\frac{\Delta N}{\Delta r} = r_{max} N \left(\frac{K - N}{K} \right)$$

Returning to the logistical growth curve, we can better understand this relationship. The smaller the population (N), the closer $(K - N)/K$ will be to 1, meaning population growth will be high. When the population reaches carrying capacity (K), then $(K - N)/K$ equals zero and growth ceases.

It is possible for a population to temporarily exceed the carrying capacity of its habitat. This, however, cannot last. Such a population causes rapid degradation of the environment. The loss of food and other resources will cause the population to crash.

How Are Age Structures Created?

Age Structure Diagrams

One demographic measure of a population is an **age pyramid**, or age structure diagram. An age pyramid is a diagram, often pyramid-shaped, that shows the age distribution of a population. This diagram can be used to determine if a population's size is growing, shrinking, or remaining relatively constant.

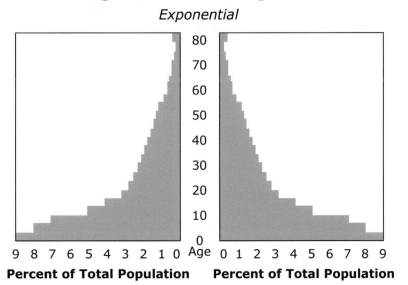

Age Structure Diagram

Exponential

Percent of Total Population   **Percent of Total Population**

GROWING POPULATION

A higher proportion of young individuals indicates a growing population. Why does this age structure suggest future population growth?

Constructing an age pyramid begins with a basic census of the population. Each organism's gender and age are determined and plotted on a graph. Males are graphed on the left, females on the right of the diagram. The genders of the individuals are graphed because the diagram will be used to determine potential growth of the population. If one gender is much higher in number, it can affect the growth rate. The number of females in particular has a greater effect on the population growth rate.

Age Structure Diagram
Declining

© Discovery Education | www.discoveryeducation.com

DECLINING POPULATION

A lower portion of young individuals indicates a declining population. What steps can countries take to avoid declining populations?

The age structure of the **population** is used to forecast the future population size. If a population has many more young individuals than older individuals, it will likely grow in size over time. As the young individuals reach sexual maturity, they will begin reproducing and increasing the population size.

If the number of young individuals is about the same as the number of individuals of reproductive ages, the population size will remain stable. If the number of young individuals is less than the number of individuals of reproductive ages, the population will decrease in size. Average reproductive rate must also be considered. If each individual produces a single offspring, the population will remain stable. If the number of offspring per individual averages less than one, the population will decline.

Age Structure Diagram
Stationary

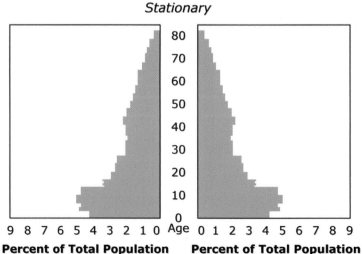

STABLE POPULATION

A stable population is one that will remain approximately the same size over time. What would be the relationship between birth rate and death rate in a stable population?

What Are the Differences between Type I, Type II, and Type III Survivorship Curves?

Survivorship Curve

A **survivorship curve** is a graph that shows rates of survival (numbers or percentage alive) for individuals at various ages in a population. Survivorship is a key factor that determines changes in population size. Reproductive rate, immigration, and emigration are other key factors. A population is characterized by one of three basic types of survivorship curves.

A type I survivorship curve describes a population in which long life spans are typical. There are high survival rates among young and middle-aged individuals. The survivorship curve begins to decrease toward older ages as death rate increases. Organisms with a type I survivorship curve tend to have long life expectancy and a long juvenile period (the pre-reproductive stage). Organisms with a type I survivorship curve tend to produce fewer offspring and provide these offspring with greater parental care. Humans and other large mammals are examples of organisms with a type I survivorship curve.

REINDEER

What factors could impact the survival of reindeer living in their natural habitat? What type of survivorship curve do you think reindeer populations exhibit?

A type II survivorship curve is similar to a straight line, as death rates are fairly consistent among individuals of all age groups. These organisms are faced with a consistent risk of mortality throughout their lives. These organisms tend to produce a medium number of offspring and provide some parental care. Some invertebrates, rodents, and most birds are examples of organisms with a type II survivorship curve.

A type III survivorship curve depicts populations in which mortality rates are significantly higher for young individuals than for individuals in older age groups. These organisms tend to produce many offspring and provide little parental care. Most insects and annual plants are examples of organisms with a type III survivorship curve.

Consider the Explain Question

▌ **Explain the factors that impact squirrel populations.**

Go online to complete the scientific explanation.

dlc.com/ca10018s

Check Your Understanding

▌ **How are density-dependent factors different from density-independent factors?**

dlc.com/ca10019s

STEM in Action

Applying Descriptions of Populations

In cases where the population size is fairly limited, such as on an island, population size can be measured directly by counting the number of individuals. For larger populations, population size must be estimated using sampling techniques. Sampling techniques vary based on the organism and location being studied.

One common sampling technique for measuring plant populations is to use a quadrat and extrapolate to the rest of the population. A sampling of at least 1 percent of the total area is often sufficient to make accurate predictions. In quadrat sampling, small sections of land are selected, and the plants within that area are either counted or the percent cover calculated. The percent cover is the measure of how much space a plant occupies. It can be estimated by measuring the size of the plant's shadow. Percent cover is an important demographic because larger, older plants have different roles in the population than do smaller saplings.

The size of the quadrat depends on the type of plant being studied. Larger plants require larger quadrats for an accurate calculation. The perimeter of the quadrats adds sources of error because counting plants on the borders can be subjective. Minimizing perimeter is one consideration, but the lay of the land is another important consideration. Plants often tend to grow in clusters around water or nutrient sources. The quadrat arrangement must take into account rivers, slopes, and other factors. One common strategy to account for these gradations in area is to use transects rather than quadrats. A transect is a long line rather than a circle or rectangle. A long rope can be laid out, and plants that fall within the range of the rope are enumerated.

SO MANY TREES!
How could you determine the population size of this tree species?

One common sampling technique for measuring animal populations is the capture-recapture method. A set number of animals is captured, tagged, and released. After some time, another set of animals from the same population is captured. A certain percentage of these will have tags from the previous capture. This count can be used to determine the total size of the population.

Example:

A population ecologist is interested in determining the size of a squirrel population. In the first trial, she captures and tags 100 squirrels. These squirrels are released back into the general population. After a month, the ecologist comes back to the same area. A month should be sufficient time for the tagged squirrels to reintegrate into the overall population. In this second trial, she captures 100 more squirrels; 20 of these were tagged from before.

The second trial is a random sampling of the population. In this random sampling, 20 percent of the squirrels were tagged. We can extrapolate that 20 percent of the entire population is tagged. From the first trial, we know that 100 squirrels are tagged. Therefore, 100 is 20 percent of the total population size; the total population is 500 squirrels.

These calculations are based on the following equation:

$$\frac{\text{\# tagged in first trial}}{\text{total population size}} = \frac{\text{\# tagged in second trial}}{\text{\# captured in second trial}}$$

Using the data from the study above:

$$\frac{100}{x} = \frac{20}{100}$$

Solving for x:

$$x = \frac{(100)(100)}{20} = 500$$

The equation for calculating total population size using this technique can be rewritten as:

$$\text{total population size} = \frac{(\text{\# tagged in first trial})\ (\text{\#captured in second trial})}{\text{\# tagged from second trial}}$$

STEM and Describing Populations

Tagging animals can help ecologists measure **population density**. Ecologists can also collect data on these animals while tagging them. Often the age, health, and other characteristics of captured animals are recorded. Returning to the same population to tag and study animals over longer periods of time can provide valuable information about the changes in the population over time.

Electronic tracking devices can provide even more information on **population demographics**. Tracking devices are able to track an animal's movements using a global positioning system (GPS). The device records interactions between tagged animals using proximity sensors and sends the data to researchers' computers via satellites. Some newer devices are solar powered to increase battery life. Tracking devices may be attached to the animals as collars, as leg wraps, or as shell attachments. New technology for these devices is focused on making them smaller and less intrusive.

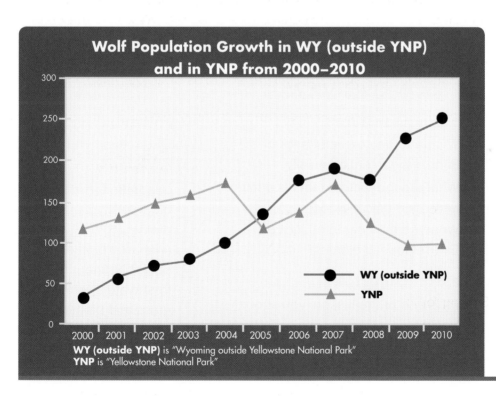

WOLF POPULATIONS IN WYOMING

Tracking devices have been used to determine the distribution of wolves in Wyoming. Why do you think wolves are declining outside Yellowstone National Park (YNP)?

Biomes

dlc.com/ca10020s

LESSON OVERVIEW

Lesson Questions

- What are the characteristics of Earth's terrestrial biomes?
- What are the factors that determine Earth's aquatic biomes?
- What are the characteristics of Earth's aquatic biomes?

Lesson Objectives

By the end of the lesson, you should be able to:

- Compare characteristics and processes of terrestrial biomes.
- Summarize mathematical representations that explain how factors affect terrestrial biomes.

Key Vocabulary

Which terms do you already know?

- ☐ adaptation
- ☐ biodiversity
- ☐ biome
- ☐ chaparral biome
- ☐ desert biome
- ☐ freshwater biome
- ☐ grassland biome
- ☐ invertebrate
- ☐ latitude
- ☐ marine biome
- ☐ precipitation (weather)
- ☐ soil
- ☐ taiga biome
- ☐ temperate deciduous forest biome
- ☐ tropical biome
- ☐ tundra biome

Image: Matt Tilghman / Shutterstock

Thinking about Biomes

When early American pioneers began moving west, they encountered the Great Plains and the prairies that covered them. Other grasslands like the prairies exist in other places around the world, such as South America, Africa, Australia, and Asia. Why do such similar, but widely separated, ecosystems exist?

dlc.com/ca10021s

EXPLAIN QUESTION

| How does climate influence the characteristics of a biome?

BUFFALOS: ANIMALS OF THE PRAIRIE

The prairies of North America are one grassland ecosystem that is part of a much larger grassland biome on a number of continents. Why do animals and plants that occupy the same biome exhibit similar characteristics?

What Are the Characteristics of Earth's Terrestrial Biomes?

Defining a Biome

Biomes are large regions defined by similarities in the abiotic factors they experience. They may not be geographically contiguous, but often occupy similar **latitudes** on the planet. Grasslands, tropical rain forests, and deserts are examples of biomes that exist on land known as *terrestrial biomes*. Biomes also exist in water, and these aquatic biomes are less well defined but are generally divided into freshwater biomes—lakes and rivers—and saltwater biomes that include estuaries, the open ocean, shallow seas, and coral reefs. Biomes are not the same as ecosystems because biomes are sets of ecosystems that are closely related to one another and have many common characteristics, including similar assemblages of organisms.

Although only 29 percent of Earth's surface is land, there is incredible diversity in that small percentage. There are great differences in latitude, altitude, and geography among Earth's terrestrial biomes.

TERRESTRIAL BIOMES

Different climates result in diverse plant and animal life across biomes. What features can be used to compare terrestrial biomes?

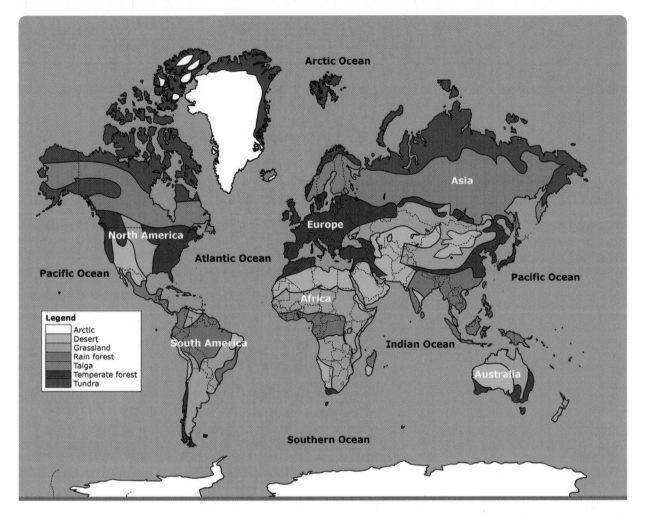

Legend
- Arctic
- Desert
- Grassland
- Rain forest
- Taiga
- Temperate forest
- Tundra

Arctic Ocean

North America

Pacific Ocean

Atlantic Ocean

Europe

Asia

Pacific Ocean

Africa

Indian Ocean

South America

Australia

Southern Ocean

EARTH'S TERRESTRIAL BIOMES

Scientists recognize seven major terrestrial Earth biomes. Look at this map, and identify what patterns you can discern in their distribution, and how you could account for these patterns.

Temperature and amount of precipitation, which are properties of climate, primarily determine which organisms live in a biome. Climate determines the types of plant species that can live in a region, and plant life, in turn, partly determines the animal species that live there.

The major terrestrial biomes on Earth include deserts, tundra, taigas, rain forests, deciduous forests, grasslands, and chaparrals.

Biome	Climate	Plants	Animals
Desert	• Usually hot in the day and cold at night • Dry • Annual precipitation <23 cm	• Sparsely distributed, often small • Include cacti and other succulents and some trees such as yuccas	• Mammals adapted to dry conditions such as camels and oryx • Burrowing animals such as lizards, snakes, and many invertebrates that can avoid the heat of the day underground
Tundra	• Cold with long, dark, extremely cold winters and short cool growing season • Annual precipitation 10–25 cm	• Grasses and low herbaceous plants • Small shrubs such as willows	• Caribou, musk ox, rodents such as hares and lemmings • Predators include Arctic foxes, bears, and wolves • Many species of birds, particularly summer migrants
Taiga (Boreal forest)	• Very cold winters and short, cool, humid, wet summers • Annual precipitation ~50 cm	• Evergreen trees such as spruce and firs	• Lynxes, bears, minks, foxes, grey wolves, and their prey: caribou, reindeers, and moose • Many species of birds, particularly summer migrants
Grassland	• Cold or cool in winter but dry and hot in the summer • Annual precipitation 25–75 cm	• Grasses and some shrubs with trees along water courses and dry riverbeds	• Large herbivores such as bison, horses, and antelopes, and their predators: wolves, lions, and hyenas • Smaller burrowing mammals such as prairie dogs and meerkats and their predators: foxes, badgers, and ferrets • Many species of seed-eating birds, snakes, and invertebrates
Chaparral	• Hot, dry summers, cool winters • Annual precipitation 25–45 cm	• Shrubs (sage brush, creosote) and small trees such as scrub oak, toyon, and yucca	• Mule deer, rabbits, and rodents, coyotes, wild goats, and horses • Many species of insects, particularly bees and butterflies

Biome	Climate	Plants	Animals
Rain forest	• Tropical rainforests are hot year-round • Temperate rainforests are cool all year round • Annual precipitation 200–400 cm	• Large trees form very diverse forests with a distinct vertical layering below the canopy	• Very high biodiversity • many arboreal mammals, such as monkeys, sloths, and rodents • Predators include cats such as leopards and tigers, large snakes, and very large birds of prey • Very high diversity of invertebrates
Temperate (Deciduous) forest	• Four distinct seasons • Warm summers and cool to cold winters • Annual precipitation 75–130 cm	• Hardwood, mainly deciduous trees such as oak, hickory, and maple species	• Deer, boar, squirrels, and many small mammals • Predators include raccoons, foxes, coyotes, wolves, and bobcats • Many bird species, particularly summer migrants • Many species of invertebrates

GIRAFFE

Giraffes live in Africa. Which type of biome are they usually found in?

What Are the Factors That Determine Earth's Aquatic Biomes?

What Abiotic Factors Affect Life in Aquatic Biomes?

Organisms in aquatic biomes are impacted by a number of abiotic factors, which include chemical and physical variables such as salinity, pH, light, and temperature. All but the shallowest wetlands, streams, and ponds are affected by changes in abiotic factors with depth. These changes may result in vertical stratification—different layers with different conditions—often occupied by different organisms.

Light is particularly important because it is absorbed by water, by any particles suspended in the water, and by floating organisms. Light intensity rapidly decreases with depth, and the quality of light also changes. Red light is absorbed more rapidly by water than blue light. Being that red light is used in photosynthesis, the reduction in the quality and quantity of light severely impairs photosynthesis below a certain depth. Biologists, therefore, recognize two zones in lakes and oceans: the photic zone, through which light penetrates, and the aphotic zone, where there is little or no light. Photosynthesis takes place only in the photic zone.

If you have ever been swimming in a sea or lake, you may have noticed the surface water is warm while the lower layers are cold. Solar radiation is absorbed by the water in the photic zone, increasing its temperature. The temperature in the photic zone typically decreases with depth because warm water is less dense than cold water. As a result, the warm water rises to the surface. This movement can cause a very rapid change between the temperatures of the warm, upper layers and cold, lower layers. The change from warm to cold is called a *thermocline*.

Oxygen and nutrients also vary with depth. Exchange of gases between water and air occurs in the upper layers, and the upper layers also contain phytoplankton, the main producers in many aquatic biomes. Phytoplankton produce oxygen as they carry out photosynthesis, and as a result, the upper layer of water typically contains more dissolved oxygen than deeper waters.

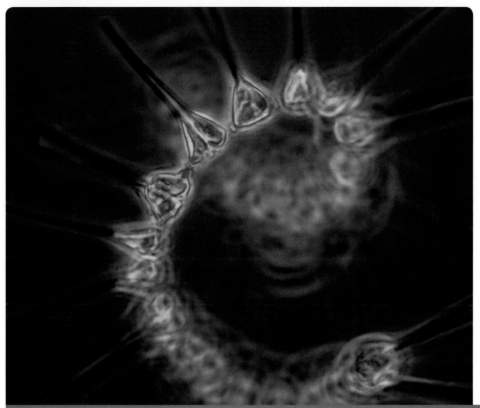

PHYTOPLANKTON

Phytoplankton are tiny plant-like organisms that inhabit the oceans. Why are phytoplankton important?

Although most producers live in the upper parts of the water column, nutrients there are scarce because organisms rapidly use up the dissolved nutrients. In addition, when an organism dies, it will eventually sink to the bottom, along with the nutrients it contains, resulting in the upper layers becoming nutrient-deficient and the lower layers becoming nutrient-rich.

The bottom of a lake or an ocean is called the *benthic zone*, and in deep water, this zone is cold and completely devoid of sunlight. The bottom may vary in composition, and it could be rocky, sandy, or muddy, and usually contains lots of organic matter, which is a rich source of food for organisms. Decomposition in this zone may decrease oxygen levels in the water and may also lower pH as the acidic products of decomposition are released.

Salinity varies with depth, because saltwater is denser than freshwater and the saltwater sinks and creates a salty layer. This salty layer is particularly common in places where the water freezes, being that ice is freshwater and the unfrozen water becomes saltier when the sea freezes. When the ice at the surface melts, the freshwater layer floats on the top.

Organisms within aquatic biomes interact in many ways, with the most obvious biotic factors being related to feeding. Trophic relationships vary with the type of biome, but in most aquatic ecosystems, microorganisms play a major role as producers. The microorganisms are mostly phytoplankton that live suspended in the water, and are eaten by microscopic animals called *zooplankton*. Above these levels, macrofauna play a key role in the food web, with aquatic food chains often being longer than their terrestrial counterparts.

OCEAN FOOD WEB

Sharks are at the top of the ocean food web. What organisms would be the producers in the ocean food web?

What Are the Characteristics of Earth's Aquatic Biomes?

Freshwater Biomes

Most bodies of freshwater are small when compared to seas and oceans and are therefore more readily influenced by changes in temperature and may freeze during the winter.

Freshwater biomes fall into two broad categories: moving water and standing water. Moving water includes rivers and streams, while standing water includes ponds, lakes, temporary pools, freshwater swamps, and freshwater wetlands. Glaciers are important bodies of frozen freshwater that move very slowly and may be considered freshwater biomes. However, few organisms are found in this biome.

River systems start at springs and small streams and increase in size as they gather water. They can be divided into zones based on position between the source and the sea, and here we divide them into three zones: source zone, transition zone, and floodplain zone. Although no two rivers are exactly alike, each of these zones has characteristic abiotic and biotic features.

Source zones are the headwaters of a river, and these streams are fed from springs or mountain lakes. These streams typically have a rocky substrate, are cold and clear, and flow rapidly. As a result, they are commonly rich in oxygen but low in nutrients. The organisms that live in these conditions are adapted to hold their positions in the strong current or hide under rocks.

The transition zone of a river occurs at lower elevations where the channel is wider, the speed of flow is moderate, and the water is warmer. The river contains more suspended matter and dissolved nutrients and sediments settle on the riverbed.

In the floodplain zone, the tributaries join to produce a big river, and the water is typically muddy and contains even more nutrients. The channel is wide, and the current is slow, with many aquatic plants growing near the banks. These rivers are often green with phytoplankton and floating plants, such as lilies, may also be present. The banks of these rivers often have many emergent plants, and a wide variety of fish are found in these rivers, depending on the local conditions. One example of this is the catfish, which often occupies parts of the river that are turbid and have low amounts of oxygen.

FLOOD PLAIN

When a river floods, the sediments deliver nutrients to the surrounding landscape. How do organisms respond to periodic flooding?

Lakes and Ponds

Lakes and ponds are standing bodies of water surrounded by land, and the communities found in lakes depend upon size and depth. Some very large lakes, such as the Great Lakes of North America, have many of the same characteristics of oceans. Depending on depth, lakes are considered to have zones that result from differences in light, temperature, oxygen, and nutrient availability.

The well-lit area close to shore, where rooted and floating plants grow, is called the *littoral zone*. Farther away from the shore is the limnetic zone, where the upper layers of water are illuminated by the sun and generally are rich in oxygen. Below this zone is dark water where photosynthesis cannot take place, and oxygen concentration and temperatures are lower. Organisms, including certain fish, have adapted to these conditions. The lake floor, or benthic zone, consists of sediment occupied by a wide range of **invertebrates** and bottom-feeding fish. Benthic zone organisms rely on detritus from above for their nutrition.

Levels of dissolved oxygen determine the types of organisms that can live in a lake, being that oxygen can enter the lake either directly from the air or through the photosynthetic activity of plants, algae, and phytoplankton. Wave action mixes lake water with the air and increases the levels of dissolved oxygen, while decomposition of organic matter by fungi and bacteria removes oxygen through the process of respiration. The removal of oxygen from the water is called biological oxygen demand or B.O.D. Due to decomposition, the amount of organic matter and other nutrients in a lake plays a key role in determining the organisms that can live in it, and consequently lakes are often classified by the amount of organic matter that they contain.

Lakes that are low in nutrients are called *oligotrophic*, and support low densities of organisms. Oligotrophic lakes are typically cold and deep, and their waters are very clear. Lakes with more nutrients support more organisms and are called *eutrophic*. Eutrophic lakes have elevated levels of nutrients, high plant growth, and may contain green-colored water as a result of the presence of phytoplankton. Mesotrophic lakes lie between oligotrophic and eutrophic lakes.

LAKES AND PONDS

Lakes and ponds are areas where the water is still and fresh. What factors determine the abundance and variety of organisms that are able to exist in a lake?

Freshwater wetlands are areas of shallow water that support the growth of aquatic plants. Marshes are covered with water year-round and are dominated by emergent plants, such as reeds and sedges. Swamps are dominated by bushes and trees, while bogs are typically found in mountain and tundra areas and are dominated by spongy moss. Most bogs have a low pH and are low in available nutrients. Fens are wetlands dominated by grasses and sedges that are typically fed by mineral-rich surface water or groundwater.

Wetlands provide humans with a wide variety of services, including flood protection, water storage, and pollutant filtration. Many wetlands have been destroyed by draining for agriculture and development.

CYPRESS SWAMP

Swamps are wetlands dominated by trees. What other types of organisms inhabit swamps?

Marine Biomes

Marine biomes have salinities above 1 percent, and most seawater is around 3 percent salt. Being that marine biomes cover such a large part of Earth's surface, they have a major impact on climate. Through photosynthesis, the phytoplankton in the ocean provide more than half the world's oxygen and absorb large amounts of carbon dioxide. Marine biomes reside in various locations, including those on the shore, the shallow seas offshore over the continental shelf, and the open ocean.

Where the ocean meets the land is the shore, or intertidal biome. This area can be a harsh place for organisms to live. Twice a day along most shorelines, tides submerge and then expose much of the substrate. The organisms that live on the shore are exposed to major changes in salinity of seawater, as well as freshwater from rain. When it is not underwater, the temperature of the shore may rise, and organisms are exposed to the sun. In cold climates, organisms may be exposed to temperatures much lower than those of seawater. Wave action regularly batters the shore, damaging or washing away shore organisms. Organisms on the shore distribute themselves according to their tolerance for these abiotic factors. This distribution creates a vertical zonation of organisms on the shore. Organisms that are submerged only at high tides, such as barnacles, lichens, and limpets, have **adaptations** that prevent overheating and drying. The middle zone has organisms, such as mollusks (limpets and mussels) and crabs that can survive, along with small fish, in rock pools. The area exposed only by the lowest tide has the most diverse shore community, with lots of seaweed and a wide array of invertebrates.

Other shores are sandy or muddy. Most of the organisms on these shores bury themselves in the substrate. In the sand or mud are small crustaceans and worms that feed on algae, archaea, bacteria, and organic matter. Birds, such as plovers and oystercatchers, are major predators. Where the tide goes out a long distance, flat intertidal marshes develop. These marshes support many different salt-tolerant grasses and reeds. Mangrove swamps are a type of marine shore found in subtropical and tropical areas. Mangroves are a group of tree species that are adapted to grow in saltwater. They form forests in shallow tidal areas. They are among the most productive ecosystems on Earth because they provide homes for a wide variety of invertebrates and act as nurseries for many fish species.

MANGROVES

Mangroves live in saltwater or a mix of saltwater and freshwater, also called brackish water. Notice the tree's unique structure. How do you think this root structure relates to its niche?

The shallow offshore areas, usually over a continental shelf, are sometimes called the *neritic zone*. The water in this region of the ocean is well illuminated and typically rich in nutrients when compared to the open ocean. It supports a wide range of fish species, aquatic algae such as kelp, and a wide variety of invertebrates, including sponges and corals.

In warm tropical areas, this zone may be dominated by coral reefs, which are often considered to be their own biome. Corals have a symbiotic relationship with algae that live inside their bodies, being that these algae, called *zooxanthellae*, photosynthesize and give off nutrients the coral needs to grow. The coral provides the algae with carbon dioxide, and because of this relationship, most corals can grow only in water that has adequate sunlight for photosynthesis. Coral reefs support an incredible diversity of marine life, possibly close to 9 million species. Although they cover a small amount of area compared to many marine biomes, this high diversity makes coral reefs very important.

Beyond the continental shelf is water that is open and often very deep. In the upper lit part of this pelagic zone live phytoplankton that form the base of a complex food web, and commonly, the next trophic level of this food web are zooplankton—numerous floating animals. Many of these zooplankton are microscopic, while bigger animals in this zone float or are free-swimming including squid, fish, turtles, and whales. At night, animals from the deep, dark parts of the ocean migrate upward to feed upon the phytoplankton and, in turn, lure their predators to the surface.

The benthic zone is located at the bottom of the deep ocean biome, at the interface between the ocean and the seabed, and the types of communities that form here depend upon the temperature and the nature of the ocean floor. Most animals that live in the benthic zone depend upon the detritus that rains from above. In the open ocean, the benthic biome is characterized by high pressure, low temperature, and darkness.

The deepest parts of the benthic zone are the abyssal zones, and animals that reside here must survive in one of the most extreme environments on Earth. Animals that live in the abyssal zone have several adaptations for living in near or total darkness, including bioluminescence, large eyes, huge jaws and teeth, and massive stomachs for catching and digesting prey.

Estuaries are the places where freshwater from rivers meets the ocean, and they typically consist of the end of a river valley that has been flooded to create a broad inlet. The water in estuaries is less salty than water in the ocean, and the salinity of the water in estuaries can vary a lot. When river flow is high, the increased input of freshwater reduces salinity; in contrast, when the flow is low, the salinity increases. Salinity also changes with changes in tidal levels; therefore, organisms that live in estuaries must be tolerant of these changes in salinity. These types of organisms are said to be euryhaline.

Consider the Explain Question

How does climate influence the characteristics of a biome?

Go online to complete the scientific explanation.

dlc.com/ca10022s

Check Your Understanding

What would be the impact of a phytoplankton boom in an aquatic biome ecosystem?

dlc.com/ca10023s

in Action

Applying Biomes

One aquatic biome crucial to life on Earth has the highest level of **biodiversity** and is mostly found in warm ocean waters. Coral reefs are naturally occurring boundaries that grow along the coasts of many areas around the equator. Coral reefs are home not only to the coral polyps that build them but also to many different species of fish, shrimp, crabs, and sea stars, among others. In addition to providing food and shelter for marine animals, coral reefs also offer a natural form of protection to the coasts of their neighboring countries. Coral reefs usually extend for miles (the Great Barrier Reef in Australian waters is 1,600 miles, or 2,575 kilometers. It is so big that it can be seen from space!) and, due to this, help reduce the amount of wave action hitting the beach. This helps to prevent erosion and other damage.

A healthy coral reef relies upon the symbiotic relationship between coral polyps and the zooxanthella algae that live inside their bodies. When there are changes that occur in the abiotic conditions under which the corals live, they become stressed. Changes in temperature, light, or nutrients may result in the expulsion, these symbiotic algae. When this happens, the corals turn white, a process called *coral bleaching*. If the conditions do not change, most of the bleached coral will die.

The abiotic factor to which the coral reefs are most sensitive is a change in temperature. Most corals can only live in water that is between 25 and 32 degrees Celsius. Temperatures outside this range can cause bleaching. In January 2010, cold water temperatures in the Florida Keys caused the corals to expel their zooxanthellae due to a water temperature drop of 6.7 degrees Celsius lower than the normal temperatures observed at that time of year. Some coral died, but luckily the temperature soon returned to normal, and most of the coral got their algae back.

But what happens to the reefs if the temperature changes for longer periods? Most coral bleaching is caused by waters that become too warm for coral.

Shifting weather patterns, such as El Niño, can bring water that is too warm to coral reefs. The Great Barrier Reef off the coast of Australia and those in Hawaii are regularly damaged by El Niño events that strike them about once every five years. There is strong evidence to suggest that climate change is causing events like this to happen more frequently and with greater intensity.

Biologists and climate scientists are working together on ways to make corals more tolerant of high temperatures. They are investigating whether the algae in some heat-tolerant corals have evolved to withstand higher temperatures or if there is some other factor that allows them to survive. If they are, in fact, tolerant, then it may be possible to inoculate heat-stressed coral with this organism.

CORAL BLEACHING

Coral bleaching happens when the symbiotic algae living within the corals are expelled. What environmental conditions can cause this to happen, and how can it be fixed?

As scientists study marine biomes, they gain a better understanding of how fluctuations in the physical environment impact the organisms that live within them.

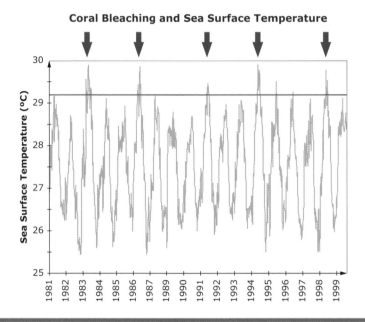

Coral Bleaching and Sea Surface Temperature

CORAL BLEACHING EVENTS OFF THE ISLAND OF TAHITI

Red arrows indicate observed bleaching event. The red line indicates minimum temperature for coral bleaching. What causes coral bleaching?

STEM and Biomes

What is the largest aquatic biome on Earth? Think about what covers more of the planet than anything else. The answer is the deep ocean floor. This part of the ocean is many kilometers down on the abyssal plain and has water that is cold and dark. The pressure this far down is hundreds of times what it is on the surface. This is due to the force of all that water pushing downward. At the surface, there is one atmosphere of pressure (which makes sense, because all of the gases of the atmosphere are sitting on top of the ocean). Every 35 feet of water adds another atmosphere of pressure. The deepest part of the ocean is called the Mariana Trench, which is 35,802 feet deep. This means that at the bottom there are close to 1,000 atmospheres of pressure. How would this impact your body? This much pressure could crush you like a bug in a matter of seconds.

Scientists who explore these areas are called deep-sea oceanographers. They have not only knowledge of how the oceans behave but also skills necessary to operate specialized technology that can go into the depths. In order to get to these depths, these scientists work closely with engineers to build machines that can help scientists survive under the precarious conditions. To date, very few existing submersibles have been able to reach the deepest part of the ocean due to the incredible depth and pressure. Only two manned submersibles have ever made it to the bottom of the Mariana Trench.

A submersible is a submarine that is used to explore the depths of the ocean. These machines are often small and can be either manned or robotic. Those that are controlled by the researchers are called ROVs, which stands for "remotely operated vehicles." These submersibles need to be very maneuverable, moving up and down as well as backward and forward in the water. The submersibles also need some form of power source. This power not only drives the vehicle but also provides electricity to run lights and data-collecting apparatuses. Many times, ROVs are tethered to the surface with very long cables to provide this power. While this ensures the submersible will be able to perform all of its functions, it does limit the depth of how far it can go. Another factor for which scientists and engineers need to compensate is the depth to which the submersible needs to travel. The ocean is very deep. Getting ROVs down to the bottom is usually fairly easy, as they often have numerous weights attached to them. The hard part is getting the machines back to the surface. The same weights that bring the submersibles to the bottom can be automatically released, which causes the subs to float back up.

ROBOTIC SUBMERSIBLE

How does the design of this ROV allow it to gather data from the deepest parts of the oceans?

Energy for Life

dlc.com/ca10024s

LESSON OVERVIEW

Lesson Questions

- What is energy and how does it contribute to maintaining life on Earth?
- What are kinetic and potential energy?
- What are the laws of thermodynamics?
- What is the difference between endergonic and exergonic reactions?
- What is the difference between oxidation and reduction reactions?

Key Vocabulary

Which terms do you already know?

- ☐ aerobic respiration
- ☐ anaerobic respiration
- ☐ cellular respiration
- ☐ chemical energy
- ☐ electron transport chain
- ☐ endergonic reaction
- ☐ energy
- ☐ exergonic reaction
- ☐ glycolysis
- ☐ oxidation
- ☐ photosynthesis
- ☐ potential energy
- ☐ redox reaction
- ☐ reduction
- ☐ thermal energy
- ☐ thermodynamics

Lesson Objectives

By the end of the lesson, you should be able to:

- Describe the concept of energy and its contributions to maintaining life on Earth.
- Distinguish among the different forms of energy.
- Describe the laws of thermodynamics.
- Distinguish between endergonic and exergonic reactions.
- Distinguish between oxidation and reduction reactions.

Thinking about the Energy for Life

dlc.com/ca10025s

After practicing for months, it is the day before the big race. Since all living things need energy, you need to be sure that the food you eat today will provide you with enough to finish the race tomorrow. What kinds of things should you eat?

RUNNING A MARATHON

Have you ever run a race? If so, then you had to use a lot of energy to cross the finish line.

EXPLAIN QUESTION

▌ **Explain how and why energy is important to living things.**

What Is Energy and How Does It Contribute to Maintaining Life on Earth?

Living Organisms and Energy

All living organisms require **energy** to perform essential cellular processes. Growth and reproduction are complex processes that need energy. Building larger molecules from smaller ones requires the input of energy; these larger molecules can also be used to store energy for later use. Moving molecules from low to high concentrations require the input of energy. Organisms also need energy for a variety of other tasks such as movement and sending electrical signals in the nervous system. Without energy, none of the processes of life are possible.

Ultimately, the energy for most organisms on Earth comes from the sun. Photosynthetic organisms such as plants, algae, and some bacteria and archaea can convert solar energy into **chemical energy**, which is energy stored in chemical bonds. Other organisms such as animals and fungi must acquire their energy from the photosynthetic organisms. When an animal ingests food, the food molecules are broken down, and the energy within is released. Some single-celled organisms are able to use inorganic molecules such as compounds containing sulfur as an energy source.

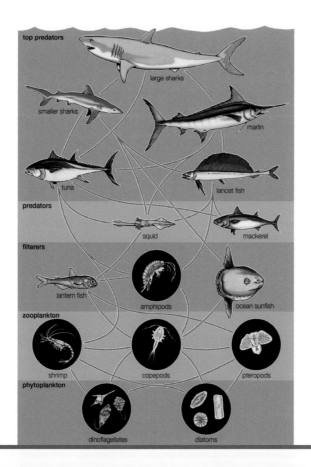

OCEAN FOOD WEB

All living things use energy. How does this energy get transferred between different organisms?

Defining Energy

All organisms require a source of energy, but what is energy? Energy is the ability to do work or cause change. The processes of living organisms such as moving and building molecules are examples of work that can be accomplished using energy. To do this work, cells convert energy from one form to another. Energy cannot be created or destroyed, but it can be transformed into different forms. Kinetic energy is the energy of motion, **thermal energy** is heat generated by the kinetic energy of atoms or molecules, and **potential energy** is stored energy. Chemical potential energy, commonly called *chemical energy,* is a form of potential energy that is stored in chemical bonds. It is the conversion of energy among these forms that keeps living organisms alive.

Measuring Energy

Energy can be measured using a number of different techniques. Energy is defined as the ability to do work, and work is defined as the force used to move an object for a certain distance (work = force × distance). The standard unit of measurement for energy is the joule (J), which is defined as 1 newton of force used to move an object 1 meter; 1 joule = 1 newton*meter.

A watt is defined as the use of 1 J/second. This measurement is often used to measure power expenditure in electrical equipment.

The energy in food is often measured in calories. A calorie (cal) is the amount of thermal energy needed to raise the temperature of 1 g of water by 1°C. The calories listed on food labels are kilocalories (1,000 calories). On food labels, kilocalories are designated as Calories with a capital letter *C.*

Energy can also be measured in ergs, which are defined as the kinetic energy of 2 g moving at a velocity of 1 cm/sec. These measures of energy relate to each other with the following conversions:

$$1 \text{ cal} = 4.184 \text{ J}$$
$$1 \text{ J} = 0.239 \text{ cal}$$
$$1 \text{ erg} = 10^{-7} \text{ J}$$

In biology, the calorie is the most commonly used unit of energy.

FOOD ENERGY

Foods contains energy. What form do you think this energy takes?

What Are Kinetic and Potential Energy?

Kinetic and Potential Energy

Energy exists in a variety of forms of kinetic and potential energy. Organisms survive by converting energy from one form to another.

Kinetic energy is the energy any object has because it is moving. Objects can have kinetic energy regardless of their mass. Vibrating atoms have kinetic energy because they are moving. A running elephant also has kinetic energy. Energy from food is converted by the elephant's muscles to make it move and give it kinetic energy. Kinetic energy is defined as the work needed to move a body of a given mass to its final velocity, or speed in a given direction.

Thermal energy is a term used to refer to heat generated by the kinetic energy of atoms and molecules. Atoms and molecules are in random constant motion. Temperature is a measure of this motion. Molecules moving more quickly have greater thermal energy than molecules moving more slowly.

Potential energy is the energy in a body or a system based on its position or configuration—it is stored energy. Potential energy exists in a number of forms. These include chemical potential energy, gravitational potential energy, and mechanical potential energy.

Chemical potential energy or chemical energy is the energy that is stored in the bonds between atoms. Chemical energy is released or absorbed during chemical reactions. When bonds are broken in chemical reactions, energy is absorbed. When bonds are made in a chemical reaction, energy is released. The balance of energy between bonds being broken and bonds being formed determines whether a chemical reaction releases or absorbs energy. Organisms store energy as chemical energy. Food compounds, like glucose, starch, or fats, contain a lot of chemical energy in their molecules. When cells metabolize food during **cellular respiration**, they react, these compounds in the presence of oxygen. This releases energy. Initially they may store some of the released energy as chemical energy in other "high energy" molecules. One of these molecules is adenosine triphosphate (ATP). This stored chemical energy is then readily available to do work within the cell. Chemical energy is required for all life processes.

Energy can be stored in other ways. A ball at the top of a hill has potential energy because of its position in relation to the center of Earth. If the ball rolls down the hill, this gravitational potential energy is converted to kinetic energy. Stretched or compressed objects, like springs or rubber bands, can also store energy. This mechanical potential energy is converted to kinetic energy when the force holding them in position is released.

What Are the Laws of Thermodynamics?

The Laws of Thermodynamics

The study of energy is called **thermodynamics**. A scientific understanding of thermodynamics has resulted in three basic laws.

The first law of thermodynamics is related to the conservation of energy and is often called the law of conservation of energy. The law states that energy cannot be created or destroyed. The total energy in the universe remains constant. Energy can, however, be transformed from one form into another.

For example, when an organism breaks down glucose molecules during cellular respiration, some of the chemical potential energy of the glucose molecules is transformed into the chemical potential energy of other molecules such as ATP, some into other compounds, and some into thermal energy. No energy disappears. The amount of energy at the beginning is the same as at the end.

The second law of thermodynamics states that the entropy of a system cannot decrease. Entropy is the measure of disorder, or chaos, in a system. Systems increase in disorder until equilibrium is reached. This law of thermodynamics explains why energy cannot be transferred from a colder body to a hotter body and why energy conversions are never 100 percent efficient. Most of the energy taken in from food is lost as thermal energy. Only a small percent of the energy taken in is used to do work. This thermal energy is why people feel hot when exercising. The conversion of potential energy to kinetic energy releases a lot of thermal energy.

The third law of thermodynamics defines the point at which the thermal energy of molecules is zero. This point is called absolute zero and is defined as 0 K (Kelvin); this occurs at $-273\,°C$. *Absolute zero* is the lowest possible temperature because atoms have ceased moving.

It is important to understand that the laws of thermodynamics apply to closed systems. A closed system is one which no energy can enter or leave. The ultimate closed system is the universe. In nature, all systems are open—energy can get in or out. Organisms are open systems within the bigger closed system of the universe. The laws of thermodynamics apply to them just as they do to the rest of the universe.

What Is the Difference between Endergonic and Exergonic Reactions?

Endergonic and Exergonic Reactions

The laws of thermodynamics can be used to classify chemical reactions into two categories: reactions that take in energy from their surroundings and reactions that release energy into their surroundings.

Endergonic reactions require a net input of energy from the surroundings. In a biological system, free energy (G) is energy that can do work if temperature and pressure are held constant. The change in free energy (ΔG) of these reactions is positive because the products of the reaction contain more energy than the reactants. Because these reactions have a positive ΔG, they are not spontaneous; that is, they are not energetically favorable and require the input of energy to proceed.

Exergonic reactions release energy. The ΔG of these reactions is negative because the products of the reaction contain less energy than the reactants. This energy is released into the surroundings and can be used to power endergonic reactions. Because these reactions have a negative ΔG, they are spontaneous; that is, they are energetically favorable and occur without the input of energy.

In cellular processes, endergonic reactions are often linked to exergonic reactions. A common exergonic reaction that is used to power a variety of cellular processes is the breakdown of ATP into ADP (adenosine diphosphate). This breaking down of larger molecules into smaller molecules is exergonic and can be used to power endergonic reactions.

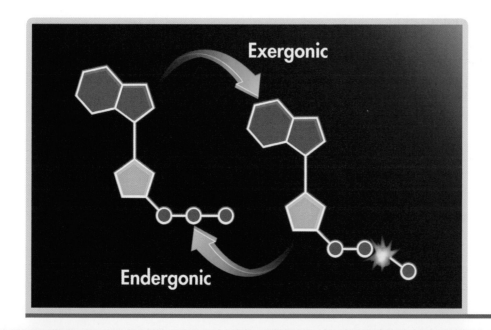

ATP

Exergonic reactions such as the breakdown of ATP to ADP are used by cells to power endergonic reactions. Why is this pairing necessary?

Cells regenerate their ATP store by adding a third phosphate to ADP; synthesizing larger molecules from smaller subunits is endergonic. Cells can break down food molecules (an exergonic process) to release the needed energy to build ATP (an endergonic process). ATP is then stored until its chemical energy is needed to do work.

What Is the Difference between Oxidation and Reduction Reactions?

Redox Reactions

Redox reactions are used to store and release energy in biological systems. Electrons can be moved from a lower energy state in one atom to a higher energy state in another atom; this serves to store energy. Electrons can also move from higher energy states in one atom to lower energy states in another, thus releasing energy. The movement of electrons from one atom to another changes the **oxidation** number of both atoms. Any chemical reaction that changes the oxidation number of atoms is called a redox reaction.

The term *redox* is a combination of the terms **reduction** and oxidation. Reduction is the gain of electrons, which decreases the oxidation state of the atom or ion. In reduction, the potential energy of electrons is increased; this stores energy. Oxidation is the loss of electrons, which increases the oxidation state of the atom or ion. In oxidation, the potential energy of the electrons is decreased, which releases energy. Oxidation and reduction reactions often occur together as one atom gains an electron from another atom. This reaction is called a redox *reaction* because one atom or ion has been reduced from the oxidation of another atom or ion.

In living things, energy is usually stored and released through redox reactions. For example, in **photosynthesis**, carbon dioxide is reduced to make sugars, and water is oxidized to form oxygen. Chemical reactions like this occur in many small steps. Each step is a small redox reaction.

What Is the Role of Photosynthesis and Respiration in the Carbon Cycle?

The Carbon Cycle

Carbon is constantly circulating between living things and the environment. As it circulates, it changes form—from gas to solid and back again. There are several ways in which carbon is stored on Earth. A large quantity of stored carbon is called a *reservoir*. Carbon reservoirs include fossil fuel deposits, biomass (living plants and animals), oceans, and rocks. Carbon is essential to life on Earth, and the carbon cycle helps keep the amount of carbon in the atmosphere relatively constant.

The exchange of carbon between biomass and the atmosphere is also referred to as the *fast carbon cycle*, because this cycle occurs relatively quickly. Carbon is taken from the atmosphere when plants use it to produce food. Then, animals consume the food and use its energy for the animal's life processes. When the animal dies, it decomposes and releases the carbon into the atmosphere or into the soil.

Photosynthesis and Respiration

Photosynthesis and respiration are two processes that exchange carbon between the atmosphere and living things in the environment. They are essential to the functioning of the fast carbon cycle.

Photosynthesis is the biochemical process by which plants use energy from the sun to produce food from carbon dioxide and water. In this way, carbon moves from the atmospheric reservoir to the biomass reservoir.

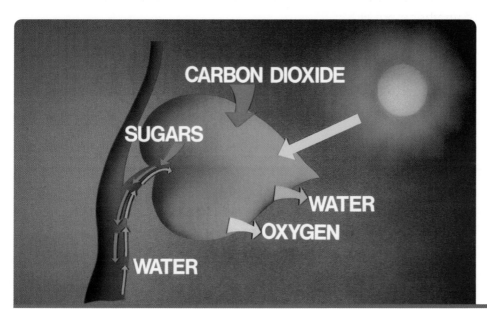

PHOTOSYNTHESIS

Plants use the process of photosynthesis to produce food from carbon dioxide and water. What role does photosynthesis play in the carbon cycle?

Cellular respiration is the set of metabolic processes by which plants and animals convert the chemical potential energy in glucose and other nutrients into adenosine triphosphate (ATP), which is then used to fuel other biochemical processes. The overall reaction for cellular respiration converts glucose into carbon dioxide (which is exhaled) and water. Thus, carbon moves from biomass back into the atmosphere.

Photosynthesis and cellular respiration not only cycle matter in the form of carbon through the carbon cycle, but they also cycle energy through the carbon cycle. Photosynthesis converts solar energy into the chemical potential energy contained in glucose and other carbohydrates. Then, cellular respiration converts the chemical potential energy into ATP, which fuels other biochemical processes.

Consider the Explain Question

Explain how and why energy is important to living things.

Go online and complete the scientific explanation.

dlc.com/ca10026s

Check Your Understanding

Go online to check your understanding of this concept's key ideas.

dlc.com/ca10027s

STEM in Action

Applying Energy for Life

As a heterotroph, you get all of your energy from eating food. No matter what you consume, all foods provide a source of energy called *calories*. A calorie is the amount of thermal energy needed to raise the temperature of 1 gram of water by 1°C. The Calories referred to on food labels are actually kilocalories—each is worth 1,000 calories (notice the uppercase *C* in the term). This information can sometimes be misinterpreted. For example, a hard-boiled egg contains 80 Calories of energy. However, since the units are actually kilocalories, the egg has 80,000 calories. Not to worry, though. The recommended caloric intake is 2,000 Calories a day, but since the units have been reduced for simplicity, the number of calories needed is actually 2 million! (Don't take that as an excuse to go eat everything in sight).

In order to maintain your weight and keep the body functioning properly, caloric intake should be balanced with energy output. This means the number of calories taken in as food should equal the number of calories used or released as energy. This energy could be released as heat, as kinetic energy when you move, or as chemical energy in the compounds you excrete or defecate. If you wish to gain weight, you need to eat more food calories than the energy you use. If you wish to lose weight, eat fewer calories than you use. It's all a matter of energy balance.

CALORIE LABEL

A calorie is a unit of energy. All of the food you eat contains calories, some more than others. Do you read the calorie labels? How does this impact what you put into your body?

Metabolic Rate of Selected Organisms

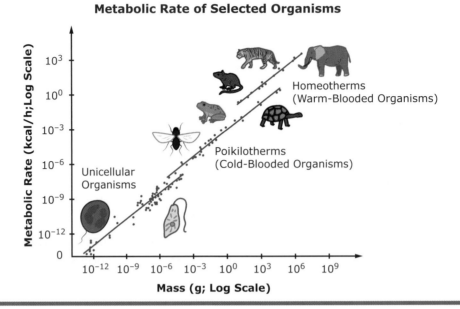

BURNING THOSE CALORIES

The graph shows the basal metabolic rate of several different types of organisms. This is the number of calories they burn due to their overall body mass. What animal shown in the graph has the highest basal metabolic rate?

While there are several different opinions on how many calories one should consume a day, the overall idea is that most weight loss is a numbers game. For example, one of the recommended matrices used for weight maintenance is to take your body weight and multiply it by 12 for men and 11 for women. This will then give you an idea of how many calories a day you need to maintain your weight. How many do you need? Let's say a man weighs 180 pounds. Doing the math (180 × 12), that means this man will need 2,160 Calories per day to maintain his weight. If he consumes less than that, he will lose weight. If he consumes more, he will gain weight. Additionally, the amount of exercise needs to be considered. If this man burns 400 calories a day running, then that increases the number of calories he can consume. The bottom line is that weight loss is all about the calories.

What is the ideal weight? All people, except identical twins, have genetic differences. This means their bodies and metabolism are different. However, studies of a large number of people have led scientists to create a tool that help individuals to determine a healthy body weight. This tool is called the *body mass index*, or BMI. The BMI is an estimate of body fat based on height and weight. It is not a precise figure, but it does tell you where you would fall compared to others. It may overestimate body fat in athletes who have a muscular build and underestimate body fat for individuals who have a low muscle mass. BMI can be determined using tables or special calculators available on the Internet.

The key to reaching and holding a healthy weight isn't about short-term changes in diet. It's not about fad diets that promise quick results. It is about healthy eating and physical activity, balancing the calories you eat with the number of calories your body uses—energy in and energy out.

STEM and Energy for Life

Converting chemical energy into kinetic energy is the basis of how cars move. The potential energy stored in petroleum products is used to power the automobile engine. This combustion produces waste products that pollute the environment and is a nonrenewable resource. This means that it will eventually get used up. Alternative fuel sources for cars are currently being researched.

Biofuels are fuels produced from biological sources. Biofuels can include using agricultural waste products, sawdust, and even corn to generate fuel such as ethanol. Corn is of particular interest because of its abundance and ease of converting into ethanol. The corn is cooked with different enzymes to convert its starch into simple sugars.

Corn production has reached all-time highs in the United States. Of the 1.5 billion bushels of corn produced in 2011, 600 million were used for biofuel. This is good news for the environment.

To meet the ever-growing demand for biofuels, crop science has become more and more popular as a course of study. Crop scientists conduct research on crops and other agricultural products to find new and improved ways to use these for fuel. A crop scientist may test several types of perennial grasses to see which can be most efficiently broken down into simple sugars. Crop scientists also work to improve crop yields by using techniques that could enhance feedstock production efforts. A career in this field would require a strong biology background, as well as a lot of field training.

CORN GROWN FOR BIOFUEL

Since there is so much corn grown in the United States, it makes sense that a lot of it is processed and converted into ethanol. How is this crop converted into energy?

Photosynthesis

dlc.com/ca10028s

LESSON OVERVIEW

Lesson Questions

- How are photosynthesis and cellular respiration related?
- How does the process of photosynthesis work?

Lesson Objectives

By the end of the lesson, you should be able to:

- Distinguish between the processes of photosynthesis and cellular respiration.
- Explain the process of photosynthesis.

Key Vocabulary

Which terms do you already know?

- [ ] adenosine diphosphate (ADP)
- [ ] adenosine triphosphate (ATP)
- [ ] autotroph
- [ ] Calvin cycle
- [ ] carbohydrate
- [ ] cellular respiration
- [ ] chlorophyll
- [ ] chloroplast
- [ ] electron
- [ ] photosynthesis
- [ ] solar energy
- [ ] stroma
- [ ] thylakoids

A Light Lunch

Visible light and other electromagnetic energy from the sun drive many of the processes on our planet, including weather systems and ocean currents, and provide the energy for life. It may seem strange that an immense ball of glowing gas 150 million kilometers away provides your lunch, but it does. How does this happen?

dlc.com/ca10029s

EXPLAIN QUESTION

Can you explain the steps involved in converting sunlight into the energy that is stored in food and compare the processes of cellular respiration and photosynthesis?

FROM SUNLIGHT TO FOOD

How do plants turn sunlight into food?

How Are Photosynthesis and Cellular Respiration Related?

Autotrophs and Producers

Organisms, such as plants, that can photosynthesize are called autotrophs. **Autotroph** means "self-nourisher." Autotrophs can make complex food substances from simple compounds. Plants use the simple compounds and energy from the sun to produce food. Not only do autotrophs produce their own food, but they also store these prepared food substances. This provides an available source of chemical potential energy in the form of organic molecules that other organisms can consume. Autotrophs produce the food that provides energy to food chains. For this reason, autotrophs are also called *producers*. **Photosynthesis** is the process that initiates, and provides biomass to, most of Earth's food chains.

GREEN ALGAE

Green algae are autotrophs that emerged nearly a billion years ago. Why did photosynthesizers precede animal life forms on Earth?

By utilizing **solar energy**, photosynthesizing organisms convert carbon dioxide and water into oxygen and **carbohydrates**. Carbohydrates are organic molecules. Carbohydrates consist of carbon, hydrogen, and oxygen. Carbohydrates store and are a source of a lot of energy. The most common carbohydrates are sugars and starches. Oxygen is a by-product of photosynthesis. Photosynthetic organisms release oxygen into the atmosphere. Animals can use this oxygen for respiration.

Plants are the main photosynthetic organisms. They include trees, flowers, grasses, herbs, vines, ferns, mosses, and shrubs. Other photosynthetic organisms include algae, some archaea, and bacteria. These are commonly found in freshwater ecosystems, the upper layers of marine environments, and salty marshes. Scientists believe microorganisms first released oxygen into Earth's atmosphere billions of years ago. They think that before that time, Earth's atmosphere contained very little oxygen. Photosynthesis is responsible for today's oxygen-rich atmosphere.

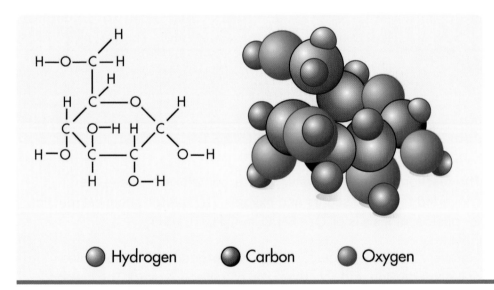

MOLECULAR STRUCTURE OF GLUCOSE

Glucose is a common carbohydrate. Can you use the information in this diagram to work out the formula for glucose?

The Photosynthesis Reaction

Like many chemical reactions, photosynthesis begins with a set of reactants (water and carbon dioxide) and uses energy to convert them into products (sugar and oxygen). Photosynthesis is therefore an endothermic or energy-absorbing reaction. The energy for photosynthesis comes from sunlight. The word *photosynthesis* literally means "using light to build." But how do plants capture solar energy for their use? What are the chemical reactants and products of this process? How do the reactants differ from the products in terms of energy?

Plants and other photosynthesizing organisms contain pigments that can absorb energy in the form of light. The main pigment in plant cells is **chlorophyll**. Chlorophyll absorbs most of the visible spectrum except green light, which it reflects, giving plants their green color. When chlorophyll absorbs light, it absorbs light energy. This light energy is then converted to chemical potential energy in the photosynthesis reaction.

CHLOROPHYLL

Chlorophyll, the pigment that makes plants appear green, is also responsible for photosynthesis. What colors of visible light is the plant converting into food?

The reaction begins with water and carbon dioxide. These are converted to simple sugars and oxygen. The overall chemical reaction for photosynthesis is $6CO_2 + 6H_2O \rightarrow C_6H_{12}O6 + 6O_2$.

For every molecule of glucose ($C_6H_{12}O_6$) produced, six molecules of carbon dioxide and six molecules of water are used. The carbon dioxide and water are the reactants, while the glucose and oxygen are the products. Notice that the amount of matter did not change but rather was rearranged. There are the same number of atoms on each side of the equation, making it balanced. This glucose may then be used to produce complex carbohydrates, such as starches or cellulose.

Comparing Photosynthesis and Cellular Respiration

Photosynthesis is performed by plants and some microorganisms. Photosynthesis uses the energy of the sun to facilitate the reaction of water and carbon dioxide gas producing the sugar (glucose) and oxygen. They use six molecules of water and six molecules of carbon dioxide to make one molecule of glucose. If photosynthetic organisms did not exist, we would not exist. We need oxygen and organic food sources obtained from plant carbohydrates to survive. Cells metabolize the products of photosynthesis to make energy by aerobic **cellular respiration**. Energy and matter derived from photosynthesis are used for the growth and maintenance of organisms.

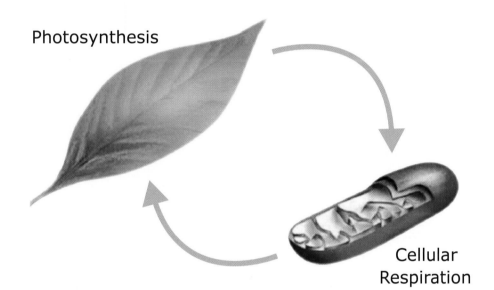

Photosynthesis

Cellular Respiration

© Discovery Education | www.discoveryeducation.com

COMPLEMENTARY PROCESSES

Photosynthesis and cellular respiration work in a cycle that uses the products of one reaction as the reactants for the other. Why is this important?

Cellular respiration is a process used by all cells to produce useful energy from carbohydrates. The form of cellular respiration used in plants and most animals is called *aerobic cellular respiration*. Aerobic cellular respiration uses oxygen and carbohydrates. Using a series of chemical reactions, aerobic cellular respiration converts the chemical energy in carbohydrates into chemical energy of another compound, **adenosine triphosphate (ATP)**. Molecules of ATP are the preferred source of energy for the cellular activity of all organisms. ATP is needed for growth, reproduction, and maintaining homeostasis. The waste products of cellular respiration are carbon dioxide and water. The aerobic respiration of one glucose molecule produces six water molecules and six carbon dioxide molecules.

The following table compares photosynthesis with aerobic cellular respiration:

Photosynthesis	Aerobic Cellular Respiration
Uses energy from the sun.	Cellular respiration releases energy.
Uses ATP (made in the early steps of photosynthesis) to make carbohydrates.	Uses carbohydrates to make ATP.
Converts six molecules of carbon dioxide and six molecules of water into one molecule of glucose.	Converts one molecule of glucose into six molecules of carbon dioxide and six molecules of water.
Removes carbon dioxide from the air.	Releases carbon dioxide into the air.
Releases oxygen into the air.	Removes oxygen from the air.
Overall chemical reaction is: $6CO_2 + 6H_2O + energy \rightarrow C_6H_{12}O_6 + 6O_2$	Overall chemical reaction is: $C_6H_{12}O_6 + 6O_2 \rightarrow 6CO_2 + 6H_2O + energy$

Photosynthesis and cellular respiration are therefore two parts of a never-ending cycle. The products of cellular respiration—carbon dioxide and water—are the reactants of photosynthesis, and vice versa. These two processes determine the amounts of carbon dioxide and oxygen in the air.

How Does the Process of Photosynthesis Work?

The overall biochemical reaction for photosynthesis is a very complex process. This complex process can be divided into two main stages: the light-dependent reaction and the light-independent reaction, or **Calvin cycle**. Both these stages take place inside the **chloroplasts**.

The Light-Dependent Reaction

In the light-dependent reaction, solar energy is converted into potential chemical energy. The light-dependent reaction takes place in the **thylakoids**—stacked, saclike structures found within the chloroplasts of plant cells. These structures contain the green pigment chlorophyll. Chlorophyll absorbs wavelengths of light other than green. Other different-colored pigments may also be present and help to absorb light. However, chlorophyll is the most important of all for photosynthesis.

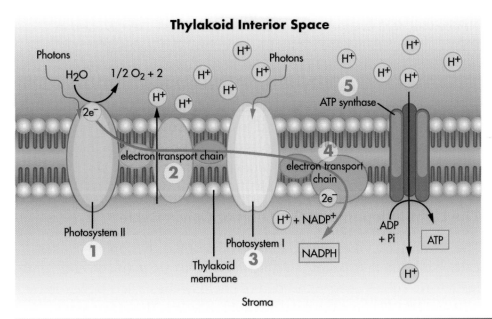

THYLAKOIDS

The light-dependent reactions of photosynthesis take place in thylakoids. Where are thylakoids located?

The light-dependent reaction has two photosystems (II and I), and takes place in the following steps:

1. Photosystem II occurs first. In Photosystem II, light is absorbed by chlorophyll molecules that excite **electrons** in the chlorophyll. These excited electrons are passed onto a series of proteins called an *electron transport chain*.

2. Electrons are passed along this chain. At each link, the electrons lose some of the energy they gained from the light. This energy is captured and used to convert **ADP (adenosine diphosphate)** to ATP (adenosine triphosphate). This process is called *photophosphorylation*. Water is split in this process. Hydrogen ions and oxygen are produced. Oxygen (from the water) is given off as a by-product.

3. In Photosystem I, the same electrons are reenergized by more light and passed down a second electron transport chain.

4. The electrons passed down the second electron transport chain are used by the hydrogen ions to convert NADP (nicotinamide adenine dinucleotide phosphate) to NADPH (nicotinamide adenine dinucleotide phosphate hydrogen).

5. The potential difference created by the electron transport chain resulting in a differing number of hydrogen ions on either side of the cell membrane causes transport of a hydrogen ion down the gradient, which provides energy for phosphorylation of ADP into ATP, mediated by ATP synthase.

Notice that light is used twice in this process. First, light is used in Photosystem II to initially excite the electrons and make ATP and then split water. Then, light is used in Photosystem I to reenergize the electrons to make NADPH. So, in the light-dependent reaction, light energy has been converted into chemical potential energy in high-energy molecules of ATP and NADPH (a source of high-energy electrons.) These high-energy molecules are passed on to the next stage of photosynthesis, the light-independent reaction.

The Light-Independent Reaction or Calvin Cycle

The Calvin cycle takes place in the **stroma** of the chloroplast. It uses carbon dioxide to make organic molecules that are then converted into sugars. No light is used in this part of photosynthesis; it is powered by ATP and NADPH from the previous light reaction. The steps are:

1. Carbon dioxide from the air is captured by existing organic compounds or CO_2 acceptors. This process is called *carbon fixation*.

2. The carbon from the carbon dioxide is then reduced through a series of steps by electrons provided by the NADPH produced from the light reaction.

3. With help from energy provided by ATP (also from the light reaction), a sugar-like compound containing three carbons called *glyceraldehyde-3-phosphate* is made. Some of this exits the Calvin cycle and is used to make glucose.

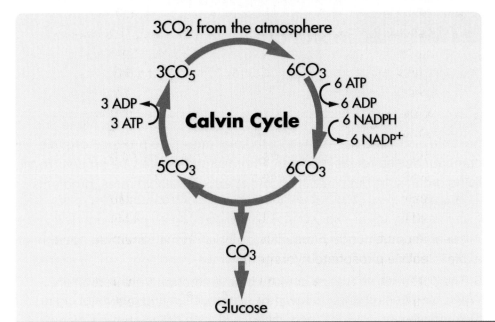

3CO$_2$ from the atmosphere

3CO$_5$

6CO$_3$

6 ATP
6 ADP
6 NADPH
6 NADP$^+$

3 ADP
3 ATP

Calvin Cycle

5CO$_3$

6CO$_3$

CO$_3$

Glucose

CALVIN CYCLE

The Calvin cycle is a series of chemical reactions that use high-energy compounds made in the light-dependent reaction to make carbohydrate. Why is the Calvin cycle sometimes called the *dark reaction*?

In the light-independent reaction, carbon from carbon dioxide is fixed into organic molecules that are then turned into sugars. These can be used to make other organic compounds. These compounds may be used by the plant directly or passed down the food chain.

Consider the Explain Question

Can you explain the steps involved in converting sunlight into the energy that is stored in food and compare the processes of cellular respiration and photosynthesis?

Go online to complete the scientific explanation.

dlc.com/ca10030s

Check Your Understanding

Why are photosynthesis and cellular respiration sometimes referred to as opposite reactions?

dlc.com/ca10031s

S T E M in Action

Applying Photosynthesis

Plants are not the only photosynthetic organisms on Earth. Algae and bacteria also have the ability to use solar energy to produce organic compounds and release oxygen. Photosynthesis is a vital process to all living organisms, but when it occurs at uncontrollable rates, problems can occur.

Algae are important ocean organisms. Under normal conditions, growth of algae is maintained at regular levels. However, conditions can be altered because of weather, temperature, toxins, or environmental pollutants. When conditions change to favor the reproduction and growth of algae, their growth can result in a population explosion called an *algal bloom*.

One of the more common algal blooms is associated with a species that produces a discoloration to the water called *red tide*. The coloring is due to photosynthetic pigments contained within the algae. Although referred to as red tide, the waters can also be brown, purple, orange, or yellow.

Red tides may or may not be harmful, depending on other circumstances. When massive amounts of algae from a bloom die, their bodies decay. This decay releases the organic compounds that make up their bodies. The release of these compounds can cause a depletion of oxygen in the water that is necessary for other organisms to survive.

RED TIDES

Algal blooms resulting in red tide can cause massive fish mortality. What is a common cause of algal blooms?

In 2011, a record-setting algal bloom covered parts of Lake Erie, one of the Great Lakes. Scientists linked the massive bloom to runoff from fertilizers used on nearby farmlands. The lake was unusually warm and still that year, keeping the fertilizer from being flushed from the system. Scientists warn that this could be a continuing problem if fertilizer-management programs are not put into place.

STEM and Photosynthesis

Fossil fuels are the remains of ancient plants and animals. As such, they were formed either directly or indirectly by the process of photosynthesis. By burning them, we are completing the carbon cycle that was delayed by their fossilization. One problem with this is that the formation of fossil fuels through the process of photosynthesis released the oxygen that makes up about one-fifth of the modern atmosphere. Burning fossil fuels will not deplete all of the planet's life-giving oxygen, but it can alter the composition of the atmosphere, increasing atmospheric levels of carbon dioxide.

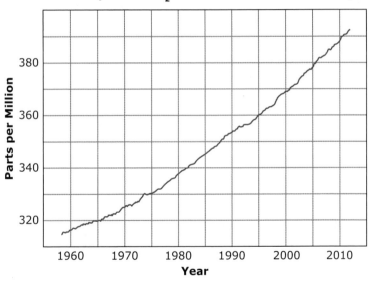

Atmospheric CO$_2$ at Mauna Loa Observatory

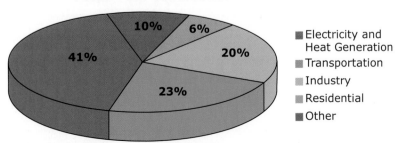

Carbon Dioxide Emissions from Fossil Fuel Combustion

- 41%
- 10%
- 6%
- 20%
- 23%

- Electricity and Heat Generation
- Transportation
- Industry
- Residential
- Other

CARBON DIOXIDE IN THE ATMOSPHERE

Photosynthetic organisms produced the oxygen that makes up about one fifth of the atmosphere. Some of these organisms were preserved in rocks and fossil fuels. What happens when we burn this stored carbon?

High levels of carbon dioxide trap heat in the atmosphere and can increase temperatures. Using fuels that can be grown fast may cycle carbon more rapidly. This could reduce the buildup of carbon dioxide. Known as *biofuels*, these products include wood, plant oils, and plant derivative products such as ethanol. Ethanol is widely used as an additive to gasoline. It is made by fermenting sugars made by plants through the process of photosynthesis.

Millions of years of evolution have proven that photosynthesis is an efficient and ideal process for harnessing energy. Taking that idea, scientists are now attempting to manufacture the products of photosynthesis in a process called *artificial photosynthesis*.

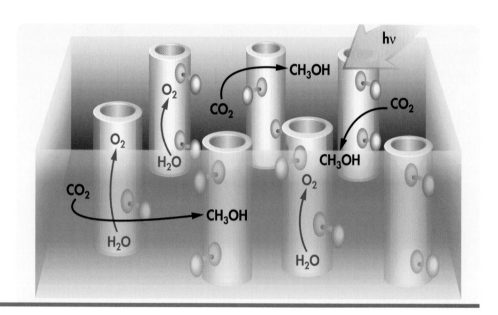

ARTIFICIAL PHOTOSYNTHESIS

Artificial photosynthesis could consist of nanotubes placed within a membrane. What might be some of the advantages of artificial photosynthesis?

The Joint Center for Artificial Photosynthesis (JCAP) is a division of the U.S. federal government's Department of Energy. The goal of scientists at JCAP is to develop methods of using Earth's own natural resources to develop a generator that uses the reactants of photosynthesis—sunlight, water, and carbon dioxide—to produce fuel. Scientists at JCAP predict that their generator could possibly be up to ten times more efficient in fuel production than typical crops. The process could theoretically be used to remove excess carbon dioxide from the atmosphere created by burning fossil fuels.

Cellular Respiration

LESSON OVERVIEW

Lesson Questions

- What are the steps involved in cellular respiration?
- What are the differences between aerobic and anaerobic respiration?

Lesson Objectives

By the end of the lesson, you should be able to:

- Model the process of cell respiration, including reactants and products, glycolysis, the Krebs cycle, and the electronic transport chain.
- Distinguish between aerobic and anaerobic respiration.

Key Vocabulary

Which terms do you already know?

- ☐ aerobic respiration
- ☐ anaerobic respiration
- ☐ cellular respiration
- ☐ electron transport chain
- ☐ energy (organisms)
- ☐ fermentation
- ☐ glycolysis
- ☐ oxidation
- ☐ oxidizing agent
- ☐ reducing agent

dlc.com/ca10032s

Fueling Fun

dlc.com/ca10033s

Running requires a lot of energy. By now you know that this energy comes from the chemical potential energy possessed in food, but how is that energy liberated? How is an energy bar, made up of fats, proteins, and carbohydrates, turned into movement?

THEY'RE OFF . . .
They're off, but what is happening inside their cells?

EXPLAIN QUESTION

How is food converted into the energy needed to move an athlete?

What Are the Steps Involved in Cellular Respiration?

Cellular Respiration

The process of releasing **energy** from food is called **cellular respiration**. When discussing cellular respiration, the term does not refer to breathing. Cellular respiration is different from breathing. It is a process that takes place inside cells. Cellular respiration involves many chemical reactions within each individual cell.

Reactants and Products

Animals and numerous microorganisms get their nutrition from organic matter that they metabolize in the presence of oxygen to obtain energy and building blocks to grow, reproduce, and survive. They rely on a type of metabolism called *aerobic cellular respiration*. For organisms that live by **aerobic respiration** of organic carbon sources, their primary source of food originates with carbohydrate-rich plants (or other organisms that eat carbohydrate-rich plants) whose mass and stored chemical energy was made during photosynthesis.

One of the simplest and most common sugar molecules used for energy is glucose, a direct product of photosynthesis. Organisms that get their nutrition from plants then use cellular respiration to metabolize, or break down, a glucose molecule into smaller molecules. Energy is released during this process and is used to make ATP. The process takes place through a series of chemical reactions.

In the case of cellular respiration, the primary reactants are glucose (or sometimes fatty or amino acids) and oxygen. Both glucose and oxygen are products of photosynthesis. When glucose is respired in the presence of oxygen, energy is released and carbon dioxide and water are produced. The basic chemical reaction for cellular respiration is shown here:

$$C_6H_{12}O_6 + 6O_2 \rightarrow 6CO_2 + 6H_2O + \text{Energy (ATP)}$$

or

$$\text{Glucose} + \text{Oxygen} \rightarrow \text{Carbon Dioxide} + \text{Water} + \text{Energy (ATP)}$$

This reaction is exothermic. The steps of cellular respiration include a series of **oxidation**-reduction reactions, or redox reactions. During these reactions, one substance gains an electron and is reduced, while another substance loses an electron and is oxidized. The substance that donates an electron is called the **reducing agent**. The substance receiving an electron is called the **oxidizing agent**. In summary, during a redox reaction, a reducing agent becomes oxidized and an oxidizing agent becomes reduced.

Redox reactions release energy because electrons move from a high-energy state to a low-energy state. Energy is given off in the process. This energy can be used to make high-energy compounds such as ATP. During cellular respiration, oxygen becomes reduced, forming water. Sugars become oxidized, forming carbon dioxide. The process takes place in three stages.

Glycolysis is the first stage of respiration. Glycolysis occurs in the cytoplasm of the cell. In eukaryotic cells such as animal cells, the products from glycolysis move into mitochondria. The second stage of cellular respiration, the Krebs cycle, takes place in the matrix of the mitochondria. Finally, the third stage takes place along the inner membrane of the mitochondria. This third and final stage is called the **electron transport chain**. In prokaryotic cells such as bacteria, glycolysis and the Krebs cycle take place in the cytoplasm, but the final stage of electron transport takes place along the plasma membrane.

For every molecule of glucose produced by photosynthesis and then oxidized by aerobic respiration, up to 38 molecules of ATP can be produced. However, the yield is more commonly around 30 ATPs. The oxygen and sugars derived from photosynthesis are respired into carbon dioxide and water. The same carbon dioxide and water can be used by photosynthetic plants, with the help of sunlight for energy, to make sugar and oxygen. The two processes are interdependent for the cycle of life to continue.

Glycolysis

The first stage of cellular respiration is glycolysis. Glycolysis is a form of **anaerobic respiration** that consists of ten stepwise chemical reactions. During these steps, a six-carbon glucose molecule, $C_6H_{12}O_6$, is broken down into two three-carbon molecules called pyruvate. A different enzyme is required for each of these reactions.

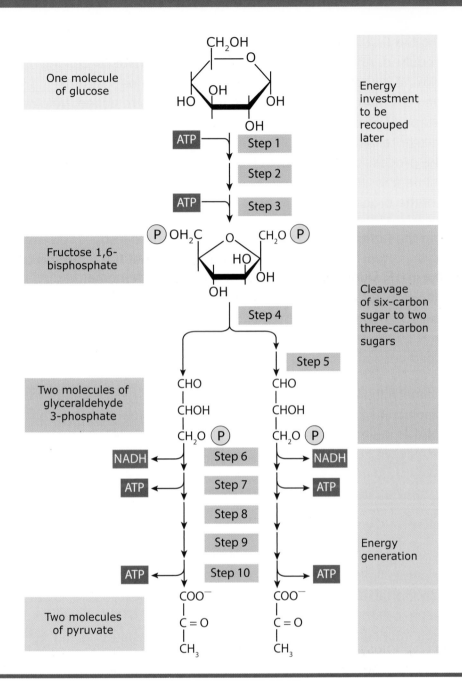

One molecule
of glucose

Energy
investment
to be
recouped
later

ATP   Step 1

Step 2

ATP   Step 3

Fructose 1,6-
bisphosphate

Cleavage
of six-carbon
sugar to two
three-carbon
sugars

Step 4

Step 5

Two molecules of
glyceraldehyde
3-phosphate

NADH   Step 6   NADH

ATP   Step 7   ATP

Step 8

Step 9

Energy
generation

ATP   Step 10   ATP

Two molecules
of pyruvate

GLYCOLYSIS

Glycolysis involves
10 stepwise chemical
reactions. What are the
reactants and products
of each reaction?

During the first few steps of glycolysis, two molecules of ATP are required. An ATP molecule loses one phosphate, becoming adenosine diphosphate, or ADP. When the bond between the second and third phosphate is broken, energy is released, helping the steps of glycolysis continue forward. Although the main purpose of cellular respiration is to release energy, some energy is required for the process to take place. Two ATP molecules are a small investment for the large amount of ATP that will be produced by the end of the process.

During the latter reactions of glycolysis, enough energy is released to produce four molecules of ATP. This means that the entire process of glycolysis involves a net production of two ATP molecules. Additionally, two more high-energy molecules called NADH are produced. *NAD* stands for *nicotinamide adenine dinucleotide*. The extra *H* on the end means "plus hydrogen," which refers to the reduced version of NAD.

In summary, the ten reactions of glycolysis require glucose and two ATP molecules for energy. The outcome includes four ATP molecules, two NADH molecules, and two molecules of pyruvate. The pyruvate molecules will continue to be broken down as cellular respiration continues to the next stage.

The Krebs Cycle

Following glycolysis, the pyruvate molecules are transported across each of two lipid bilayers of mitochondria. They enter the inner mitochondrial matrix. Each molecule is then converted to another molecule called *acetyl coenzyme* A, or acetyl CoA. This is the starting molecule for the next stage of cellular respiration. In the first step of the Krebs cycle, acetyl CoA donates its two-carbon acetyl group to another molecule. The resulting molecule is called *citrate*. Citrate is then modified in each of the next steps of the Krebs cycle. By the end of the cycle, the original molecule that reacted with acetyl CoA is actually regenerated. This allows the cycle to begin again and continue with each new molecule of acetyl CoA.

There is a total of eight reactions in the Krebs cycle. Like glycolysis, each reaction requires a unique enzyme. Three molecules of NADH, one molecule of ATP (or GTP), and a molecule of $FADH_2$ are all produced. $FADH_2$ is another high-energy molecule and stands for *flavin adenine dinucleotide*. Again, the H_2 indicates a reduced version of the FAD molecule.

Remember that there are two pyruvate, and thus two acetyl CoA, molecules resulting from a single glucose molecule. This means that for each glucose molecule, two full turns of the Krebs cycle occur. Therefore, the energy-containing products from the Krebs cycle are six NADH, two ATP, and two $FADH_2$.

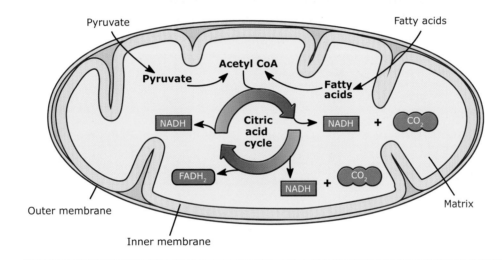

KREBS CYCLE

The Krebs cycle, also known as the *citric acid cycle*, involves many chemical reactions. Which reactions does this diagram show?

The Electron Transport Chain

By the end of glycolysis and the Krebs cycle, a molecule of glucose has produced a net of only four ATP molecules. It is during the next and final stage of cellular respiration that most ATP production occurs. During the electron transport chain, the other high-energy molecules NADH and $FADH_2$ go to work.

The electron transport chain is a series of protein complexes. It is embedded in the inner mitochondrial membrane. These complexes are "electron carriers." NADH and FADH$_2$ donate electrons to the first complex in the series. Electrons are passed down the chain, from one protein complex to the next. Each subsequent protein complex donates the electrons to its neighbor, one by one, and energy is released at each step. These transmembrane protein complexes also include ion pumps. The energy that is released in each electron-passing step is used to pump H$^+$ ions across the membrane. The H$^+$ ions are released from NADH and FADH$_2$ at the same time that they donate their electrons. As these free H$^+$ ions accumulate in the mitochondrial matrix, the ion pumps in the chain pump them from the matrix into the intermembrane space.

THE ELECTRON TRANSPORT CHAIN

The electron transport chain produces most of the ATP released during cellular respiration. What are the reactants and products of each step of the electron transport chain?

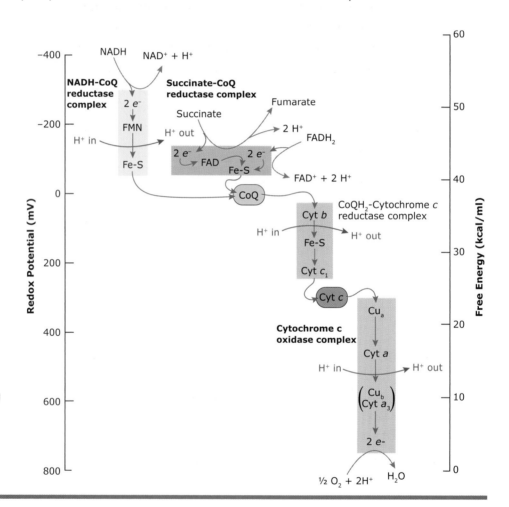

Two important final steps occur in the electron transport chain. One might wonder what happens to the donated electrons once they reach the final protein complex of the chain. This is when the critical oxygen molecule becomes a factor. Oxygen serves as the final electron acceptor. When an O_2 molecule accepts electrons, it becomes negatively charged. It then picks up free-floating H^+ ions, forming two molecules of H_2O.

Finally, the main question remains: How is ATP produced by the electron transport chain? The answer involves another very special transmembrane H^+ protein channel. In the final step, the large numbers of H^+ ions that have been pumped into the intermembrane space now form a concentration gradient between the intermembrane space and the matrix. This concentration gradient causes them to flow back into the matrix through a channel called *ATP synthase*. The H^+ ions passing through this channel cause a rotor within the channel to spin. This spinning rotor creates the energy needed to synthesize large amounts of ATP from ADP. This spinning force is only possible due to the large H^+ concentration gradient between the intermembrane space and the mitochondrial matrix.

Approximately 32 to 34 molecules of ATP are produced during the electron transport chain. A net total of 36 to 38 molecules of ATP can be produced from a single molecule of glucose. However, in reality, because of various losses in the process, around 30 are usually made.

What Are the Differences between Aerobic and Anaerobic Respiration?

Aerobic Versus Anaerobic Respiration

Aerobic respiration refers to the production of ATP using oxygen as a final electron acceptor in the **electron transport chain**. Aerobes are organisms that obtain oxygen or absorb oxygen from their environments. These organisms typically produce ATP using **aerobic respiration**.

Some organisms live in oxygen-poor environments or experience circumstances of low oxygen. They would not survive if they required oxygen to produce ATP. Many of these organisms undergo a process similar to aerobic respiration, but they use a different molecule as the final electron acceptor. The process is called anaerobic respiration. Examples of alternative final electron acceptors are sulfate (SO_4^{2-}), nitrate (NO_3^-), and sulfur (S).

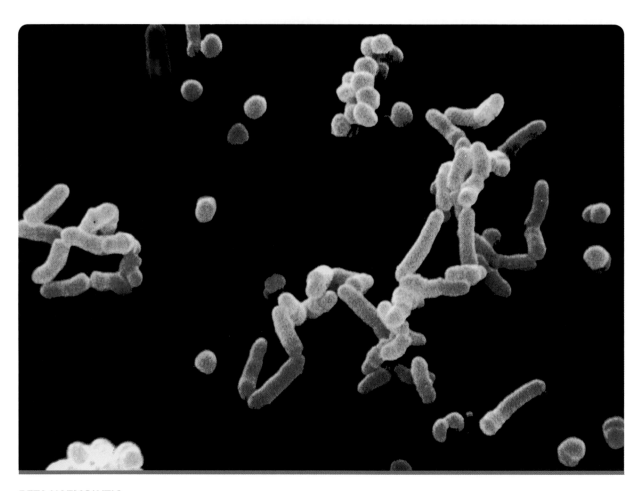

BETA HAEMOLYTIC STREPTOCOCCI BACTERIA

In the absence of oxygen, some bacteria are able to use anaerobic respiration. How does this relate to the environments in which bacteria often live?

Cells can obtain energy from food without the use of oxygen or an electron transport chain. **Fermentation** is an anaerobic process by which cells ensure that glycolysis takes place repeatedly to generate as much ATP as possible. Fermentation involves the conversion of pyruvate to another molecule. Pyruvate may be converted to lactate or ethanol. During these reactions, the NADH produced by glycolysis is oxidized back to NAD^+. By ensuring a steady supply of NAD^+, a cell can continue to undergo glycolysis uninterrupted.

Fermentation is very useful in cases where oxygen is in short supply. However, with only the small ATP yield from glycolysis, it is a much less efficient way to metabolize food than aerobic cellular respiration.

Consider the Explain Question

How is food converted into the energy needed to move an athlete?

Go online to complete the scientific explanation.

dlc.com/ca10034s

Check Your Understanding

What is the difference between aerobic and anaerobic respiration?

dlc.com/ca10035s

STEM in Action

Applying Cellular Respiration

Why do muscles sometimes get sore when we exercise? What has this got to do with cellular respiration?

Many animal cells use a form of fermentation that produces lactate. This occurs in conditions of reduced oxygen availability. For example, during vigorous exercise, an athlete's muscles need more ATP. The muscle cells may not be able to get enough oxygen to supply this ATP through aerobic respiration. Instead, they temporarily switch to using anaerobic respiration. This produces lactate, which builds up in the muscles. When the athlete stops exercising, and an adequate amount of oxygen becomes available, this lactate will be converted to pyruvate and then oxidized in aerobic respiration.

CRAMPS

Why does this athlete have a stitch and cramped muscles? Could anaerobic respiration be partly responsible?

Muscle soreness during or after exercise may in part be caused by the buildup of the lactate in your muscles. When the buildup reaches a certain point, a burning sensation can be felt, and the muscles may actually lock up or cramp. However, this accounts only for the temporary soreness immediately after exercise since the lactate is usually converted into pyruvate minutes after exercise has stopped.

Longer term muscle soreness is caused by damage to muscle fibers and other parts of the muscular system. These microtraumas cause inflammation and pain that can last for days. In addition to the injured fibers, increased blood flow to the muscles causes muscle tissues to swell. This causes pressure that stimulates pain receptors. So painful muscles often have microscopic tears and are swollen. The fix for longer term muscle soreness is quite simple: if you stretch and warm up properly before the activity and gradually increase the endurance and strength of your muscles, you will not get so sore.

STEM and Cellular Respiration

Humans benefit from fermentation in many ways. Bacteria and yeast produce some of the foods people eat through fermentation. One common type of lactic acid-producing bacteria is *Lactobacillus bulgaricus*. These and other lactic acid bacteria ferment milk to produce yogurt. Sauerkraut and kimchi are other foods produced by the fermentation of vegetables.

Brewers also make use of ethanol fermentation in yeast. All alcoholic beverages are produced by the fermentation of fruits, grains, and vegetables by yeast. For bakers, yeast is an important ingredient in bread dough. One of the byproducts of the fermentation reaction is carbon dioxide (CO_2). The basic formula for the ethanol fermentation reaction is:

$$C_6H_{12}O_6 \rightarrow 2C_2H_5OH + 2CO_2$$

A unique enzyme catalyzes this reaction in which NADH is converted to NAD^+. The chemical formula for ethanol is C_2H_5OH. The carbon dioxide gas given off during fermentation is necessary for bread to rise.

FERMENTATION VATS

The industrial fermentation vats in this yogurt dairy are big. What sort of condition would be needed to ensure that the process inside them is anaerobic?

Another important use for ethanol fermentation is in the production of ethanol as an energy source. In the United States, corn is the primary crop used for ethanol production. Other countries, such as Brazil, make ethanol mainly using sugar from sugar cane. The ethanol produced is a biofuel and can be used as an alternative energy source.

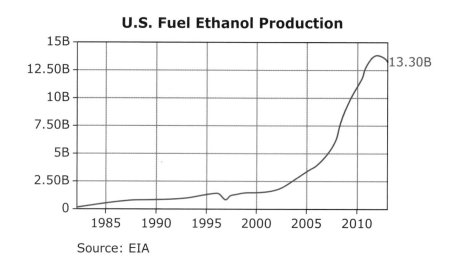

FERMENTING FUEL

This graph shows U.S. Fuel Ethanol Production since 1980. About how much ethanol was produced in 2009?

CONCEPT
2.4

Nutrient Cycles

LESSON OVERVIEW

Lesson Questions

- What are the processes and features of the water cycle?
- What are the processes and features of the carbon cycle?
- What are the processes and features of the nitrogen cycle?
- What are the processes and features of the phosphorus cycle?

Lesson Objectives

By the end of the lesson, you should be able to:

- Model the processes, features, and significance of the water cycle.
- Model the processes, features, and significance of the carbon cycle.
- Model the processes, features, and significance of the nitrogen cycle.
- Model the processes, features, and significance of the phosphorus cycle.

Key Vocabulary

Which terms do you already know?

- [ ] adenosine triphosphate (ATP)
- [ ] Archaea
- [ ] bacteria
- [ ] biofuel
- [ ] carbon cycle
- [ ] condensation
- [ ] Industrial Revolution
- [ ] nitrogen cycle
- [ ] nucleic acid
- [ ] phosphorous cycle
- [ ] phosphorus cycle
- [ ] sustainable
- [ ] topsoil
- [ ] water cycle

dlc.com/ca10036s

© Discovery Education | www.discoveryeducation.com

Recycle and Reuse

dlc.com/ca10037s

Does nature have its own recycling systems? How, for example, are carbon, nitrogen, phosphorus, and water, which are the basis of all life on Earth, recycled within ecosystems?

RECYCLING RESOURCES

These plastic bottles can be broken down and remade into useful products. How is recycling of man-made materials similar to nutrient cycling through the environment?

EXPLAIN QUESTION

▌ **How do water and nutrients cycle through the environment?**

What Are the Processes and Features of the Water Cycle?

The Water Cycle

More than 97 percent of all water on Earth is stored in the oceans as salt water. However, humans and many other organisms depend on freshwater for survival. Indeed, freshwater is one of Earth's most precious resources. The total amount of water on Earth is constant and continuously moves through the **water cycle**. Parts of the water cycle transform salt water into freshwater that can be used by living organisms.

The water cycle (also called the *hydrologic cycle*) includes three primary processes: evaporation, **condensation**, and precipitation. Evaporation refers to the transformation of a liquid to a gas. In the water cycle, the sun heats up water in oceans, lakes, rivers, streams, and other aquatic bodies, resulting in evaporation during which liquid water evaporates into water vapor. Evaporation also takes place from the leaves of plants. This form of evaporation is called *transpiration*. Plants play an important role in determining the rate of evaporation from vegetated areas.

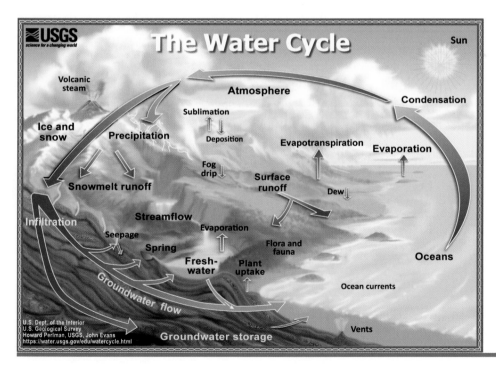

THE WATER CYCLE

One example of a route through the water cycle is evaporation from the oceans, precipitation over the mountains, and flow through rivers back to the ocean. What parts of the water cycle do you encounter in your daily life?

Although the concentration varies, air always contains a certain amount of water vapor. The amount of water in the air is called *humidity*. The amount of water that can be held by the air depends upon temperature. The warmer the air, the more water it can hold. When air is holding the maximum amount of water at a certain temperature, it is said to be saturated.

Condensation occurs when a gas cools into a liquid. Condensation occurs when saturated air is cooled. Most condensation occurs when clouds are formed. Clouds consist of tiny water droplets that have condensed out of the air.

Precipitation occurs when water droplets suspended in clouds become too heavy to remain in suspension. These water droplets fall as rain, hail, sleet, or snow. Precipitation may collect as surface water, which then drains into lakes, rivers, streams, and other bodies of water. In contrast to surface water, groundwater is water residing in the soil and rock below land surface. Groundwater may collect to form an aquifer. Wells can be drilled into aquifers in order to obtain water for human activities.

Most of our planet's freshwater is locked up in ice. Most of this ice is found near Earth's poles. Some is found in glaciers that exist at lower latitudes. The amount of water locked up in ice depends upon Earth's temperature. In the past, Earth often had more ice cover than it does today.

The continual recycling of water and its precipitation plays an important role in determining the nature of Earth's surface. Water is the major agent of weathering and erosion on Earth. Water can dissolve and break apart rocks. Water freezing in cracks in rocks can physically break them apart.

PERITO MORENO GLACIER

Earth's glaciers and ice caps are rapidly melting. What global consequences will this melting have?

Water transports rock fragments, a process called *erosion*. Erosion carries rock particles from elevated to lower areas. Eroded sediments suspended in water can be carried large distances. These sediments increase the erosive capabilities of streams and rivers. Glaciers also erode the landscape. Typical landforms formed by water are valleys, canyons, underground caves, and sinkholes.

Eroded sediments are deposited in low-lying areas or out to sea. These sediments may produce river deltas and wetlands. Substances that are dissolved by water can be recrystallized when the water evaporates. Examples of this can be seen in salt lakes and pans.

What Are the Processes and Features of the Carbon Cycle?

The Carbon Cycle

Carbon is present in all living things and is the fundamental element of all organic compounds. All organisms depend on organic compounds such as fats and sugars for energy.

Organisms that make their own food from simple substances are called *autotrophs.* Most of these organisms, such as plants, algae, and some **bacteria** and **archaea**, photosynthesize carbon-based food molecules using carbon dioxide from the atmosphere. Heterotrophs, on the other hand, depend on autotrophs, either directly or indirectly, for their food supply—they eat other organisms. The process of cellular respiration breaks down carbon-based compounds to yield energy. Carbon dioxide gas is given off in this process and is released from the organism back into the atmosphere.

The **carbon cycle** refers to the cycling of carbon through the environment. This includes cycling from reservoirs (rocks, sediments, and the ocean), to the atmosphere (mostly as CO_2), to organisms in food webs, and back to reservoirs.

Carbon moves through the carbon cycle by multiple processes. Photosynthesis removes carbon dioxide from the atmosphere and uses it to build food molecules. Cellular respiration involves the breakdown of these food molecules, resulting in the release of carbon dioxide gas.

Organisms store carbon compounds in their bodies. When the organisms die, they decompose. Through the process of decomposition, much of their carbon is returned to the atmosphere as carbon dioxide. Some of this carbon is locked up in sedimentary rocks, such as limestone or chalk. Thus, the weathering of limestone rock, or its use in cement manufacture, contributes to carbon transfer through the carbon cycle. Some of this buried carbon forms fossil fuels such as coal, gas, and oil. The burning of fossil fuels releases carbon dioxide into the atmosphere.

Dead organisms occasionally become trapped under certain conditions that do not allow decomposition to take place. In these situations, the carbon from these organisms becomes buried deep within Earth.

Volcanic eruptions also release carbon dioxide into the atmosphere.

Many human activities, such as burning fossil fuels and forests, produce carbon dioxide. For a few thousand years before the **Industrial Revolution**, the amount of carbon dioxide in the atmosphere remained fairly constant. However, it is estimated that atmospheric carbon dioxide has increased by about 35 percent since the Industrial Revolution around the early 19th century. This increase closely matches humankind's increasing dependence on burning fossil fuels. The increase in atmospheric carbon dioxide is closely matched by a recent rise in average global temperatures. Why does this relationship exist?

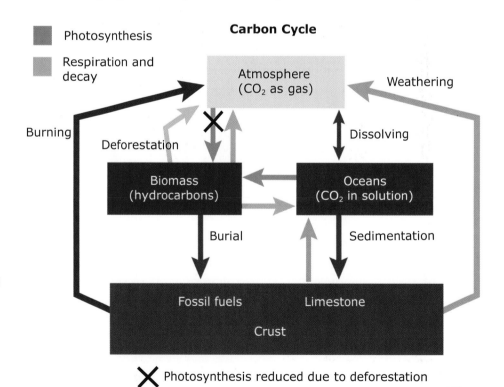

CARBON CYCLE

Human activity is leading to increased levels of atmospheric carbon dioxide. What are two human activities that move carbon dioxide into the atmosphere?

Carbon dioxide is called a greenhouse gas because it has the property of retaining radiant heat. The presence of increased concentrations of greenhouse gases like carbon dioxide in Earth's atmosphere therefore causes average global air temperatures to rise. Nowadays about half the carbon dioxide produced by natural and human processes is remaining in the atmosphere. So human activities, even when other factors are taken into account, are contributing to the trend of increasing global temperature.

What Are the Processes and Features of the Nitrogen Cycle?

The Nitrogen Cycle

Nitrogen is an important component of amino acids and **nucleic acids**, which are critical to all living things. On land, this nitrogen is made available to living things when plants absorb it as a nutrient from the soil.

Nitrogen makes up about 80% of Earth's atmosphere, which is the reservoir of nitrogen for living things. However, plants can only use nitrogen in the forms of ammonium (NH_{4+}), nitrate (NO_{3-}), and organic forms such as amino acids. Animals can only use nitrogen in organic forms that they get from food. Atmospheric nitrogen is primarily made available to these organisms through nitrogen-fixing bacteria.

The **nitrogen cycle** is the series of chemical reactions by which nitrogen is converted among its various chemical forms. The nitrogen cycle can be broken down into five main phases:

- Some species of bacteria and archaea convert atmospheric nitrogen into nitrogen compounds into the soil.
- Plants absorb nitrogen compounds from the soil and change it into their own molecules.
- Animals receive nitrogen compounds when they eat plants.
- Both animals and plants return nitrogen compounds to the soil through waste and decomposition.
- Some bacteria decompose nitrogen compounds in the soil into nitrogen gas.

The processes of the nitrogen cycle include fixation, mineralization (ammonification), nitrification, and denitrification. The primary way in which usable nitrogen enters an ecosystem is through nitrogen-fixing bacteria. Many of these live in close association with plants. Some live inside the roots of plants in root nodules. In the fixation process, certain species of bacteria convert N_2 gas from the atmosphere into ammonia (NH_3). Some bacteria perform nitrification, during which ammonium ions (NH_{4-}) are converted into nitrate. Once nitrogen has been converted into ammonium or nitrate ions, it can be absorbed by plants.

NITROGEN-FIXING BACTERIA

Nitrogen-fixing bacteria live on soybean roots. Does this benefit the bacteria, the roots, or both?

The process of mineralization or ammonification decomposes organic nitrogen into ammonium compounds.

Other bacteria use nitrate instead of oxygen during cellular respiration. These bacteria are performing denitrification, converting nitrate back into N_2 gas.

Biological systems work to achieve and maintain balance. However, the ecological function of the microorganisms can both contribute to maintaining the health of organisms and ecosystems, and contribute to disrupting the health of organisms and ecosystems.

For example, since the agricultural boom in the 19th and 20th centuries, there has been an increased use of nitrogen-containing fertilizers. There are many problems associated with over-fertilization. Excess inorganic nitrogen added to soil can be harmful to plants. Also, these fertilizers often lack other important minerals naturally found in soil. Continuously growing crops using such fertilizers without adding these mineral supplements can decrease the concentration of these minerals, making soil less productive.

Runoff rich in nitrogen compounds can also cause problems in aquatic environments. Nitrogen compounds can fertilize algae, causing them to grow at an accelerated rate, producing an algal bloom. The algae can become overcrowded and die. Microorganisms, such as bacteria, use the oxygen in the water as they decompose the dead algae. The microorganisms can use so much oxygen that other living things in the water, such as fish, suffocate.

What Are the Processes and Features of the Phosphorous Cycle?

The Phosphorous Cycle

Phosphorus is an important element to all living organisms. It is a major component of nucleic acids, phospholipids, and **adenosine triphosphate (ATP)**. It is also an important component of animal bones and teeth. In contrast to carbon and nitrogen, phosphorus is not present in a gaseous form in the atmosphere. The greatest quantities of phosphorus are found as minerals in oceanic rock. Large amounts are deposited on the ocean floor.

The **phosphorus cycle** involves the transfer of phosphorus, primarily in the form of phosphate (PO_4^{3-}) between rocks, soil, water, and organisms. The weathering of rocks is the primary way that phosphate enters the soil. Plants absorb phosphate through their roots. Animals obtain the phosphorus they need from eating plants and other food. Phosphorus is returned to soil by decomposition and waste from organisms. Phosphorus compounds are lost from the soil in runoff.

PHOSPHORUS

Unlike other essential plant nutrients such as nitrogen and carbon, phosphorus does not exist as a gas. How is phosphorus able to move through the different stages of the phosphorus cycle?

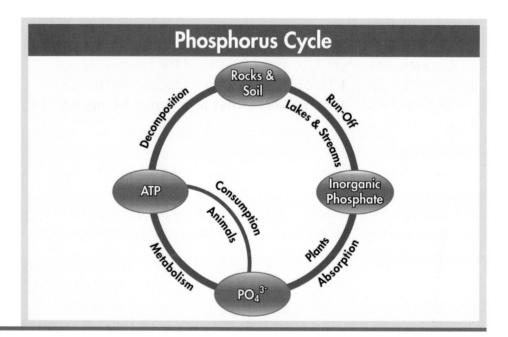

Farmers and gardeners replace phosphorus compounds lost from the soil using manures and fertilizers. Bone meal is one important source of phosphorus compounds that is used by gardeners. Most farmers use inorganic fertilizers rich in phosphates. As with nitrogen, over-fertilization can add too much phosphorus to soil and water. In water, too much phosphorus can cause algae to overgrow and die. When microorganisms decompose the algae, they use oxygen in the water. Without enough oxygen, fish and other organisms in the water may die.

Consider the Explain Question

❚ **How do water and nutrients cycle through the environment?**

Go online to complete the scientific explanation.

dlc.com/ca10038s

Check Your Understanding

❚ **Can you model the carbon and nitrogen cycle?**

dlc.com/ca10039s

STEM in Action

Applying Nutrient Cycles

Water, carbon, nitrogen, and phosphorus are strongly tied to agriculture. Our agricultural industry is responsible for providing us with the food we eat. Modern agriculture makes extensive use of inorganic fertilizers without which we could not feed the world's rapidly growing population. However, this dependence on inorganic fertilizers and other synthetic agricultural chemicals has led to some unsustainable agricultural practices. These practices have created environmental and health problems. They also disrupt the natural flow of the nutrient cycles.

INDUSTRIAL FARMS
Industrial agriculture in the United States tends to be input-intensive, meaning a lot of fertilizers and water are required to grow our food. How might the application of nitrogen fertilizers across large areas affect nutrient cycles?

One damaging agricultural practice is the excessive use of manure and fertilizer. Nutrients from these sources contain both nitrogen and phosphorous compounds. The nutrients that are not absorbed by plants may enter runoff or seep into groundwater. This nutrient pollution eventually enters rivers, lakes, and estuaries. The excess of nutrients can cause algae in these ecosystems to rapidly reproduce, which leads to hypoxic or anoxic conditions in the water. Other organisms in the food chain are often negatively affected. In fact, when nutrient runoff from farms along the Mississippi River washes into the Gulf of Mexico, large hypoxic dead zones can result, leaving fisheries in dire straits.

Environmental scientists have engineered solutions to the problem of nutrient runoff from agricultural fields. One solution is what is known as a *denitrifying bioreactor*. Designs vary, but these are usually large open pits filled with wood chips or other organic matter placed between the drainage outlet of a field and any nearby waterways. Bacteria occupying small pores in the wood chips convert the nitrate in the drainage water into harmless N_2 gas, which enters the atmosphere. With nitrogen content greatly reduced by this process, the water can safely drain into streams.

STEM and Nutrient Cycles

Carbon dioxide and methane are greenhouse gases. Under normal circumstances, Earth's surface is warmed by incoming solar radiation, and Earth emits infrared radiation outward toward space. The greenhouse gases that are present in the atmosphere trap the infrared radiation and then re-emit the radiation back to Earth. This potentially warms average temperatures on Earth and disrupts weather patterns.

Most climate scientists today argue that human-produced greenhouse gases in the atmosphere contribute to global warming. The burning of fossil fuels generates large amounts of CO_2. Plants cannot uptake the huge amounts of CO_2 released by motor vehicles, power plants, and factories all over the world. Furthermore, millions of acres of forest have been destroyed to make space for land development and agriculture. These forest trees were a vital absorber of carbon dioxide.

While some debate surrounds the exact contribution increased CO_2 levels from human activities have upon global warming, burning fossil fuels clearly has a negative impact on the natural balance of the carbon cycles it adds various forms of potentially harmful carbon gases and metal particulates to the atmosphere. Most people agree that the answer to this problem lies in the use of renewable energy sources rather than fossil fuels. These sources include solar, wind, and thermal energy, as well as **biofuels**. Biofuels are composed of, or produced from, renewable biological materials such as animal waste and plants. The largest source of plant-based biofuel currently is corn, which can be converted into ethanol. However, plant breeders are busy developing dedicated biofuel crops—such as perennial grasses and fast-growing trees—which can be grown on marginal land, leaving the prime agricultural land for food production. Bioengineers have developed technologies to convert cellulose from biofuel crops, and new biorefineries are being built around the country.

Mechanical and Chemical Weathering

LESSON OVERVIEW

Lesson Question
■ How do mechanical and chemical weathering change Earth's surface?

Lesson Objective
By the end of the lesson, you should be able to:

■ Separate and compare the weathering processes that affect Earth's land surface.

Key Vocabulary
Which terms do you already know?

- ☐ abrasion
- ☐ carbonate
- ☐ chemical weathering
- ☐ climate
- ☐ differential weathering
- ☐ elevation
- ☐ erosion
- ☐ exfoliation
- ☐ geology
- ☐ hydrolysis
- ☐ ice wedging
- ☐ karst
- ☐ mineral
- ☐ oxidation
- ☐ sediment
- ☐ topography
- ☐ weathering
- ☐ weathering (physical)

dlc.com/ca10040s

Observing Mechanical and Chemical Weathering

dlc.com/ca10041s

What forces over a significant period of time cause changes in buttes and other landforms? How does the process of weathering change the look of a mountain or other rocky surface?

BUTTE WEATHERING

Rocky surfaces gradually change over time. What forces have likely contributed to the appearance of this butte?

EXPLAIN QUESTION

What effect does weathering have on the surface of landforms such as mountains, buttes, mesas, and plateaus?

How Do Mechanical and Chemical Weathering Change Earth's Surface?

Mechanical Weathering

Mechanical **weathering** is the natural breakdown of rock into **sediments** by physical changes. Mechanical weathering is sometimes called **physical weathering**.

Common causes of mechanical weathering are **ice wedging** and root growth. Ice wedging occurs during cycles of melting and freezing as temperatures change daily or seasonally. When liquid water freezes, it expands in volume by about 10 percent. When liquid water seeps into cracks in rocks and then freezes, the expansion of the ice is a force powerful enough to crack the rock further. When temperatures rise and the ice melts, the resulting water seeps deeper into the cracks. Freezing continues the cycle by further expanding the cracks. Eventually, the cracks cause rock to crumble away.

Root growth is another major cause of mechanical weathering. Tree roots grow down into cracks in bedrock. As a tree grows, its roots thicken, causing the cracks to widen. Tree roots continually delve deeper into the ground in search of water, further widening cracks in the rock.

Other causes of mechanical weathering include **abrasion**, impacts, and **exfoliation**. Abrasion is the scouring or scraping of rock, usually caused by the action of glaciers as they creep slowly down mountains or by friction with windblown sand. Impacts of meteorites can blow rock into bits and form craters.

© Discovery Education | www.discoveryeducation.com ● Image: Paul Fuqua

ABRASION

Glaciers carved this groove by abrasion as they moved slowly over the rock. What can scientists learn about Earth's history from geologic features like this?

Exfoliation is a type of weathering in which thin layers of rock peel off exposed rock surfaces like slivers of an onion. This typically happens to bedrock that has been buried beneath other layers of rock. If the overlying rock is removed, the tremendous release of pressure causes the exposed rock to expand. As the rock expands, cracks appear in its surface, weakening the rock so that its outer layers may be stripped away one by one.

EXFOLIATION

The peeled look of these stones is due to exfoliation. What processes cause exfoliation?

The Properties of Water

Water is found almost everywhere on Earth—in the ocean, rivers, lakes, and ponds. Water is a compound consisting of hydrogen and oxygen atoms bonded together. In a water molecule, two atoms of hydrogen and one atom of oxygen are bonded together. Water has several physical and chemical properties that make it a unique substance. These properties include water's exceptional capacity to absorb, store, and release large amounts of energy as it changes state. Water is also able to transmit sunlight, to expand on freezing, and to dissolve and transport numerous materials. It also lowers the viscosity and melting points of rocks when mixed with the hot, solid rock in Earth's mantle. Each of these properties plays a role in how water affects most natural processes on Earth, such as ice wedging, which contributes to mechanical weathering, and the ocean's thermal capacity to balance temperature differences.

Water exists in three states as solid, liquid, and gas. As liquid water, it carries soil and rocks from one place to another and supports the variety of life-forms that live on Earth. Water is found as a gas, called *water vapor,* and as ice crystals high in the atmosphere. It remains suspended as droplets in clouds, falls as precipitation, or rests as solid ice on mountains and in glaciers.

Energy from the sun causes evaporation, and gravitational force and Earth's rotation propel oceanic and atmospheric circulation, which transports water around the globe through the water cycle. About 97 percent of Earth's water is salt water found in an ocean or lake. The remaining 3 percent is freshwater accumulated in glaciers, underground aquifers, streams, bays, freshwater lakes, and rivers.

Water is considered a significant factor in the mechanical weathering of Earth's crust. For example, as liquid water flows downhill or turns to solid ice, changes in landscapes occur through the breakdown of rock materials into sediment.

The physical properties of water include polarity, which causes adhesion and cohesion, as well as capillary action, density, and color. Water's chemical properties, such as conductivity and pH, on the other hand, are the basis of **chemical weathering**.

HORSESHOE BEND, ARIZONA

This photo shows a bend in the Colorado River called Horseshoe Bend. What forces have shaped, and continue to shape, this formation?

Chemical Weathering

When chemical reactions change one or more of the **minerals** in rock into different substances, chemical weathering occurs. Unlike mechanical weathering, chemical weathering changes the chemical makeup of rock and other substances.

Water is a common reactant in chemical weathering reactions. Many minerals, including halite (salt), dissolve in neutral water. Acidic water reacts with **carbonate** minerals, including calcite. Carbonation reactions convert minerals into a bicarbonate form that dissolves in water. Natural waters can be mildly acidic. Acid rain due to air pollution speeds chemical weathering of carbonates. In **hydrolysis** reactions, water becomes slightly ionized and reacts with silicate and carbonate minerals.

Water can also be an agent of chemical weathering through hydration. When a rock takes up water, it may react with the molecules that make up the rock. This can transform the rock's molecular structure, causing it to break down more easily.

Oxidation reactions are also commonly involved in chemical weathering. Hard, iron-bearing minerals can react with oxygen to form soft rust. Iron minerals are common in granite. When they rust, the hard granite crumbles.

ACID RAIN DAMAGE
What effect did acid rain have on this marble building decoration?

Rates of Weathering

Although the breakdown of rock is generally a slow process, in some cases it can proceed more quickly. The rate or speed at which weathering occurs depends on many variables, such as:

- the composition of the rock
- the rock's surface area that is exposed to air and water
- **climate** conditions, including humidity and temperature
- the shape of the landscape (**topography**)
- **elevation**
- the actions of living organisms

Mechanical and chemical weathering are also key processes in the functioning of the rock cycle.

Sometimes different rocks in the same landform weather at different rates. This is called **differential weathering**. Differential weathering can sometimes produce dramatic, sculpture-like effects, such as the stone arches that dot the western United States. This type of weathering can be both chemical and mechanical.

DIFFERENTIAL WEATHERING

This red sandstone arch was formed by differential weathering and erosion. What happened to the rocks that once filled the arch's center?

Consider the Explain Question

What effect does weathering have on the surface of landforms such as mountains, buttes, mesas, and plateaus?

dlc.com/ca10042s

Go online to complete the scientific explanation.

Check Your Understanding

How does metamorphism happen?

dlc.com/ca10043s

STEM in Action

Applying Mechanical and Chemical Weathering

Weathering does not only affect the outside of landforms. As water seeps through mountains and other rocky surfaces, weathering is also taking place on the inside. One of the best examples of weathering that takes place inside landforms is the formation of solutional caves. Solutional caves are formed in limestone and other soluble rock and are some of the most common and largest caves on Earth.

Carbonate rock layers, such as those containing significant amounts of limestone, are slowly dissolved through chemical weathering. As groundwater hits the outside of the landform, it seeps down through the soil and into the carbonate rock. As it travels through the rock, the water dissolves the carbonate present in the rock and releases carbon dioxide into the atmosphere and carbonic acid into the water. While water alone is not enough to change the chemical composition of rock, the carbonic acid makes the water weakly acidic. This gives it the power to act as an agent in the chemical weathering process. As the acidic water flows through the rock, it dissolves the minerals found there. This forms small pockets that gradually grow larger and expand into caves.

MOAI

These statues are found on Easter Island. They were made around 500 years ago from a soft volcanic rock called tuff. What is likely to be their appearance a few thousand years into the future?

STEM and Mechanical and Chemical Weathering

Natural landforms are not the only stone formations that experience the effects of weathering. Many ancient buildings, statues, and monuments were made of stone. Over time, both mechanical and chemical weathering have had an effect on the appearance of these ancient attractions. Some have succumbed to the forces of weathering and are no longer recognizable, while others, through the help of restoration efforts, continue to stand today.

In the case of the Sphinx, both rain and blowing sand have caused significant wear and tear on the famous monument. Over the years, experts have attempted to restore the Sphinx to help it regain some of its original grandeur. However, not all restoration attempts were successful. The Sphinx is constructed largely of limestone, which is very porous, meaning water is able to pass through it. A porous stone is a positive trait in an environment prone to weathering by wind. In one restoration, however, experts repaired the Sphinx using cement, a non-porous material. As a result, the proportions of the Sphinx started to change as the weathering affected the cement differently than the limestone.

THE SPHINX

What impact has weathering likely had on the appearance of the Sphinx?

Knowing about chemical and mechanical weathering helps architects, engineers, and urban planners choose the best locations and materials for their building projects. They must consider how the landscape will change over time. For example, an urban planner must consider the effects of chemical and physical weathering when planning a new community on a hillside. An engineer may determine that a structure built in an area prone to high winds will need to be built with extra supports or be moved to an area with slightly lower wind levels to ensure the ground around it will stay secure. They must also consider how a structure will change over time and make design choices with that information in mind. For example, structures made from limestone or marble may be affected by chemical weathering in the form of acid rain. When building in an area that is prone to acid rain, architects may opt to use a stronger material, such as granite, that is better able to handle the chemical effects of the acid rain.

MOAI

What details show the effects of chemical and mechanical weathering on the Moai?

Erosion and Deposition

LESSON OVERVIEW

Lesson Questions

- How do rock and soil undergo erosion and deposition?
- What are the specific agents of erosion, and what factors control deposition?
- How can engineering design solve problems caused by erosion?

Lesson Objectives

By the end of the lesson, you should be able to:

- Distinguish between the processes of erosion and deposition.
- Identify patterns of erosion as surface processes change Earth's crust.
- Distinguish depositional environments encountered during transport of eroded material.
- Summarize engineering challenges due to negative effects of erosion and deposition.

Key Vocabulary

Which terms do you already know?

- ☐ deposition (sedimentary)
- ☐ gravity
- ☐ logarithmic
- ☐ sediment
- ☐ suspension

dlc.com/ca10044s

Waterfalls

dlc.com/ca10045s

Waterfalls are one of the most powerful agents of erosion, but what other types of erosion can make a big impact?

YOSEMITE FALLS, CALIFORNIA

The tallest waterfall in the United States, Yosemite Falls is formed where Yosemite Creek drops over a granite precipice. Will Yosemite Falls last forever?

EXPLAIN QUESTION

▌ **How do erosion and deposition shape Earth's surface?**

How Do Rock and Soil Undergo Erosion and Deposition?

The Relationship between Weathering and Erosion

Erosion is the overall process that results in movement of rocks and soil from one place on Earth's surface to another. Erosion is facilitated by a series of processes, including chemical and mechanical weathering, that wear down rocks and minerals at Earth's surface. When rock has been weathered into smaller pieces, it is transported by forces such as wind, flowing water, and **gravity**. These processes modify the surface features of Earth, leveling and removing many landforms.

Weathering is a prerequisite for erosion. Mechanical weathering occurs when rock is broken into smaller pieces by physical means. This process does not alter the chemical nature of the minerals in the rock. Chemical weathering is the process of breaking a rock into smaller particles by altering the chemical structure of the minerals in the rock. Exposure to water is a common cause of chemical weathering. Chemical weathering processes can weaken a rock, making it easier for mechanical weathering processes to break the rock into even smaller pieces.

MITTEN BUTTE

Erosion forms buttes and mesas, such as the Mitten Butte in Arizona. What agents of erosion could have formed Mitten Butte?

Erosion and Deposition of Sediment

Chemical and mechanical weathering processes break down rock into smaller particles. These particles are called *detritus*. These smaller particles are loosened and removed from their original site. This process is called *erosion*. The agents of erosion include water, wind, ice, gravity, and occasionally lava flows. Organisms can also act as agents of erosion and deposition. For example, marine invertebrates may take up **sediment** during feeding in one area and expel it in another. However, these effects are typically so small compared to those of nonliving agents that organisms are not commonly considered to be important agents of erosion or deposition.

The rock particles being carried by erosion are called *sediments*. When sediments accumulate in new areas, the process is called **deposition**. Deposition occurs when the speed of the medium transporting the sediments diminishes, allowing the sediments to lose speed, fall, and eventually come to rest. Over time, sediments accumulate in low-lying regions called *sedimentary basins*.

A sedimentary basin is a low area in Earth's crust. It does not have to be shaped like a basin, or bowl; sometimes a sedimentary basin is just a gently sloping surface. In this low area, sediments accumulate. Some sedimentary basins can be as small as a few hundred meters, while others are as large as an ocean.

Deposition always follows erosion. Most sediments originate on land. Some are deposited on land, but many are transported by rivers into lakes and ultimately end up in the ocean. These sediments may accumulate on the ocean floor near tectonic plate boundaries where ocean and continent meet. Along these boundaries, the accumulating sediments are forced upward as the ocean crust is subducted beneath them. This creates a wedge of uplifted accreted material. Over long periods of tectonic plate convergence, these sediments can be uplifted to extreme elevations and incorporated into mountain belts. Such examples of uplifted sediments can be observed at extreme elevations in places such as the Andes in South America, the Alps in Europe, and the Himalayas in Asia.

THE HIMALAYAS
Continental collisions created the world's highest mountains, the Himalayas. Which colliding land masses were responsible for creating this mountain range?

Where a sedimentary basin is trapped between colliding continental plates, the sediments are also compressed and uplifted to form mountains. For example, where the Indian subcontinent meets Asia, the sediments trapped along their edges have been uplifted to form the Himalayas. This is why fossils of sea animals are found on the peaks of some of Earth's highest mountains. If we look at most mountain chains around Earth, we can trace their origins to current or ancient plate collisions. Sedimentary basins also form in low areas on continental plates when the tectonic plates are stretched by extensional forces. Where tectonic plates are stretched, these basins can form. These fill with sediments that may be compressed and folded to form mountains by later plate activity.

What Are the Specific Agents of Erosion, and What Factors Control Deposition?

Methods of Sediment Transport

Sediments are transported from one location to another by several methods. Water is by far the most powerful means of eroding sediment. Bed load describes the sediment carried in rivers. How sediment is eroded in the bed load depends on the speed of the water and the size of the sediment grains.

Rivers carry their bed load by three processes: traction, saltation, and **suspension**. Traction occurs when water does not have enough energy to pick up the sediment grains. Instead, the water slides or rolls the sediment particles along the riverbed. Saltation occurs when the water has only enough energy to pick up sediment grains and transport them short distances. As the water slows down, the sediment grains are deposited on the riverbed. This process is repeated over and over again. The sediment grains appear to skip or hop across the bottom of the riverbed. Suspension occurs when the speed of the water is fast enough to pick up sediment grains and transport them for long distances. The water is too energetic to permit small sediment grains to fall out of the current. Fine particles suspended in water require very calm conditions to be deposited.

Like water, winds are capable of eroding and depositing sediments. Wind transports sediments by suspension, saltation, and surface creep. These processes mimic the suspension, saltation, and traction that take place in a river. Except under unusual conditions like hurricanes, winds are seldom strong enough to transport large sediment grains. When large supplies of loose sediment accumulate in areas with little vegetative cover, the wind can strip land bare.

Gravity is a force that acts on all objects on the planet. The gravitational force is directed downward toward the center of Earth. Sediments located on an incline will move downhill under the force of gravity. A steeper incline produces greater movement and can lead to increased erosion. Gravity is responsible for the mass movement of sediment of all sizes during rock falls, landslides, and mudflows.

Ice is another mechanism for eroding sediment. During an ice age, fingers of ice grow and extend from the polar regions, producing massive ice sheets over previously uncovered land. Even during warmer periods, glaciers can form in polar regions and at the tops of tall mountains. As the ice plows across continental crust, it picks up rocks and sediments of all shapes and sizes, even as large as boulders. When the weather warms and the ice melts and retreats, it deposits sediments of all sizes. The deposited sediments produce unique glacial features such as moraines. The sediments are also carried to the ocean in icebergs that break off from large shelves of ice floating on the water's surface. The icebergs follow surface ocean currents. As they enter warmer waters and melt, they deposit sediments across the ocean floor.

Sediment Size and Deposition

Sediment size provides a clue to the energy needed to transport and deposit sediment. Sediments are classified by grain size into seven major categories. The Wentworth scale is centered at 2 millimeters, marking the boundary between sand and gravel. The sand category contains sediment grains that range in size from 0.125 millimeters to 2 millimeters. (Sand may be further subdivided as very coarse, coarse, medium, and fine.) The silt category contains sediment grains that range from 0.0039 millimeters to 0.125 millimeters. The clay category describes the smallest particles, smaller than 0.0039 millimeters in size. On the coarser end of the Wentworth scale, sediments that range in size from 2 millimeters to 4 millimeters are classified as gravel. Sediments that range in size from 4 millimeters to 64 millimeters are classified as pebbles. The cobble category includes sediments that range in size from 64 millimeters to 256 millimeters. The boulder category contains sediments that are larger than 256 millimeters.

Wentworth Classification	Size (mm)
Boulder	>256
Cobble	64–256
Pebble	4–64
Gravel	2–4
Very coarse sand	1–2
Coarse sand	0.5–1
Medium sand	0.25–0.5
Fine sand	0.125–0.25
Silt	$\frac{1}{256} - 0.125$
Clay	$< \frac{1}{256}$

The grain sizes and load of the sediments eroded depends on the energy of the water or wind, which is a function of their speed. Hjulstrom's diagram is a graph that depicts the speed required of a stream to erode, transport, and deposit sediment of different sizes. The x-axis depicts the sediment grain size. The y-axis shows the change in speed. The diagram uses a double **logarithmic** scale, so that the units on each axis increase by factors of 10. Water traveling at a speed of 100 centimeters per second, for example, will erode a sand grain that is 0.1 millimeter in diameter. If the water slows to 10 centimeters per second, it will not be strong enough to pick up additional sediment grains of that size, but it can still transport the grain in the direction that the water is moving. As the water slows below 1 centimeter per second, it no longer has enough energy to transport the sediment grain. At this point, the grain will fall out of the water and be deposited.

HJULSTROM'S DIAGRAM

Hjulstrom's diagram provides a way to associate the speed required to move a particle of sediment with grain size, thereby relating the processes of erosion and deposition. What does the area labeled Deposition indicate?

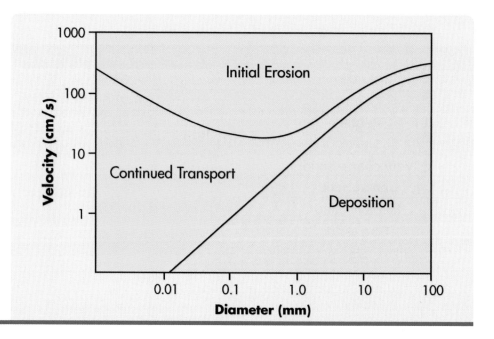

When examining Hjulstrom's diagram, it is clear that fine-grained sediments like clays and silts require lower water speeds to be eroded or transported than do sand grains. So, clay and silt grains are suspended in the water and transported for longer distances than sand. The deposition of clay and silt particles requires an environment characterized by slow water or wind movement.

How Can Engineering Design Solve Problems Caused by Erosion?

Beach Erosion

Many erosional problems are caused or exacerbated by human activities. Coastlines are eroded continually as seawater ebbs and flows and waves crash upon the shore. These are natural forces, but humans also contribute to erosion. For example, as people build homes, roads, and other structures along beaches, they alter the natural topography. Construction often eliminates protective sand dunes and weakens bluffs, exposing even more of the beach to erosion. Eroded shorelines may be especially vulnerable to hurricanes and other storms. As sediments are washed away and the shoreline changes, human-made structures may be damaged or even destroyed.

EROSION

The beach between this home and the ocean has been heavily eroded. How could engineers protect this home from damage?

Engineers have developed a number of strategies to protect coastlines and coastal structures from erosion. Different strategies have different advantages and disadvantages; some strategies actually may cause more erosion than they prevent.

- **Shoreline hardening** involves building seawalls and other hard structures along a coast. These methods are primarily intended to protect property from waves. Unfortunately, the hard structures reflect wave energy to other parts of the coast that may be less protected and thus more vulnerable to erosion.

- **Sand retention structures**, such as groins, stick out from the shore. As flowing water carries sediments along a coastline, the sediments are trapped along the retention structure. This can prevent erosion on one side of the structure, but it can exacerbate erosion on the other side because sediments that normally would be carried to other parts of the beach are prevented from moving there.

- **Beach nourishment** is the process of replacing eroded sand with new sand from other locations, including inlets, healthier beaches, and offshore sources. The new sand is added to the eroded beach or used to shore up the continental shelf or dunes farther inland. When properly designed, a nourished beach may incorporate a variety of natural and human-made structures that help reduce further erosion. Disadvantages of beach nourishment include high cost. Furthermore, because nourishment does not stop erosion from happening, the beach typically must be replenished with new sand every few years.

- **Soft stabilization** involves adding plants and other organic substances to an eroded shoreline. These "soft" materials can trap sediments while preserving the natural features of the shoreline. They also can create new habitats for organisms, thereby contributing to the ecosystem's biodiversity. Unfortunately, soft stabilization may not always be a practical solution, especially in environments with high-energy waves.

PROTECTING COASTLINES

Barriers can be built to protect coastlines but, in the long-term, erosion always wins. How will building seawalls and other hard structures help to prevent beach erosion?

© Discovery Education | www.discoveryeducation.com ● Image: Brian van der Brug / Contributor / Los Angeles Times / Getty Images

Erosion is a natural process that never can be stopped completely. Limiting construction along coastlines can slow the rate of erosion, but the best way to avoid coastal erosion problems is to avoid building along the coast in the first place. As this rarely is a realistic option, engineers continue to look for better ways to protect coastal structures from the erosion that happens when wind and water meet land.

River Erosion: Niagara Falls

Humans do not cause every problem related to erosion. Flowing water, blowing wind, and other agents of erosion continually are reshaping Earth's surface, regardless of human activities. Consider the spectacular waterfalls at Niagara Falls, which provide enough hydroelectric power to generate one-quarter of the electricity used in the state of New York and the Canadian province of Ontario. Niagara Falls also attracts millions of tourists each year. Yet each year, the tourists find the waterfalls a little farther upstream. Thousands of cubic meters of water rush over the falls every second, slowly eroding the surrounding rock. Scientists estimate that for centuries the falls receded one meter or more each year.

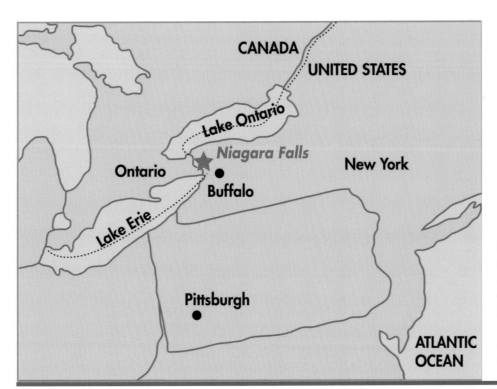

NIAGARA FALLS

Niagara Falls is located along the Niagara River, which connects Lake Erie to Lake Ontario. How are engineers slowing the rate of erosion at Niagara Falls?

To slow the rate of erosion, engineers have built underground tunnels that carry large amounts of water away from the falls; much of this water is redirected to the hydroelectric plants and used to generate electricity. Where possible, engineers also have reinforced the rocks along the falls. As a result of these efforts, Niagara Falls now recedes approximately one foot per year. At that rate, the waterfalls may disappear completely in 50,000 years (though a rapidly flowing river will remain). Scientists think the rate of erosion may be reducible to one foot per decade. Even so, we probably cannot keep the falls from someday eroding away completely.

Consider the Explain Question

How do erosion and deposition shape Earth's surface?

Go online to complete the scientific explanation.

dlc.com/ca10046s

Check Your Understanding

What is the difference between erosion and deposition?

dlc.com/ca10047s

© Discovery Education | www.discoveryeducation.com

STEM in Action

Applying Erosion and Deposition

The coast is a popular destination both for visiting and permanent living. For Earth, the coast is an intersection where mankind leaves its footprint on nature, perhaps more than anywhere else in the world. About 80 percent of the U.S. population lives near the coastline, causing a huge impact on resources needed for humans. Most impact from humans on the coastlines is negative due to building, using resources, and pollution.

Erosion can cause catastrophic events on those who choose to live in these areas. Sediments near coastlines are very unstable and mass movement, waves, and winds can all affect those who choose to live there. Human habitation on the coasts also affects marine life in coastal waters. Although the coastline makes up only 1 percent of Earth, the marine life that live in these coastal areas constitute major ecosystems that are needed to help regulate ocean environments. Predatory and migratory patterns originating at the coast affect all other marine life in the ocean. Keeping these ecosystems intact and lessening the amount of human impact on erosion can only help sustain our way of life for years to come.

EROSION

What should scientists do to protect beaches from erosion?

NORTHERN CALIFORNIA COAST

What problems arise from population growth on the coastlines?

All around the world, beaches are being eroded by waves and wind every day. The Pacific coast is subjected to much erosion due to the tectonic margin and very steep offshore areas. Because of the makeup of the rocks and marine clays that form the coastline, many areas are in danger of collapsing.

Scientists examine these coastlines to avoid problems for people who live in these areas. Efforts to stop erosion in one area often cause erosion in other areas. Engineers are tasked with implementing plans that cause the least amount of damage to the natural cycle, while keeping the coasts protected. The least disruptive way to protect the homes in these areas is to relocate them rather than disrupt the natural erosion process. When the population on the coast increases, local governments build expensive infrastructures in the pathways of high-energy marine processes such as hurricanes and tsunamis. The global problem with the development of shoreline is not always compatible with natural processes. How can local governments and businesses work together with citizens to find a happy medium between economic development and nature?

STEM and Erosion and Deposition

Cape Hatteras is one of a series of barrier islands that make up the Outer Banks of North Carolina. The Cape Hatteras lighthouse was built in 1870. Its distinctive black-and-white "candy cane" design has become a landmark of the North Carolina coastline. The lighthouse stands 198 feet high and weighs 4,830 tons. It was built to warn oncoming ships of the Diamond Shoals, a region of shallow water that extends far into the ocean. When the lighthouse was constructed, it stood 1,500 feet from the shoreline. By 1987, this historic landmark stood a mere 160 feet from the ocean.

Barrier islands are naturally unstable because wind and water erode and deposit sand along the beach. Stationary structures along the beach are threatened by shifting sands. The Cape Hatteras lighthouse was left exposed to waves and inclement weather. Many feared it would succumb to nature and be lost to the ocean forever.

CAPE HATTERAS LIGHTHOUSE

Beach erosion is a problem where people have built on shorelines and barrier islands. What factors drive construction along coastlines?

Beginning in the early 1930s, a number of erosion control measures were put into effect at Cape Hatteras. The community tried to protect the lighthouse with groins, seawalls, jetties, and beach nourishment with varying degrees of success. In spite of these attempts, the lighthouse remained in peril from the encroaching ocean. The residents of the area knew something more had to be done and began to research and develop a plan. They submitted a series of proposals to the National Academy of Sciences to perform an independent review and decide the best long-term plan to save the lighthouse. A relocation scenario was approved in 1988.

It took 11 more years to draw up and approve engineering plans, as well as to raise the $12 million necessary to pay for the relocation. On June 17, 1999, the lighthouse relocation began. In preparation for the move, engineers removed 800 tons of granite at the base of the lighthouse. They replaced the granite with a steel support structure. Hydraulic jacks lifted the lighthouse 6 feet in the air. Engineers used five hydraulic pushjacks to move the lighthouse farther inland. The pushjacks carried the lighthouse at 5-foot increments.

It took 23 days to move the lighthouse 2,900 feet to its new home 1,600 feet from the shoreline. The successful relocation was celebrated during a special relighting ceremony in November that year. The lighthouse relocation was an engineering marvel that was awarded the Outstanding Civil Engineering Achievement Award by the American Society of Civil Engineers in 2000.

The History of Life on Earth

LESSON OVERVIEW

Lesson Questions

- What are different scientific explanations for how and when life on Earth evolved?

- What are biological diversity, episodic speciation, and mass extinction?

- What is an evolutionary tree diagram?

- What are some possible scientific explanations for aspects of the fossil record such as gaps and the sequential nature of fossils?

Key Vocabulary

Which terms do you already know?

- [ ] bilateral symmetry
- [ ] biodiversity
- [ ] biome
- [ ] Cambrian explosion
- [ ] ecosystem
- [ ] endocytosis
- [ ] episodic speciation
- [ ] evolutionary tree diagram
- [ ] extinction rate
- [ ] extinction rate
- [ ] fossil
- [ ] invertebrate
- [ ] mass extinction
- [ ] paleontology
- [ ] Pangaea
- [ ] phylogenetics
- [ ] phylum
- [ ] prokaryotic cell

dlc.com/ca10048s

Lesson Objectives

By the end of the lesson, you should be able to:

- Summarize the sequence of life on Earth, including evidence for evolution and mass extinction.
- Differentiate the terms *biological diversity, episodic speciation,* and *mass extinction*.
- Use taxonomic concepts to construct an evolutionary tree diagram.
- Explain aspects of the fossil record such as gaps and the sequential nature of fossils in terms of evolution, extinction, and environmental change.
- Cite empirical evidence for common ancestry and biological evolution.
- Formulate tests for solutions designed to reduce adverse impacts of human activity on biodiversity.
- Cite evidence for how environmental changes cause population increases, the evolution of new species over time, and the extinction of species.

Key Vocabulary continued

- ☐ subduction
- ☐ tarpit
- ☐ taxonomic level
- ☐ taxonomic unit
- ☐ The Theory of Evolution
- ☐ trace fossil
- ☐ unconformity
- ☐ vertebrate

Examining the History of Life on Earth

How do scientists know anything about what life was like before humans came along? And what do they know about the earliest life and how it gave rise to the many different life forms that cover the planet today?

EXPLAIN QUESTION

How can scientists construct a timeline for the history of life on Earth?

DINOSAUR FOOTPRINTS

How do fossils act like a snapshot of time?

What Are Different Scientific Explanations for How and When Life on Earth Evolved?

Early Earth

Scientists think it is unlikely that organisms existed on Earth when it was first formed. They continuously search for ancient rocks or meteorite fragments to help provide new insights into the origins of Earth and life.

Scientists have determined that Earth is about 4.55 billion years old. Evidence from moon rocks and other solar system objects indicates that Earth and the rest of our solar system formed around the same time.

Earth and the other planets in the early solar system were formed from gas, dust, and rocks in a giant molecular cloud. Material in the cloud collided and, attracted by the force of gravity, combined to form larger bodies. One of these became planet Earth. At this early stage, Earth was made up almost completely of magma, or hot liquid rock. Radioactivity and collisions with meteorites generated a lot of heat, raising the temperature of Earth's surface to about 1000 degrees Celsius. It is likely that this sea of molten rock swirled for thousands of years. Denser compounds in the magma eventually sank to the center of the planet to form Earth's core. The structure of the planet began to differentiate into the layers we find today. The magma eventually cooled, which allowed a thin crust to form on Earth's surface.

Earth's initial environmental conditions made it difficult for life forms to arise. Yet Earth's surface continued to change, and familiar features like continents and ocean basins began to form. Eventually, Earth's crust began to cool. Steam released from the crust cooled and condensed. Together with water from incoming icy asteroids and comets, this water began to form the oceans. Chemicals rich in carbon and nitrogen that were present in the crust and the atmosphere began to dissolve in the newly formed bodies of water. The early atmosphere was quite unlike today's atmosphere. It was rich in carbon dioxide and ammonia. Over millions of years, the atmosphere began to change. Sunlight split the ammonia (NH_3) into nitrogen and hydrogen. Levels of nitrogen began to build up, but there was still no significant amount of oxygen in the atmosphere. Most life that we are familiar with could not have survived in this atmosphere.

Attempts have been made to simulate conditions on early Earth. Scientists hope that these types of experiments will provide clues to life's origin. They have been able to produce numerous organic compounds from inorganic precursors in simulated early Earth environments. Some of these experiments produced amino acids—the building blocks of proteins—from simple inorganic compounds. None of them produced life or self-replicating molecules.

Early Organisms

Nobody is sure how the first organisms evolved. It has been suggested that, very early on, self-replicating molecules provided the material upon which natural selection could act. Some scientists have suggested that these early precursors to life were based on RNA. They think that these RNA systems were later replaced by more stable DNA-based ones. Other suggestions include the possibility that life on Earth was "seeded" by organisms carried in meteorites. Although this possibility would explain how life came to exist on Earth, it does not explain how life arose elsewhere to be carried by meteorites.

CARBONIZATION

Carbonization occurs when some of the original material of an organism decays, leaving behind a coating of carbon that comes from the carbon in the organism's body. What is a possible advantage of this carbon coating?

Fossil evidence suggests that the earliest forms of life were prokaryotic cells. Fossils of these cells have been dated to about 3.4 billion years ago. Prokaryotes do not contain a cell nucleus, and are usually unicellular (single-celled). These organisms are extremely small, typically less than two microns, or two millionths of a meter, in size. These prokaryotes thrived in the harsh environment of early Earth. For this reason, some scientists think these early prokaryotes may have first evolved in conditions similar to those found around deep ocean thermal vents, where similar forms are found today.

The process of photosynthesis first evolved on Earth about three billion years ago. Prokaryotes called cyanobacteria were able to use photosynthesis to turn carbon dioxide into water, oxygen, and glucose. This provided the basis for food chains for other organisms. It also began to change the composition of the atmosphere. The amount of carbon dioxide in the atmosphere began to decline and the amount of oxygen began to rise.

Around two billion years ago, eukaryotic cells evolved. Unlike prokaryotic cells, eukaryotic cells contain nuclei and membrane-bound organelles. According to the endosymbiotic theory, evidence suggests that some of these organelles arose from prokaryotes "working together" to form early eukaryotic cells. The theory states that eukaryotic cells evolved through the inclusion, or endocytosis, of prokaryotes within a host ancestral anaerobic bacterium. According to this theory, mitochondria are the result of the endocytosis of aerobic bacteria—bacteria that need oxygen—and chloroplasts are the result of the **endocytosis** of photosynthetic cyanobacteria. This theory is supported by the fossil record. Eukaryotic cells did not appear until after the evolution of both anaerobic and aerobic bacteria. It also accounts for the fact that both chloroplasts and mitochondria have their own DNA, independent of the DNA in the eukaryotic cell's nucleus. The DNA in these organelles closely resembles bacterial DNA.

One major difference between eukaryotes and prokaryotes is that most eukaryotes rearrange genetic material during meiosis, a form of cell division that occurs during sexual reproduction. Meiosis involves rearranging chromosomes in such a way that the resulting cells are genetically different than the parent cells. This mixing increases the genetic diversity in a population of organisms. Meiosis therefore provides more variation upon which natural selection can act. It is likely that meiosis helped speed up the evolution of multicellular life forms. Multicellular organisms appeared about two billion years ago. What did these early multicellular life forms look like?

Early multicellular organisms were flat discs. Only a few fossils of these soft-bodied organisms have been found. They did not appear until photosynthetic organisms had produced an oxygen-rich atmosphere. Fossil evidence shows that a rapid expansion of animal diversity occurred about 1.5 billion years after the oxygenation of the atmosphere.

Land plants first evolved about 475 million years ago. Next, plants with seeds evolved about 400 million years ago. The ancestors of modern flowering plants evolved approximately 130 million years ago.

The Rise of the Animals

The fossil record tells scientists that a rapid increase in the diversity of animals started around 550 million years ago. It was about this time that conditions on Earth began to change. The planet got warmer. Also during this time, animals evolved eyes. It seems likely that the evolution of eyes started an evolutionary arms race. Predation ramped up as hunters became more efficient. Hard protective body parts rapidly evolved.

These hard body parts fossilize more easily than those of earlier soft-bodied organisms like sponges and jellyfish. As a result, our record of life on Earth at this time is much better than that of earlier times.

This rapid increase in the diversity of animals is called the **Cambrian explosion**. The Cambrian explosion actually took place over tens of millions of years. Most of the major phyla (sing. **phylum**) of animals that exist today appeared at this time. Fossils show the emergence of animals such as early arthropods, precursors to modern-day insects and crabs.

TRILOBITE FOSSILS

Trilobites are early arthropods that lived 550 million years ago. How do fossils help scientists reconstruct the history of life on Earth?

The following list shows approximate periods during Earth's history in which new life forms probably appeared:

■ About 650 million years ago: The first simple animals appeared. Sponges, jellies, and other small marine creatures were some of the first animals to evolve on Earth.

■ About 580 million years ago: The first animals with **bilateral symmetry** evolved. At first, these were very simple, but over millions of years, these invertebrates developed into more complex, worm-like animals.

■ About 550 million years ago: Early arthropods, which are also invertebrates, first appeared. Trilobites are examples of these early arthropods. Much later, these organisms eventually became the first life forms to walk on land. (Crabs, spiders, and centipedes are examples of modern-day arthropods that resemble these ancient life forms. Insects, a broad category of arthropods, did not evolve until about 170 million years later.) The earliest fish-like organisms also appeared about this time. These later diversified into the vertebrates.

- About 500 million years ago: Proto-amphibians (animals having characteristics of both fish and amphibians) first appeared. Some of these mostly sea-dwelling species began to develop lungs, which allowed them to leave the water and colonize the land. These **vertebrate** life forms had symmetric limbs and fully functioning lungs.

- About 360 million years ago: Amphibians evolved out of their "proto" phase to become some of the most dominant animals on land. Frogs and toads are examples of modern-day amphibians that resemble these ancient life forms.

- About 300 million years ago: Over the course of several million years, some amphibians evolved into organisms that scientists call "reptile-like amphibians." These animals developed short legs and long bodies and were able to live almost exclusively on land. These organisms in turn evolved into reptiles.

- Reptiles' tough skin, varied diets, and ability to lay eggs on land helped protect them from the severe climate changes that arose at this time. Crocodiles and turtles are examples of modern-day reptiles that resemble these ancient life forms. According to scientists, the dinosaurs were reptiles that evolved about 230 million years ago and died off about 65 million years ago. The dinosaur line that evolved into birds survives to this day.

- About 225 million years ago: Mammals first appeared on Earth. Scientists use fossils to trace the evolution of one group of reptiles into early mammals. These fossils provide evidence that the teeth, jaws, and other physical traits changed significantly as some reptile groups evolved into mammals. Rats and opossums are examples of modern-day mammals that resemble these ancient life forms.

- About 150 million years ago: Birds evolved from a different line of reptiles. These winged animals are thought to have evolved from a group of two-legged dinosaurs known as theropods, or possibly from a group of four-legged reptiles. Birds also went through a number of major physical changes as they evolved. One important change is that their tails shortened, allowing for improved balance and flight.

Name	Eohippus	Mesohippus	Merryhippus	Pliohippus	Equus
Skull Structure					
Forefoot Structure					
Representation					
Time period (millions of years from present)	50–55 mya	40–20 mya	20–11 mya	5–11 mya	2 mya–present

HORSE EVOLUTION

This diagram shows images of fossils from horses and their descendants collected over time. Do you think this evidence shows all the types of horses that evolved?

- Around 65 million years ago: The first primates evolved. These ancestors of modern apes, including humans, were small, tree-dwelling, tarsier-like mammals.

- About 2.5 million years ago: The genus *Homo* first appeared on Earth. Modern humans and a number of related but now extinct species all belong to this genus. These species represent a very large jump in the evolution of mammals. The brain capacity of early Homo species was relatively large, eventually allowing them to learn to use tools for hunting, farming, and other tasks. Members of the *Homo* genus had long, hairy arms and a large lower jaw bone.

- As early as 300,000 years ago: Modern humans emerged. These mammals are known as *Homo sapiens*.

- Around 25,000 years ago: Neandertals became extinct. Neandertals were a human-like species belonging to the genus *Homo*. This extinction left *Homo sapiens* as the only surviving members of the *Homo* genus. All humans alive today belong to the species *Homo sapiens*.

What Are Biological Diversity, Episodic Speciation, and Mass Extinction?

Biological Diversity

In simple terms, biological diversity, or **biodiversity**, can be thought of as the variety of life in an area. Earth's biodiversity is the variety of life on Earth. Scientists also talk about the biological diversity of biomes and ecosystems. Most commonly, biodiversity refers to the number of species in an area—species diversity. Species diversity arises due to natural selection acting upon genetic diversity within populations.

Biodiversity varies greatly from one **biome** or **ecosystem** to another. Some biomes and their ecosystems contain a high diversity of organisms. For example, tropical forests and coral reefs are very diverse. Others, such as the tundra or desert, are not as diverse. They contain fewer species of organisms. As a general rule, biodiversity is greatest at low latitudes (nearer the equator) and lowest at high latitudes (nearer the poles).

When an ecosystem comes under stress, its biodiversity is usually reduced. For example, pollution may kill off some species of invertebrates in a river. This reduces the biodiversity of the river ecosystem. Changes in biodiversity are therefore an indicator of the overall "health" of an ecosystem. For example, if an ecosystem maintains its biodiversity, it is probably not under severe environmental stress. The organisms living in that area are likely healthy and probably not threatened with extinction. If an area experiences a significant decrease in biodiversity, then something is threatening the health of the area. Biological diversity can therefore be a useful tool for tracking the health of an ecosystem.

Threats to biodiversity include habitat loss, the introduction of non-native species or diseases to an area, exploitation of resources (such as overfishing, overhunting, and deforestation), pollution, or climate change. Large or rapid changes in conditions can lead to extensive loss of biodiversity. This has taken place a number of times during Earth's history. Widespread, rapid losses in biodiversity in which large numbers of species cease to exist anywhere on Earth are referred to as mass extinctions.

Speciation and Extinction

A species is a group of organisms that have the potential to breed together to produce fertile offspring. North American elk (*Cervus canadensis*) are an example of a species. Male and female elk from any part of the continent have the potential to breed with each other and produce fertile offspring. Many species can interbreed, but their offspring are infertile. For example, when a horse (*Equus ferus caballus*) breeds with a donkey (*Equus africanus asinus*), a mule is produced. The mule looks quite different from either of its parents, but it is not a species. Mules are infertile and cannot produce young.

How do species arise? The process through which a new species forms is called speciation. All new species have ancestors from which they have descended. The formation of new species relies on the existence of barriers that prevent breeding between populations of the same species. These barriers may be geographic (like oceans or mountain ranges) or biological (like behavior). These barriers prevent gene flow between populations. The populations' gene pools become isolated.

Once isolated, the populations evolve independently. Eventually, they become so different that they can no longer interbreed and produce fertile offspring. At this point, the populations are said to belong to new, different species. Speciation typically occurs most rapidly in small, isolated populations exposed to new selection pressures. Details of speciation processes are provided in the concept Evolution.

Darwin envisaged speciation as a slow process, requiring many millions of years to produce new species. From the human perspective, speciation is a slow process, but scientists have determined that at times it can be much faster than Darwin thought. This is particularly true during and after periods of major environmental change. **Episodic speciation** refers to how new species evolve when there are major shifts in the environmental conditions of an area, such as changes in climate.

Some environmental shifts are so great that they cause a large fraction of species to die out completely. A look back at the **fossil** record shows paleontologists that most of the species that have existed in the past have disappeared. The process of losing a species is called extinction. Species become extinct for a wide variety of reasons. Environmental change and competition from new species are common causes of extinction.

Just as new species are continually being formed through speciation, species are continually becoming extinct. This background **extinction rate** is about one species per million species per year. On average, most species only survive 5 to 10 million years before they become extinct. Normally, speciation easily keeps up with this rate of extinction. However, at certain times in Earth's history, the **extinction rate** has increased rapidly. In some cases, more than half of Earth's species have disappeared in a few million years. These events are called mass extinctions.

The fossil record suggests that five major mass extinctions have taken place during Earth's history. In each of these mass extinctions, more than half of Earth's species became extinct.

Earth's Major Extinction Events

Extinction Event	Ma* (* Ma = millions of years ago)	Possible Cause	Impact on Life
Cretaceous-Paleogene (known as the K-T event)	66	asteroid impact	About three-quarters of species were lost, including most of the non-avian dinosaurs.
Triassic-Jurassic	200	volcanic activity associated with the breakup of Pangaea, perhaps combined with asteroid impact	This event occurred in two pulses. About 75% of species were lost, including early reptiles and most large amphibians. This reduced competition for the dinosaurs.
Permian-Triassic	252	major volcanic eruptions in Siberia increased global temperatures	About 96 percent of marine species and 70 percent of land vertebrates became extinct.
Late Devonian	370	unknown	About 70 percent of species disappeared.
Ordovician-Silurian	445	movement of the supercontinent Gondwana to the South Pole cooled shallow seas and reduced sea level	About 65 percent of all species, most of which lived in shallow seas, disappeared.

One of these **mass extinction** events occurred when an asteroid crashed into North America about 65 million years ago. The asteroid impact caused the skies to darken, the temperature to rise dramatically, and the atmosphere to fill with toxic gases. Most scientists accept the theory that dinosaur species and many others became extinct as result of this impact. Some species survived for a short while, but they were not able to adapt to the climate changes that occurred around the globe.

Episodic speciation occurs after mass extinction events. New species fill the vacant niches. In the case of the dinosaurs, many of these niches were filled by mammals and birds.

It has been suggested that we are currently in the middle of a period of mass extinction. This sixth mass extinction is the result of human activities and their impact on biological systems. Scientists estimate that the current extinction rate is around a hundred to a thousand times the background extinction rate.

What Is an Evolutionary Tree Diagram?

Evolutionary Trees

All existing organisms have evolved from other organisms. If we could trace the history of life back in time, we would discover that all organisms have a common ancestor. This theory is supported by a wide variety of evidence, including fossils and DNA similarities.

The realization that all life is related was at the heart of Darwin's ideas about evolution. It provides us with way of looking at and classifying life. If all organisms are related, then they must all be members of the same "family" tree. If we create a tree built around different species, we can see how they are related. This type of tree is an evolutionary tree, a model of evolutionary relationships between organisms.

Evolutionary trees provide scientists with a way to map extinction and speciation. Evolutionary tree diagrams show theoretical evolutionary relationships among organisms. The biggest evolutionary tree is the tree for the history of all life on Earth. This tree is huge. For ease of use, scientists typically look at small branches from this tree of life. Each branch also starts with a common ancestor—the main stem. This stem forks when the common ancestor evolves into two species. In turn, these species may branch off new ones. Many twigs begin to form. Each new species is a new twig. The tree grows. If a species becomes extinct, then the twig no longer grows. It becomes a dead end.

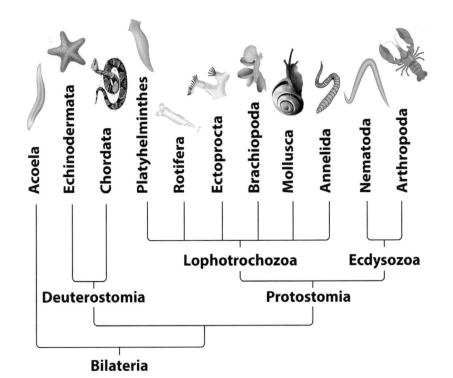

PHYLOGENIC TREE

This evolutionary tree shows most of the animal kingdom. Which of these groups do you belong to?

The relationships on an evolutionary tree may be based on similarities and differences among physical traits. If data are available, such relationships may be confirmed or refined using genetic similarities of the organisms involved. Since **phylogenetics** is the study of evolutionary relationships, evolutionary trees are sometimes called phylogenetic trees. Organisms that have very similar characteristics are in close proximity on the tree. If the **fossil** record is not complete, a tree can be drawn with branches that represent hypotheses about intermediate species. If new intermediate forms are found, the tree can be modified accordingly. Scientists have used phylogenetic trees to predict the existence of species. Some of these species—or fossil evidence of them—have later been discovered.

Taxonomists use phylogenetic trees to represent the classification of organisms. Each tree branch represents a **taxonomic unit** called a clade. All organisms that have a common ancestor are in the same clade. The methodology used to make a phylogenetic tree is therefore called cladistics. Depending on the level of detail needed, evolutionary trees may not include species or other taxonomic levels. However, the tree model can be applied to any **taxonomic level**.

What Are Some Possible Scientific Explanations for Aspects of the Fossil Record Such as Gaps and the Sequential Nature of Fossils?

Interpreting the Fossil Record

When interpreting and explaining the history of life, scientists use a variety of evidence to support their scientific explanations. The **fossil** record provides a record of the history of life and has been important for developing evolutionary theory. However, the fossil record is incomplete. It does not provide a complete record of all living things that have lived on Earth. There are many reasons why the fossil record is incomplete.

Fossils can be formed from either the remains of an organism or the marks, such as footprints or borrows (trace fossils), left by an organism. When most organisms die, they rot and leave no trace of their existence. Therefore, fossils are formed very rarely. Most fossils form in environments where deposition is taking place. Sediments, such as mud or fine volcanic ash, provide the best environment for fossilization. Organisms that die on dry land are less likely to be fossilized than those that die in lakes or shallow seas. This means that environments such as lakes and shallow seas produce lots of fossils. Organisms that lived or died in these environments are common in the fossil record.

Some organisms fossilize more easily than others. Soft tissues rot fast and, even under ideal conditions, rarely fossilize. This means that organisms that only have soft body parts rarely form fossils. Hard body parts fossilize more easily. Therefore, hard animal parts, such as shells and bones, and certain plant parts, such as hard pollen grains, are over-represented in the fossil record when compared with soft-bodied organisms, such as worms or sea anemones. This makes it difficult to determine all the organisms that occupied a particular ancient environment.

Fossils are continually being formed, but the process is typically very slow. Therefore, fossils may be very close or mixed together in the fossil record, even though the organisms that formed them may have lived thousands of years apart.

Fossils are also being continually destroyed. As sedimentary rocks that contain fossils are eroded, their fossil record is lost. Often paleontologists encounter gaps in the fossil record where rocks containing fossils were eroded and then newer rocks were deposited on top of them. This type of **unconformity** can create the false impression that life has evolved very fast over a short period of time. Many fossils are destroyed when the moving plates of Earth's crust are subducted. In **subduction**, parts of the crust are pushed deep into Earth's interior.

The dinosaur dies in a river.

The body is covered with sediment. The meat decomposes. The dinosaur becomes a fossil.

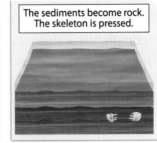
The sediments become rock. The skeleton is pressed.

The earth's movements raise the layers of the rocks to the surface.

The rock erodes, exposing the fossil.

FOSSIL FORMATION

Fossils can form after an organism dies, is buried in sediment, and the sediment becomes rock. How does a fossil become exposed at Earth's surface?

Fossils are formed in rock and most rock is hidden from human view. Only in those cases where rock is exposed naturally, or through human activities such as mining, are fossils likely to be found. As more mining and exploration takes place, new fossils are found. Many of the fossils found in museums were found as a result of quarrying. For example, *Archaeopteryx*, considered to be ancestral to modern birds, was found in a stone quarry in Germany.

Despite all these problems, paleontologists have uncovered huge numbers of fossils and have been able to assemble them into a detailed representation of the history of life on Earth.

What Are Some Possible Scientific Explanations for Aspects of the Fossil Record Such as Gaps and the Sequential Nature of Fossils?

The Sequential Nature of the Fossil Record

Fossils are laid down in sequence. Older fossils are laid down before the younger ones. This creates a sequential record of life on Earth. Fossils can be dated using rock sequences and by radiometric dating. In some cases, fossils are present in a complete sequence. Most often they are not. Paleontologists are often able to assemble sequences from rocks from different areas. In other cases, there are gaps in the **fossil** record. Some of these gaps are marked by the apparent sudden appearances of new life forms.

The sequential nature of the fossil record has enabled scientists to trace the evolution of groups of organisms from common ancestors. One example is the evolution of whales.

Fossils formed over the last 60 million years suggest that whales evolved from a land-based ancestor. These fossils show a gradual transition between the land-dwelling ancestor—*Pakicetus*—and modern whales. *Pakicetus* was a carnivorous, semi-aquatic quadruped that lived in shallow, freshwater habitats. It didn't look much like a whale, but its skull bears some resemblance those of modern whales. The ear region was surrounded by thick bone, a characteristic only found today in whales. This minor detail has helped paleontologists connect together a series of fossils that are part of the whale evolutionary tree. Links in the evolution of this tree show a variety of species with intermediary body forms.

One transitional fossil is the more recent *Ambulocetus* (dated to about 48 million years ago). Its body form suggests that it was amphibious. While its forelimbs showed the features of a land animal, its hind limbs and undulating tail were adapted for swimming. Isotope analysis shows that it lived in near-shore marine habitats. A chain of more recent fossils shows a further transition to a whale-like body without legs, better adapted for swimming. These organisms were able to live in the sea. Eventually, these populations evolved into modern dolphins and baleen whales. While the fossil evidence indicates that these animals are relatives of each other, it does not provide conclusive evidence showing that one is a direct ancestor of the other.

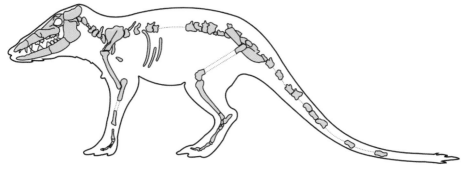

Pakicetus

THE EVOLUTION OF THE WHALE

The sequential nature of fossils can help scientists hypothesize about the common ancestor of a clade of organisms. What kinds of evidence might lead scientists to hypothesize that these organisms descended from a single ancestral species?

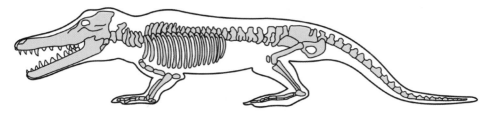

Ambulocetus

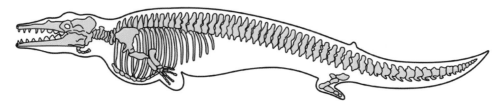

Basilosaurus

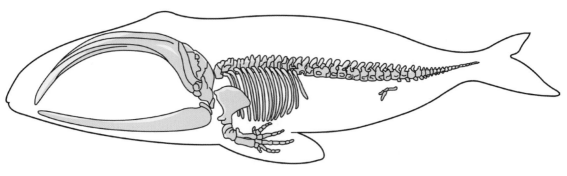

Balaena

There is increasing evidence from fossils that birds evolved from small carnivorous dinosaurs called theropods. *Tyrannosaurus* belonged to this group of dinosaurs. This dinosaur-bird connection was first suggested after the discovery of a transitional fossil—with reptile and birdlike characteristics—called *Archaeopteryx*. The fossil *Archaeopteryx* has been dated to around 150 million years old. The fossils show that *Archaeopteryx* had feathered wings and other features similar to birds. It also had a long bony tail, clawed fingers, and teeth, similar to reptiles. More recent fossils show that some dinosaurs had feathers long before they evolved wings. These early feathers probably functioned as insulation; they were colored, so may have also been used for display or camouflage. Some of these feathers were downy. Others were much stiffer, more like the wing feathers of birds. Fossils found in China and South America show evolutionary changes in nesting behavior, feathers, jaws, and skeletons that connect feathered dinosaurs to modern birds.

BIRDS EVOLVED FROM DINOSAURS?

This image is an artist's rendition of the dinosaur *Archaeopteryx*. What birdlike features did *Archaeopteryx* have?

Whales and birds are just two examples of how sequential fossils can be used to build up a picture of evolutionary history.

The fossil record shows that evolution is not a smooth process in which some forms slowly transform into others over millions of years. Many organisms have existed unchanged for many millions of years. They then appear to undergo apparent rapid evolution. One example is the evolution of the Foraminifera, a group of single-celled protists. Over the last 10 million years, the Foraminifera underwent a series of relatively quick morphological changes separated by longer periods of stasis. This pattern fits in well with current ideas about evolution. Within an isolated population, genetic drift and natural selection can result in rapid evolution that may leave no fossil record. The reintroduction of the changed population to the wider population may lead to a "sudden appearance" in the fossil record, breaking the period of stasis.

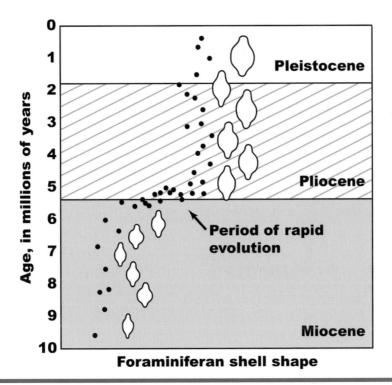

Age, in millions of years

Foraminiferan shell shape

Pleistocene

Pliocene

Miocene

Period of rapid evolution

EVOLUTION OF THE FORAMINIFERA

The diagram shows the evolution of the Foraminifera, a common type of marine protist. How does the diagram of foraminiferan evolution provide evidence of stasis in the fossil record?

One thing all scientists agree on is that there are gaps in the fossil record. Some of these gaps have been filled in by "missing links" or transitional fossils. Other gaps still remain. Because the fossil record is incomplete, scientists also rely on molecular, genetic, and anatomical evidence to support theories of evolution.

Consider the Explain Question

| How can scientists construct a timeline for the history of life on Earth?

Go online to complete the scientific explanation.

dlc.com/ca10050s

Check Your Understanding

| Was Earth a suitable environment for living things when it first formed billions of years ago?

dlc.com/ca10051s

STEM in Action

Applying Explanations for the History of Life on Earth

Studying the history of life on Earth is similar to a real-life treasure hunt. Biologists, geologists, paleontologists, and archaeologists are examples of scientists who search for clues, such as fossils and other remnants that tell them about Earth's past. Fossils are like snapshots of time because scientists can often tell from where the fossilized organism came, how old it is, and what the conditions of Earth were like during its existence. Specialized tools are used carefully to find, gather, and study fossils. For instance, a chisel may be used for delicately splitting fine-layered shale. Brushes are often used to dust off a fossil once it is located. Magnifying glasses are used to study fossils to get a closer look at their structure. Computers and substance dating materials are also important for modern day scientists in the storage and analysis of data.

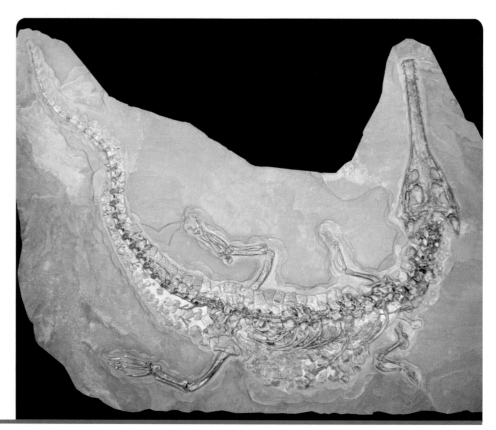

CROCODILIAN FOSSIL

This Jurassic crocodilian fossil was found near Holzmaden, Germany. What can scientists learn from collecting and studying fossils?

Fossils can be used to provide evidence that Earth is a dynamic planet whose surface is changing all the time. Some fossils of the same species have been found along the east coast of South America and the west coast of Africa. These fossils provide evidence that South America and Africa were once part of one supercontinent. This supports the theory of continental drift, which states that Earth's continents move together and apart over time. This drift is due to tectonic plate movement. Continental drift is further supported by finding the fossils of tropical organisms in places that are now on land in colder climates. These locations on the continents were once closer to the equator, but they have shifted over time with the movement of tectonic plates.

STEM and the History of Life on Earth

Paleontologists study the fossil record to learn more about life on Earth, such as extinct species and evolution. The fossil record can even be used to discover ancient ancestors of modern humans. Excavating fossils is a delicate process, as fossils can break or become damaged when they are being unearthed. Some creatures, such as trilobites, have tough shells that create great records of fossils. Scientists have learned a great deal about how long and where these creatures lived because so many of them were fossilized.

Once the fossils are discovered and excavated, they can be analyzed and studied further. Electrical and environmental engineers design and operate technology that helps tell how old the fossil is and what kinds of minerals and other elements it contains. Computer technology may also be used to create simulations of three-dimensional views of the fossils. This helps fill in the gaps where scientists are unsure about how the fossilized organism may have looked.

The Development of Earth

dlc.com/ca10052s

LESSON OVERVIEW

Lesson Question

■ What were the conditions of early Earth?

Lesson Objectives

By the end of the lesson, you should be able to:

■ Summarize the evolution of Earth's geosphere, oceans, and atmosphere.

■ Cite evidence that is consistent with a model of Earth's formation and early history.

Key Vocabulary

Which terms do you already know?

- [ ] asthenosphere
- [ ] atmosphere
- [ ] Cambrian explosion
- [ ] continental crust
- [ ] crust
- [ ] cyanobacteria
- [ ] deposition (sedimentary)
- [ ] evaporation
- [ ] geosphere
- [ ] inner core
- [ ] kinetic energy
- [ ] lithosphere
- [ ] magnetic field
- [ ] mantle
- [ ] oceanic crust
- [ ] outer core
- [ ] ozone
- [ ] photosynthesis
- [ ] radioactive isotope
- [ ] sediment
- [ ] solar wind

© Discovery Education | www.discoveryeducation.com ● Image: InkkStudios / E+ / Getty Images

Reflecting on the Development of Earth

Scientists calculate that the universe sprang into existence about 13.7 billion years ago when an area of extreme temperature and intense gravitational pressure began to expand. This event is known as the big bang. What do you already know about the big bang theory?

dlc.com/ca10053s

EXPLAIN QUESTION

| What evidence is there to support the statement that conditions on the surface of Earth have changed since it was first formed?

AN ACTIVE VOLCANO

A volcanologist collects data from an active volcano. How do you think information from volcanoes can help scientists discover conditions from Earth's beginnings?

What Were the Conditions of Early Earth?

The Structure of Earth

After the planet formed about 4.6 billion years ago, several processes released heat that kept the surface a molten pool of metals.

1. The young planet was bombarded by material from space. The kinetic energy of the incoming material transformed into heat as it struck the planet. This heat kept early Earth's surface molten.

2. Accretion describes the addition of material to the planet from space. Each new addition added mass to the planet. When bodies from space collided with Earth, they often stuck to each other. This process is called impact accretion. The increase in Earth's mass led to an increase in the planet's gravitational force. Gravitational compression made Earth's volume less. In the process, heat was released.

3. Differentiation describes how molten materials changed position in the planet based on density. Molten metals like nickel and iron sank toward Earth's center, while less dense materials like molten silicon rose to the planet's surface. This separating process released heat from the planet's interior.

4. Radioactive isotopes are unstable atoms. These atoms release energy in the form of heat as they transition to more stable states.

VOLCANIC ERUPTION

Molten rock escapes from the mantle to Earth's surface. How can newly forming rock help us determine the conditions of early Earth?

Earth's composition consists primarily of six elements: iron (Fe), oxygen (O), silicon (Si), magnesium (Mg), nickel (Ni), and sulfur (S). Early Earth consisted primarily of dense, liquid metals. The liquid iron and nickel sank to the planet's center. The less dense liquid materials, primarily aluminum and silica, rose to the planet's surface. Over time, the molten materials separated into three layers.

Earth's core is composed almost exclusively of iron with a small amount of nickel. It is divided into two parts, the solid **inner core** and the liquid **outer core**. The inner core lies 5,150 to 6,370 kilometers below Earth's surface. It accounts for 2 percent of Earth's total mass. The average density of the inner core is 13.5 g/cm^3. Scientists estimate the temperature of the inner core at 5,000 to 7,000°C. However, the inner core experiences intense pressure in excess of 1,400,000 gigabars, or 1.4×10^{14} bars greater than the pressure at sea level. Despite the high temperature, the intense pressure keeps the material in the inner core solid.

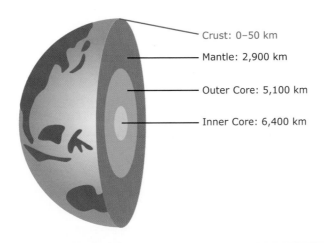

Crust: 0–50 km
Mantle: 2,900 km
Outer Core: 5,100 km
Inner Core: 6,400 km

EARTH'S INTERNAL LAYERS

During Earth's formation, molten rocks separated into layers due to density differences. How does the composition of these layers differ?

The outer core lies 2,891 to 5,150 kilometers below Earth's surface. It accounts for 30 percent of Earth's total mass. The outer core temperature ranges between 4,400 and 6,100°C. The outer core remains liquid because it experiences lower pressure.

The **mantle** is the thickest layer in Earth's interior. It lies 2,891 to 40 kilometers below Earth's surface and accounts for 70 percent of the planet's volume. The mantle is composed primarily of aluminum, iron, magnesium, and silica. The mantle has a density that ranges between 4 and 10 g/cm^3, which is less dense than the core. The mantle's temperature is about 870°C. The **asthenosphere** is the upper portion of the mantle. It comes in direct contact with the rigid rock layer overlying Earth's surface, called the **lithosphere**, on which sits the **crust**. The asthenosphere is a solid that behaves plastically—in other words, the asthenosphere moves fluidly, like putty.

The rocks found on the planet's surface form the crust. The crust is relatively thin and adds very little to the overall mass or volume of the planet. The first rocks formed on Earth's surface around 4.0 billion years ago. Earth's oldest rock was discovered in 2008 along Hudson Bay in northern Quebec. Researchers from McGill University think this rock is a portion of Earth's primordial crust—the first crust on the planet.

Earth's Early Atmosphere

The **atmosphere** is comprised of gases that surround the surface of Earth. The composition of gases in the atmosphere has changed through time. The earliest atmosphere was composed primarily of hydrogen and helium gases. These gases were too light for the planet to retain. Many scientists think that **solar wind** (charged particles from the surface of the sun) carried the young atmosphere away. Today, solar winds are deflected from the planet by the **magnetic field**, but the early planet did not have this protection. Earth's magnetic field did not form until the Earth's core formed. As a result, gaseous hydrogen and helium in the original atmosphere were lost to outer space and remain relatively rare on Earth today.

VOLCANIC GASES

Volcanic gases formed most of the early atmosphere of Earth. What can scientists learn about Earth's early atmosphere from gases emitted by volcanoes?

Many scientists propose that Earth's "first atmosphere" developed from the release of gases from volcanoes to the atmosphere. This early atmosphere would have contained mostly hydrogen and large amounts of water vapor, carbon dioxide, and hydrogen sulfide. It also would have contained smaller amounts of nitrogen, carbon monoxide, methane, and other gases. It is thought that this atmosphere was blown off the planet by a catastrophic impact with a huge Mars-size body that blew off huge volumes of material when it collided with primitive Earth about 4.5 billion years ago. Much of that material later condensed, forming the moon. The intense energy released by the impact left much, if not all, of Earth in a molten state.

EARTH'S FIRST ATMOSPHERE

A meteor the size of Mars would have left Earth in a molten state and released gases to form the first "atmosphere." What gases would that early atmosphere contain?

About 4 billion years ago, the composition of the atmosphere changed again. The planet was still in the process of cooling. Volcanic activity at the planet's surface expelled a variety of gases into the atmosphere, primarily water vapor, carbon dioxide, hydrogen sulfide, and trace amounts of nitrogen, carbon monoxide, methane, and ammonia. Many of the gases reacted with minerals on land or dissolved in the ocean. The gases that did not react began to accumulate and form Earth's "second atmosphere." The sun's light broke down the ammonia from the volcanoes. The nitrogen that was released by this process slowly increased in the atmosphere.

Formation of the Oceans

Early Earth was an inhospitable place. The processes that released heat in Earth's interior kept the planet's surface a pool of molten materials. The earliest rocks formed when molten material at Earth's surface cooled, forming a thin, brittle crust. The composition of the early crust was similar to the molten material originating in the planet's interior and brought to the surface during volcanic eruptions today.

Over time, the early crust was melted and re-formed many times. With each episode of melting and cooling, the chemical composition of the crust began to change. Two types of crust emerged: continental and oceanic. The two types of crust differ in composition and thickness. **Continental crust** is composed of minerals made up primarily of aluminum and silica. The average density of continental crust is 2.7 g/cm^3. Continental crust ranges in thickness from 30 to 40 kilometers. **Oceanic crust** is composed of iron- and magnesium-rich minerals. It has a density of about 3.5 g/cm^3. Oceanic crust is thinner—5 to 6 kilometers thick on average.

Earth's oceans formed when the continents began to separate or rift apart. When this happened, material from Earth's molten interior rose to the surface and cooled, producing oceanic crust. As the process continued, water condensed out of the atmosphere, fell as rain, and flooded the rifted area. In the new oceans, however, water evaporated, rain re-flooded the land and entered the ocean, and water evaporated again, through several cycles. During these periods of **evaporation**, rocks like halite and gypsum were formed. Eventually, coarse-grained **sediment** eroded from the surrounding continental crust and covered the deposits remaining after the evaporation. As the spreading continued and more water flooded the regions, ocean sediments began to collect in the newly formed basins. As more oceanic crust was added, the rifted continents were pushed farther apart and the ocean basins grew as they filled with water.

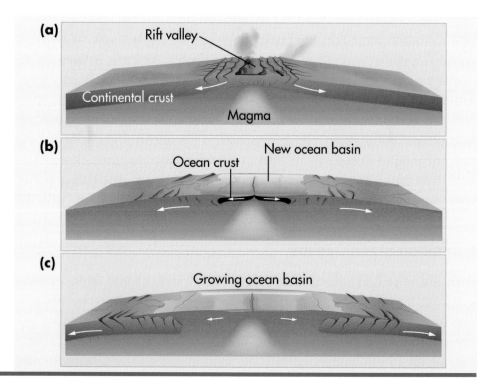

A NEW OCEAN

As a continent rifts apart, a new crust forms and grows, forming ocean basins. What hypothesis explains the origin of the water that fills these basins?

The Lack of Oxygen

Almost all life on the planet depends on oxygen, but the early atmospheres lacked any free oxygen. It is important to understand how this element became so abundant in the atmosphere of today.

Oxygen in the atmosphere was released by ancient blue-green bacteria (**cyanobacteria**). These organisms conducted **photosynthesis**, which is a chemical reaction that converts carbon dioxide and water to glucose, a simple sugar. A byproduct of photosynthesis is oxygen gas. As the population of bacteria increased, the concentration of oxygen in the atmosphere slowly began to increase.

The Concentration of Oxygen Increases

Blue-green bacteria formed mound-like structures called stromatolites in the ocean. The oldest stromatolite fossils have been dated to almost 4 billion years ago. The free oxygen these organisms produced began to react with other elements in the ocean, like iron. The reactions produced iron-rich minerals. These minerals include hematite, magnetite, siderite, pyrite, and olivine. As the concentration of iron in the ocean diminished, photosynthesis carried out by the bacteria began to release free oxygen into the atmosphere.

STROMATOLITES

Stromatolites are one of the earliest fossil evidence of life on Earth. Why do scientists hypothesize that these structures contributed to Earth's atmosphere as we know it today?

At first, this oxygen in the atmosphere did not accumulate. Instead, it reacted with other elements on land. Oxygen is very reactive and will not form free oxygen if there are other elements to bond with. Once these elements were exhausted, the oxygen began to accumulate in the atmosphere.

Around 2.5 billion years ago, there was little oxygen in the atmosphere. In fact, oxygen made up only 1 percent of the atmosphere. By 2 billion years ago, the concentration began to increase. By 700 million years ago, it had increased to 20 percent. As oxygen built up, more **ozone** (another molecule made of oxygen atoms) formed. The layer of ozone in the atmosphere blocked some of the sun's harmful ultra-violet radiation. The formation of the ozone layer allowed more terrestrial life in Earth's **geosphere** to survive and evolve. The rise in oxygen (and ozone) began near the start of the **Cambrian explosion**, a period of rapid evolution that began about 540 million years ago.

Consider the Explain Question

What evidence is there to support the statement that conditions on the surface of Earth have changed since it was first formed?

dlc.com/ca10054s

Go online to complete the scientific explanation.

Check Your Understanding

How have Earth's oceans and atmospheres evolved since the planet formed?

dlc.com/ca10055s

STEM in Action

Applying the Development of Earth

Studying the levels of carbon dioxide in the **atmosphere** can help us determine the atmospheric conditions in the past and in our future. The concentrations of greenhouse gases in Earth's atmosphere fluctuate over time. Ice cores provide a wealth of information on atmospheric chemistry, and scientists have learned about past levels of carbon dioxide, methane, nitrous oxide, oxygen, and dust. Air bubbles trapped in the cores are condensed and transferred to a gas chromatograph. The concentration of each gas in the mixture is measured, and scientists compare these data to the composition of the current atmosphere. These comparisons illustrate how atmospheric chemistry has changed over time.

RETREATING GLACIER
Climate change is speeding up the melting of glaciers, releasing more water into our oceans. What could higher ocean levels mean for Earth?

One of the most widely studied greenhouse gases is carbon dioxide. Ice core records reveal that the concentration of atmospheric carbon dioxide varies naturally over time. During interglacial episodes, the concentration is approximately 280 parts per million. During glacial episodes, the concentration is approximately 180 parts per million. Using data collected at the Mauna Loa Observatory, scientists document temperature trends around the world.

The overall trend of atmospheric carbon dioxide concentration is up. According to the National Oceanic and Atmospheric Administration (NOAA), the average surface temperature has warmed 0.5°C since the 1970s. Furthermore, the average surface temperature is warming at a rate of about 0.01°C every decade, or 1.7°C every century. Daily maximum and minimum temperatures confirm this warming trend. Land tends to warm faster than ocean water. In addition, winter months are warming faster than summer months. The Intergovernmental Panel on Climate Change has drawn several conclusions from these data. First, global average surface temperature has risen substantially since the mid-20th century. Second, human activities are likely a primary cause of this increase. Since 1880, the warmest years on record have all occurred in this century. If we continue to release carbon dioxide into the atmosphere more quickly than we are able to store it through natural processes, we may make irreversible changes to the environment and the type of living things that populate Earth.

STEM and the Development of Earth

Geologists, geochronologists, physicists, and archaeologists collaborate in laboratory studies to perfect techniques of radiometric dating to determine ages of rocks and organic remains.

Radiometric dating is based on the principle that the nucleus in a radioactive element naturally and spontaneously splits. This process forms different isotopes or elements from the original, or parent, element. The rate at which an element splits, or decays, over time is constant. So we can use the ratio of the amount of parent isotope to daughter isotope in a rock to calculate backwards to the date when the parent formed 100 percent of the total amount.

Developed in the 1940s, radiocarbon dating is an application of radiometric dating that is appropriate for archaeological and anthropological research into relatively young organic material. This technique is based on the fact that all living things absorb carbon until they die. The total carbon at the time of death is in two forms, one radioactive and the other nonradioactive. The radioactive carbon isotope decays after the death of the organism; the other does not. The ratio of the amount of one carbon isotope to the other changes at a known rate. By measuring the carbon ratio in decaying organic matter, biologists and archaeologists can calculate the length of time that has passed since the death of the organism.

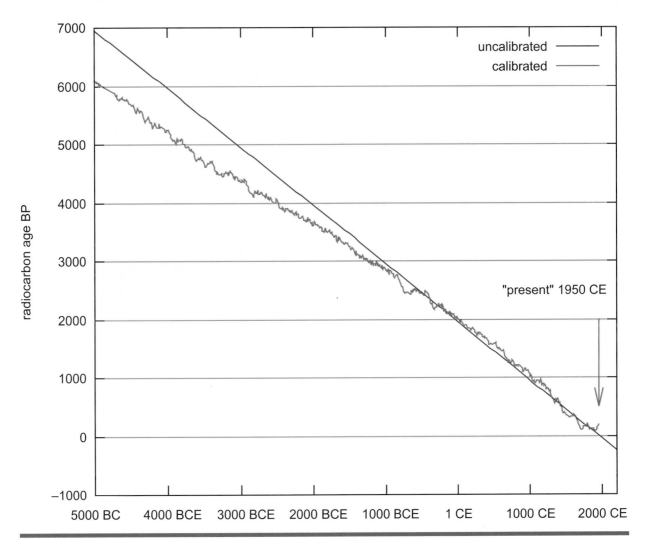

Radiocarbon measurements are effective only when dating material that is less than about 50,000 years old. Geologists and stratigraphers have other radiometric tools available to date rocks that are much older, including the oldest rocks on Earth. They are even able to use these techniques to date rocks from the moon and meteorites from Mars and the asteroid belt. These rocks all contain naturally occurring isotopes of radioactive elements. The oldest ages in the geologic column are based on the decay rates of several isotopes of uranium.

Radiometric dating has shown that the oldest minerals on Earth and in meteorites and asteroids are all about 4.5 billion years old. Geologists and planetologists, therefore, conclude that all the planets in the solar system formed at about the same time, 4.5 billion years ago!

THE CARBON RATIO

The carbon ratio in decaying organic matter indicates the length of time that has passed since the death of the organism. What is the radiocarbon age BP of an organism that died around 2000 BCE?

CONCEPT
3.3

Evidence for Plate Tectonics

dlc.com/ca10056s

LESSON OVERVIEW

Lesson Questions

■ What is the process of seafloor spreading?

■ What evidence supports the theory of plate tectonics?

■ What are the processes thought to drive the motion of tectonic plates?

Key Vocabulary

Which terms do you already know?

☐ asthenosphere
☐ atmosphere
☐ climate
☐ continental crust
☐ continental drift
☐ convection
☐ convergent boundary
☐ core
☐ divergent boundary
☐ Earth
☐ fossil
☐ geologic time
☐ inner core
☐ lithosphere
☐ mantle
☐ mid-ocean ridge
☐ outer core
☐ plate motion

Lesson Objectives

By the end of the lesson, you should be able to:

- Summarize the process of seafloor spreading.
- Identify evidence that supports the theory of plate tectonics.
- Summarize the processes thought to drive the motion of tectonic plates.

Key Vocabulary continued

- ☐ plate tectonics
- ☐ radioactive decay
- ☐ radioactivity
- ☐ ridge push
- ☐ rift valley
- ☐ rift zone
- ☐ seafloor spreading
- ☐ slab pull
- ☐ subduction zone
- ☐ transform boundary

Evaluating Evidence for Plate Tectonics

dlc.com/ca10057s

Fossils of an extinct reptile called *Mesosaurus* and of an extinct fern called *Glossopteris* were discovered on both the eastern coast of South America and the western coast of Africa. But how could fossils of the same genera of organisms be found in places so widely separated by so much ocean?

PLANTS CAN'T SWIM

Fossil *Glossopteris* leaves are found in South America, Africa, and in Australia, where this specimen came from. The plants lived from 245 to 286 million years ago. How did the same species exist in places that are separated by whole oceans?

EXPLAIN QUESTION

What evidence do scientists have that Earth's crust is divided into moving plates?

What Is the Process of Seafloor Spreading?

Seafloor Spreading

Earth's crust and the upper part of the **mantle** make up the relatively cool, rigid outer layer of the planet. This cool, rigid layer is called the **lithosphere**. The lithosphere is separated into tectonic plates. The tectonic plates are constantly moving together and apart. This phenomenon is known as the theory of **plate tectonics**.

The theory of plate tectonics explains how Earth's surface is recycled over time. Plate movements are responsible both for the formation of certain features on Earth's ocean floor and **continental crust** and, to a lesser extent, for the distribution of Earth's rocks and minerals. Tectonic plates are destroyed at **subduction zones**. Subduction zones are areas where a denser plate slides beneath a less dense plate. The denser plate then melts in Earth's mantle. New oceanic crust is formed at mid-ocean ridges. This happens through the process of **seafloor spreading**.

Mid-ocean ridges are oceanic rift zones. They consist of long mountain chains along a central **rift valley**. Mid-ocean ridges are divergent plate boundaries. At mid-ocean ridges, tectonic plates move apart and seafloor spreading occurs. Seafloor spreading is the process by which new oceanic lithosphere forms at mid-ocean ridges. As tectonic plates move away from each other, magma rises from Earth's interior. It then cools and solidifies in the center of the ridge. The rising magma pushes up between the plates and drives them further apart.

As new crust is forming at the spreading center, it pushes the older crust apart. Because of this, the oceanic crust contains symmetrical patterns of crustal rock ages. These rocks increase in age as their distance from the mid-ocean ridge increases.

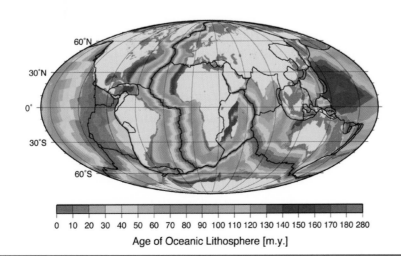

Age of Oceanic Lithosphere [m.y.]

OCEANIC LITHOSPHERE

This map shows that the ocean floor gets older the further it is from the mid-ocean ridges. What makes the ocean floor move away from the mid-ocean ridge?

Learning from Mid-Ocean Ridges

The patterns that form at mid-ocean ridges reveal additional information about Earth's history at the time the older crust was formed. For example, Earth's magnetic field occasionally reverses its polarity.

Earth's magnetic field is generated by the flow and circulation of the liquid **outer core** around the solid **inner core**. This field is not static—it moves all the time. For this reason, magnetic north and true north (the north end of Earth's rotational axis) do not always correspond. True north is a fixed geographic location, but magnetic north is what attracts the needle in a compass. Magnetic north migrates over time in a phenomenon called polar wandering. So, magnetic north does not always match up with true geographic north. The angle of this difference at any given location is called the declination. The declination can be set on a compass to correct for this difference; maps often indicate it as well.

Polar wandering is a continuous process that occurs on a human time scale. Magnetic north has shifted several degrees within a period of a few decades. In addition to the poles wandering over the northern and southern hemispheres, Earth's magnetic poles completely flip. Throughout geologic history, Earth's magnetic field has completely reversed many times. When Earth's magnetic field reverses polarity, the same end of the compass needle still points to the magnetic north pole. However, the magnetic north pole would be located closer to the geographic south pole. After another pole reversal, the poles switch back so that magnetic north is again closer to geographic north.

These reversals have happened many times throughout Earth's history, but they do not happen at a predictable rate. Over the last 20 million years, there has been a magnetic pole reversal on average about every 200,000 to 300,000 years. However, much longer periods have passed without any pole reversals. Scientists can study these magnetic pole reversals by studying the magnetic polarity of rocks in Earth's crust. Spreading centers are an ideal place to study this phenomenon because rocks on either side of mid-ocean ridges can be matched and correlated. The oceanic crust contains symmetrical bands of alternating magnetic polarity on each side of mid-ocean ridges.

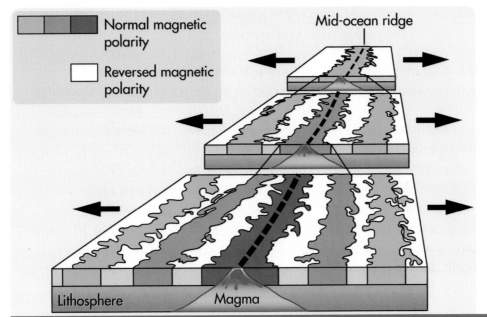

Normal magnetic polarity

Reversed magnetic polarity

Mid-ocean ridge

Lithosphere

Magma

MAGNETIC STRIPING ON THE OCEAN FLOOR

Earth's magnetic field occasionally reverses its polarity. How do rocks on either side of mid-ocean ridges reflect that phenomenon?

Scientists are not sure exactly what the effects of a magnetic field reversal would be on living things. However, it is unlikely that a reversal would be harmful to most life on Earth. Although Earth's magnetic field protects the planet from solar radiation, the **atmosphere** also protects the planet from the sun's harmful rays. Animals that rely on magnetic fields for navigation and migration would likely be able to adapt since pole reversals seem to occur very slowly in relation to an individual's life span.

What Evidence Supports the Theory of Plate Tectonics?

Wegener's Evidence for Continental Drift

Scientists are gaining more knowledge of plate tectonics every day. However, the theory of plate tectonics is a relatively new one, becoming widely accepted only in the 1970s. One of the first things that scientists noticed that supports plate tectonics is the apparent fit of the continental coastlines. This is particularly apparent in the way that eastern South America and western Africa seem to fit like a jigsaw puzzle. This evidence led to the hypothesis of **continental drift**, developed in the early 1900s by a German scientist named Alfred Wegener.

Wegener marshaled a variety of evidence in support of his idea that the continents may once have been joined:

- Similar landforms are distributed across oceans. For example, mountain ranges sometimes appear to be continuous on opposite sides of an ocean. The Appalachian Mountains in North America and the Caledonian Mountains in Greenland and Northern Europe formed when all three land masses were joined in the supercontinent Pangaea. As Pangaea broke apart, what had been a continuous mountain range broke apart as well. Today these mountains are separated by the Atlantic Ocean and several northern seas. Rock sequences have also been matched on opposite sides of an ocean.
- Wegener noticed that deposits of glacial sediment have been found on opposite sides of an ocean. The position of these glacial deposits did not make sense with the continents in their current positions. Continental drift seemed the only explanation for their distribution.
- Similar fossils have been discovered in distant locations. The Mosasaurs fossils found in Brazil and western Africa are only one example of this phenomenon. Paleontologists continue to find more and more fossils that match on opposite sides of an ocean.

Evidence for Plate Tectonics

Initially, the hypothesis of continental drift was rejected. This was because Wegener could not determine the mechanism by which the continents drifted together and apart over **geologic time**. Wegener died in 1930, before scientists truly began to accept his ideas.

Technological advances allowed scientists to more thoroughly explore the ocean floors. Using new, sophisticated instruments, they began to understand this mechanism. Scientists realized that Earth's surface is divided into tectonic plates containing both continental and oceanic tectonic plates. The hypothesis of continental drift then became incorporated into the theory of plate tectonics. Scientists used Wegener's evidence supporting continental drift to support the theory of plate tectonics. Scientists also discovered further evidence of tectonic plate movement.

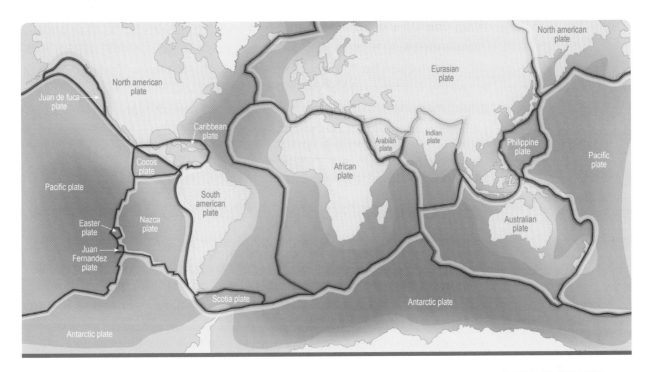

The following labels appear on the map:

North american plate

Juan de fuca plate

Caribbean plate

Cocos plate

Pacific plate

Easter plate

Nazca plate

Juan Fernandez plate

South american plate

Scotia plate

Antarctic plate

Eurasian plate

Arabian plate

Indian plate

African plate

Philippine plate

Pacific plate

Australian plate

Antarctic plate

North american plate

PLATE TECTONICS

This map shows Earth's main tectonic plates. On which tectonic plate is the continental U.S.?

Plate tectonics is supported by the relatively young age of the oldest oceanic crust. Earth's crust first solidified approximately 3.85 billion years ago. Earth's crust is constantly recycled through plate tectonics. If it were not, all of Earth's crust would be expected to be the same age: approximately 3.85 billion years old. Yet new oceanic crust is continually being formed at seafloor spreading centers. Older crust is continually being destroyed at subduction zones. Therefore, the oceanic crust that exists today is only 200 million years old, much younger than the age of the continental crust, which can be older than 3.85 billion years.

Seafloor spreading centers provide other evidence for plate tectonics as well. Scientists can observe where the oceanic crust used to match up. This oceanic crust has now been pushed apart on either side of the mid-ocean ridge. Scientists have discovered the symmetrical age patterns of oceanic crust on either side of the mid-ocean ridges. They have also discovered symmetrical magnetic reversal patterns. These matching patterns show very clear evidence that the oceanic crust is moving apart at the divergent boundaries of mid-ocean ridges. Magma wells up between the two moving plates, forming new crust. Scientists can directly observe new crust being formed at seafloor spreading centers. They can then infer that older crust must be destroyed elsewhere on the planet. Otherwise, Earth would be expanding. Observations of old crust being destroyed at subduction zones confirm this hypothesis.

Plate tectonics is also supported by precise measurements of relative **plate motion**. Scientists can use global positioning systems (GPSs) and other devices to track the movement of tectonic plates. Scientists now know the average rate of movement of each tectonic plate. Some of the plates move faster than others. The average rate of plate movement is just a few centimeters per year.

What Are the Processes Thought to Drive the Motion of Tectonic Plates?

Processes That Drive Plate Tectonics

Scientists now have very solid evidence to support the idea that tectonic plates are moving all the time. However, like Wegener's **continental drift** hypothesis, the theory of plate tectonics cannot be accepted without an explanation of the processes that drive it. Fortunately, scientists now have clear explanations for these driving processes.

The tectonic plates that make up Earth's lithosphere "float" above the mantle. The mantle is a solid, not a liquid. However, because it is so hot, it is soft enough that it can flow slowly, similar to how putty flows. Hot material in the mantle rises toward the lithosphere, cools, and sinks back down toward the **core**. This cycling of mantle material is called mantle **convection**.

Mantle convection—the slow convection of mantle rock caused by the uneven distribution of thermal energy in Earth's interior—is thought to be a driving force of tectonic plate motion. As the convection cycles occur within the mantle, the tectonic plates above are moved as if on a very slow conveyer belt. This mantle convection pushes plates together at convergent boundaries such as subduction zones. As the denser plate begins to subduct beneath the less dense plate, gravity starts to pull the subducting plate into the mantle. This further drives tectonic plate movement in a process called **slab pull**. Slab pull—the sinking of cooler, denser oceanic lithosphere at subduction zones—is thought to be another driving force of tectonic plate motion.

At seafloor spreading centers, the mid-ocean ridge constitutes an area of high elevation on the seafloor. Oceanic plates can slide down this higher elevation toward a subduction zone. This further drives tectonic plate movement in a process called **ridge push**. Ridge push—the sliding of oceanic lithosphere down and away from a mid-ocean ridge due to the higher elevation of the mid-ocean ridge relative to a subduction zone—is thought to be another driving force of tectonic plate motion. In fact, ridge push and slab pull often work together to move tectonic plates.

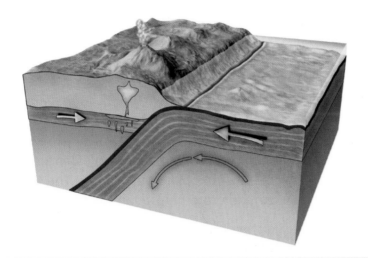

SUBDUCTION ZONE

An oceanic plate dives below a less dense continental plate. What types of landforms might you find along a subduction zone like this?

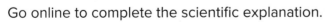

Through the processes of mantle convection, slab pull, and ridge push, scientists can now explain the driving forces behind tectonic plate movement. As our understanding of these processes has increased, the theory of plate tectonics has become widely accepted.

Consider the Explain Question

| **What evidence do scientists have that Earth's crust is divided into moving plates?**

Go online to complete the scientific explanation.

dlc.com/ca10058s

Check Your Understanding

▌ **What evidence supports the theory of plate tectonics?**

dlc.com/ca10059s

STEM in Action

Applying Evidence for Plate Tectonics

Thanks to the evidence supporting the theory of plate tectonics, scientists know that segments of Earth's crust move together and apart. They also know that the movement of the tectonic plates can cause earthquakes, volcanism, seafloor spreading, and mountain-building events. But how do scientists know where the boundaries of tectonic plates are? And what types of boundaries they are dealing with? What can they do with this information?

EARTH'S FIERY BOUNDARIES

Data from volcanoes and earthquakes have allowed scientists to map the boundaries of plates all across Earth. Have the boundaries always been in the same place?

Volcanism occurs very often at subduction zones. The subducting plate begins to melt as it approaches the mantle. The resulting magma rises and builds up pressure in the crust. If enough pressure builds, a violent volcanic eruption will occur. Less violent volcanism also occurs as magma wells up at seafloor spreading centers. Volcanism rarely occurs in association with transform plate boundaries. The type and presence of volcanism can therefore help scientists to ascertain the type of plate boundary.

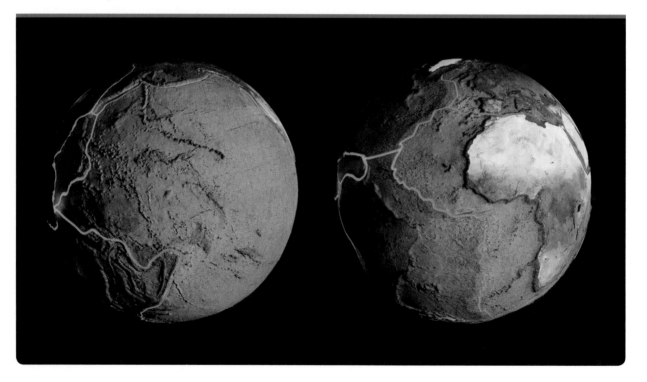

When plates push against each other at convergent boundaries or slide past each other at transform boundaries, pressure builds. When this pressure becomes too great, it is released in the form of an earthquake. The pressure of two plates pushing together at convergent boundaries can also form mountain chains. Earthquakes also occur at divergent plate boundaries but they are less frequent and less violent.

By tracking the areas where earthquakes and volcanic eruptions have occurred throughout history, scientists can discover patterns. These patterns, along with the locations of mountain chains, allow scientists to determine the boundaries of tectonic plates. This information can be used to determine where earthquakes and volcanic eruptions are likely to happen.

STEM and Evidence for Plate Tectonics

Geologists continue to find evidence that the continents have changed position, on every continent they conduct fieldwork. *Glossopteris*, one of the fossils that originally raised the idea of **continental drift** when it was found in South America and Africa, has also been found in Antarctica. **Fossil** evidence also reveals that Antarctica, now under a polar ice cap, once had trees, ferns, and a variety of animals, including dinosaurs and later, mammals. The fossil records show when the Antarctic animal populations started to be isolated from the ones on nearby continents, such as Australia. The records also provide tantalizing clues about when living things died out from an increasingly cold **climate**.

Fossils are not the only evidence scientists rely on to reconstruct the movements of the ancient supercontinents. Geologist John Goodge travels to Antarctica to unravel the geologic history of the continent. Millions of years ago, the continent of Antarctica was not in the middle of a plate, as it is now. Its rocks contain clues to ancient rifts, now quiet, as well as subduction zones that raised mountains before sealing themselves off and holding still.

During the Antarctic summer, from October through February, Goodge travels by plane and snowmobile to camp out in the snow hundreds of miles from the nearest base camp, in order to collect rocks to analyze back in the lab.

In the lab, Goodge uses a variety of technological equipment to unlock the rocks' secrets. Specimens are analyzed using scanning electron microscopes as well as radioactive dating for igneous rock, and analysis of grains of the mineral zircon in sedimentary rocks. The ages of the rocks, the types of minerals present, as well as the shapes, sizes, and geographic orientation of the grains, are all clues to the rock's formation. Some of the data Goodge's team has collected suggest that Antarctica and North America were once close neighbors. However, this is not consistent with the overwhelming evidence that these two bodies of land were separated by what is now Africa, back when the continents were joined in one supercontinent. Goodge points out that his team is researching a much older period of Earth's history, and that more data are needed.

Exploring Europa

The *New Horizons* space probe made this image of Jupiter's moon, Europa, capturing the moon in its orbit around the gas giant planet. Data from the *New Horizons* mission raised the possibility of plate tectonics on Europa, which has an icy crust.

EXPLORING EUROPA

What instruments do you need to search for evidence of plate tectonics?

A new mission to Europa is in the planning stages. The new space probe will contain a number of scientific instruments, each of which must be engineered both to collect the desired data and to fit on the probe. The Proposed Instrument list describes the capabilities of each available instrument.

Proposed Instruments

- Plasma Instrument for Magnetic Sounding (PIMS): Measures surface ice crust thickness and ocean depth
- Interior Characterization of Europa using Magnetometry (ICEMAG): Measures the magnetic field of Europa
- Mapping Imaging Spectrometer for Europa (MISE): Identifies materials making up Europa and maps location of the materials
- Europa Imaging System (EIS): Cameras to produce high-resolution maps of surface features
- Radar for Europa Assessment and Sounding: Ocean to Near-surface (REASON):Ice-penetrating radar system that reveals hidden structure of crust and ocean beneath
- Europa Thermal Emission Imaging System (E-THEMIS): Heat detector identifies locations of active vents spewing water from within the moon
- Mass Spectrometer for Planetary Exploration/Europa (MASPEX): Determines composition of surface and subsurface ocean
- Ultraviolet Spectrograph/Europa (UVS): Detects water plumes
- Surface Dust Mass Analyzer (SUDA): Measures the composition of small solid particles ejected from the moon's surface, similar to the way volcanoes eject particles on Earth

Relative Dating

LESSON OVERVIEW

Lesson Questions

- What broad, underlying assumptions or philosophies do scientists use to explain Earth's history?
- What dating techniques do scientists use to determine the relative ages of rocks?
- How do scientists describe gaps in the rock record?

Lesson Objectives

By the end of the lesson, you should be able to:

- State the underlying assumptions that scientists use to explain Earth's geologic history.
- Identify relative dating techniques and explain how scientists use them.
- Explain how scientists describe gaps in the rock record.

Key Vocabulary

Which terms do you already know?

- [ ] angular unconformity
- [ ] disconformity
- [ ] nonconformity
- [ ] principle of inclusions
- [ ] principle of lateral continuity
- [ ] principle of superposition
- [ ] rock cycle
- [ ] superposition

dlc.com/ca10060s

Image: Brad McGinley Photography / Moment / Getty Images

Thinking about Relative Age

How do scientists use relative age dating? Why is it so important when beginning to understand the history of Earth?

dlc.com/ca10061s

EXPLAIN QUESTION

▐ **What is relative dating, and how can it be determined?**

FAMILY GATHERING

This family decided to take a break from their daily lives to take a picture. Can you organize the family from oldest to the youngest based on certain characteristics they possess?

© Discovery Education | www.discoveryeducation.com • Image: Jack Hollingsworth / DigitalVision / Getty Images

What Broad, Underlying Assumptions or Philosophies Do Scientists Use to Explain Earth's History?

Two Geologic Philosophies

For thousands of years, people have attempted to solve many of the mysteries of Earth's past. During the past few centuries, people have focused on two broad, underlying philosophies to explain Earth's geologic history: catastrophism and uniformitarianism.

RANGER TALKING ABOUT DINOSAUR BONES

Fossilized dinosaur bones are evidence that life in Earth's past was very different than it is today. Look at this image. What do you think deposited first, the bones or the rocks around them?

Catastrophism

For early scientists, some of the most perplexing clues about Earth's past came from fossils of marine organisms found on dry land. Also, many fossils appeared to be from organisms that couldn't be found living on Earth. One early explanation suggested that these organisms lived in the past and were totally wiped out by disastrous catastrophes. Catastrophism is the idea that Earth has been mainly shaped by sudden, violent events such as floods or volcanic eruptions.

Uniformitarianism

In the late 1700s, James Hutton proposed an idea that opposed the idea of catastrophism. For many years, he observed how natural processes such as weathering and erosion gradually changed the landscape on his farm in Scotland. He thought that, given enough time, these same natural processes could eventually wear down mountains and change the shape of Earth's surface. The principle of uniformitarianism states that processes that occurred in the past operate in the same way as they do in the present. Uniformitarianism includes the idea that many changes occur gradually over millions of years.

Today, uniformitarianism is the guiding philosophy used to explain Earth's geologic history. Recently, however, scientists have developed a more inclusive and integrated view. According to this view, some catastrophic events—such as the asteroid impact that caused the extinction of the dinosaurs—also play major roles in shaping Earth's history. However, although infrequent in historical terms, such events are, when looked at from the perspective of geological time, a normal part of Earth's history.

What Dating Techniques Do Scientists Use to Determine the Relative Ages of Rocks?

Principles of Relative Dating

Scientists use several principles or dating techniques to determine the relative ages and chronological order of rocks in an outcrop. These include the **principle of superposition**, the principle of original horizontality, the **principle of lateral continuity**, the principle of cross-cutting relationships, and the **principle of inclusions**.

Superposition

The word *superimpose* means to lay or place something on or over something else. Imagine placing dirty clothes in a laundry hamper each day for a period of one week. By the end of the week, the "oldest" clothes will be on the bottom and the most recent clothes will be on the top. The same principle applies to layers of sedimentary rocks. The principle of **superposition** states that sedimentary rocks are laid down such that younger layers are deposited above older layers.

Original Horizontality

The principle of original horizontality states that sedimentary rock formations were originally formed in horizontal layers. This principle is easily observed by pouring pancake batter into a frying pan. The batter doesn't stand up vertically—it spreads out in a relatively flat horizontal layer. The same thing occurs when sediments are originally deposited. Gravity causes the sediments to be deposited in horizontal layers, which then turn to rock.

This principle is important when analyzing folded or tilted layers of rock. A fold is a bend in rock that was caused by movement in Earth's crust. Folds are commonly produced when horizontal pressure causes layers of rock to buckle or bend. For example, folding can occur when Earth's tectonic plates collide at convergent boundaries. A common analogy is a rug that buckles when it is pushed sideways. Tilting often occurs when rock layers are uplifted unevenly, causing the layers to no longer be horizontal. The principle of original horizontality indicates that folding and tilting events occurred after the original rock layers were formed.

Lateral Continuity

Imagine a construction crew digging a ditch through an asphalt-covered roadway to insert a drainage pipe. When the job is complete, the ditch will separate two sides of the asphalt from each other. Originally, the asphalt was continuous, but now both sides terminate against the drainage pipe.

The preceding example demonstrates another principle of relative dating. The principle of lateral continuity states that sedimentary layers extend laterally in all directions. For example, identical rock layers on both sides of a valley or canyon can be assumed to have originally been continuous. Before the Colorado River carved out the Grand Canyon, the layers of rock on both sides of the canyon formed one connected layer.

SEDIMENTARY ROCKS

Even though sedimentary rock layers might be separated by deep canyons, they were originally continuous and extended laterally in all directions—sometimes for many kilometers. Which kind of events could interrupt rock layers?

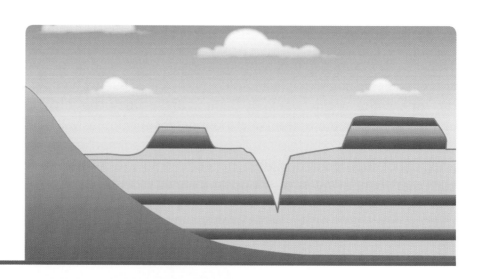

Cross-Cutting Relationships

To understand the principle of cross-cutting relationships, it is helpful to first learn a bit about some geologic features. This principle is often used in reference to geologic features such as rock formations, faults, intrusions, dikes, and sills. A rock formation is a laterally continuous body of associated rocks that have a wide distribution. For example, the Morrison Formation is a sedimentary layer from which dinosaur fossils have been discovered in Montana, Wyoming, Utah, Colorado, and South Dakota. A fault is a fracture in rock along which movement has occurred. An intrusion is a mass of igneous rock that was forced into or between other rocks while it was still molten (magma) and later solidified into solid rock. A dike forms from magma that is forced into a vertical crack in a rock formation and later solidified. A sill forms from magma that is forced into a horizontal crack in a rock formation and later solidified.

The principle of cross-cutting relationships states that any geologic feature that cuts partially through or completely across another geologic feature is the younger of the two features. For example, suppose a car has a crack in the windshield. Which is younger—the crack or the windshield? Answer—the crack. The windshield can't have a crack if the windshield didn't exist in the first place. Hence, faults, intrusions, dikes, and sills are younger than the geologic features they cut across—including other faults, intrusions, dikes, or sills they cut.

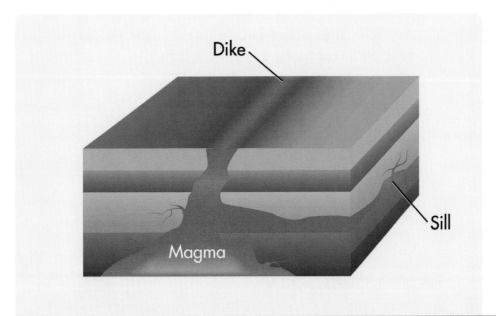

IGNEOUS ROCKS

According to the principle of cross-cutting relationships, dikes and sills are younger than the rocks they cut across. What type of rock is a dike made from?

Inclusions

The principle of inclusions is used by geologists to determine places in the rock record where erosion has removed large sequences of strata. Inclusions represent pieces of one rock that have been incorporated into another rock. This happens when rocks are fragmented by faulting, volcanic activity, or compression from deposition and burial. When these things take place, older, preexisting rocks are often incorporated into the matrix of younger, overlying rocks.

The boundary between two adjacent rock layers is known as a contact. When inclusions are observed in a layer along a contact, the younger layer is easily identified by the inclusions. In most situations, such inclusions are found in the top layer. However, it is possible for the layers to be tilted and even overturned. In such situations, inclusions of older rock in the younger rock may be found in the lower bed. Conglomerate and breccia are sedimentary rocks that are often found along contacts between older and younger rocks. In such situations, pebbles of older rocks are embedded in the matrix of younger rocks.

CONGLOMERATE

According to the principle of inclusions, the small fragments of rock are older than the material that surrounds and connects them. What processes might account for the formation of this conglomerate?

How Do Scientists Describe Gaps in the Rock Record?

Unconformities

Imagine reading a history of the United States written on loose-leaf pages bound together in a three-ring notebook. As you begin to read through the chapters, you notice a steady pattern of advancement in technology. The history begins with the horse-and-buggy days of the American Revolution. It proceeds to the steam locomotive and telegraph of Civil War times. Then Suddenly, the next chapter is about the Iraq War. You read about computers, jet aircraft, and laser-guided missiles. Even though you don't initially notice anything missing from the stack of papers, you know something is out of place. The steady progression of technology in the preceding chapters is suddenly inconsistent with the technology in the latter chapters. It seems as though someone removed some of the middle chapters. In other words, the preceding information does not conform to the information that comes later.

The sequence of Earth's sedimentary rock layers forms a geologic record of past events much like the chapters in a history book. Earth's history can be studied by examining and interpreting rock sequences that form the geologic rock record of past events. However, most rock sequences are not complete. Much of the rock material has been worn away by weathering and erosion. Later, new rock material is deposited on the old, eroded surface. Where this has happened, a gap or break appears in the rock record.

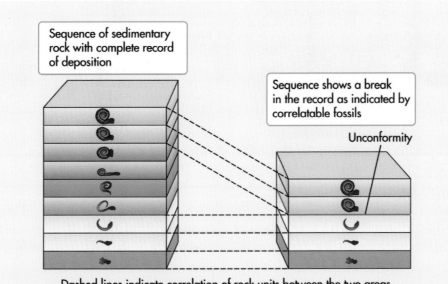

Dashed lines indicate correlation of rock units between the two areas

Sequence of sedimentary rock with complete record of deposition

Sequence shows a break in the record as indicated by correlatable fossils

Unconformity

UNCONFORMITY

An unconformity occurs when portions of Earth's rock record are eroded away before the next layers of sedimentary rock are deposited. How would you recognize an unconformity?

Gaps in the rock record are called unconformities. An unconformity is simply an erosional surface that separates two rock masses of different ages. It represents a missing segment of Earth's history at that location. The three main types of unconformities are angular unconformities, disconformities, and nonconformities.

Angular Unconformity

An **angular unconformity** is an erosional surface in which the sedimentary rock layers below the surface form an angle with the sedimentary rock layers above the surface. This type of unconformity is probably the easiest to recognize during a field observation.

A typical angular unconformity forms in the following way. First, multiple horizontal layers of sediment solidify into several horizontal layers of sedimentary rock. Next, the horizontal layers of sedimentary rock are uplifted, tilted, or folded. Then, the rock layers are eroded in such a way that an erosional surface cuts across several of the layers. This new surface forms at an angle to the layers. Later, new horizontal layers of sediment are deposited onto the eroded surfaces of the underlying rock layers. Finally, the overlying layers of sediment form horizontal layers of sedimentary rock above the underlying tilted or folded layers.

ANGULAR UNCONFORMITY

The angular unconformity is indicated by the red line in D. Which events could cause the folding in the second step?

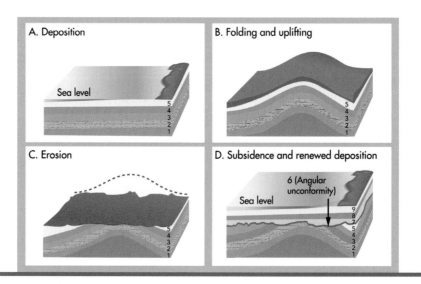

A. Deposition

Sea level

B. Folding and uplifting

C. Erosion

D. Subsidence and renewed deposition

6 (Angular unconformity)

Sea level

Disconformity

A **disconformity** is an unconformity between parallel layers of sedimentary rock. Like the angular unconformity, a disconformity also is a buried erosional surface that separates two rock masses of different ages. However, along a disconformity, the lower rock mass has not been tilted or folded. Instead, the sedimentary layers of the lower rock mass remain parallel with the sedimentary layers of the upper rock mass.

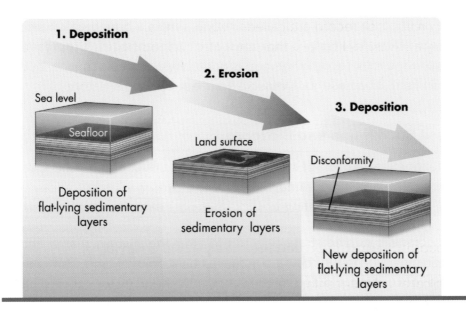

1. Deposition

2. Erosion

3. Deposition

Sea level

Seafloor

Deposition of flat-lying sedimentary layers

Land surface

Erosion of sedimentary layers

Disconformity

New deposition of flat-lying sedimentary layers

DISCONFORMITY

The sedimentary rock layers are arranged horizontally above and below a disconformity. How could this affect the relative dating of the layers?

When viewed from a distance, a disconformity might be difficult to distinguish from ordinary parallel layers of sedimentary rock. However, the irregular shape of the erosional surface separating the two rock masses becomes more apparent when it is examined from a closer distance.

Nonconformity

Both of the preceding unconformities occur between layers of sedimentary rock. But this is not the case with a **nonconformity**. A nonconformity is an unconformity between sedimentary rock and metamorphic or igneous rock. In this situation, metamorphic or igneous rock is eroded. Later, sedimentary rock forms on the eroded surface of the metamorphic or igneous rock.

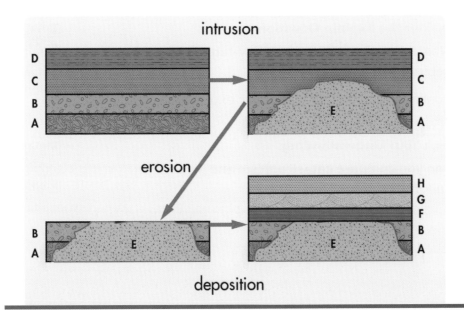

intrusion

erosion

deposition

D C B A

D C B A

E

B A

E

H G F B A

E

NONCONFORMITY

A nonconformity occurs where sedimentary rock is deposited onto the eroded surface of igneous or metamorphic rock. Of which type of rock does the intrusion consist?

Like all unconformities, a nonconformity is simply a buried erosional surface that separates two rock masses of different ages. It represents a gap in the rock record. This gap is not a physical gap of space, but a gap in time. It represents a missing segment of Earth's history.

Fossil Succession and Biozones

A biozone is a section of strata containing fossils characteristic to a specific geologic time frame. Biozones are used in biostratigraphy. This is the study and dating of rock units based on the fossils present.

As geologists studied strata, they noticed that the animals, plants, and their distribution in the rock record have changed over time. This change in the rock record is called fossil succession. The early rock record has very little biodiversity. Animals were mostly shelled animals, similar to clams and other marine molluscks or animals with jointed exoskeletons, like crabs. Over geologic time, biodiversity increased to include a bigger variety of animals (including vertebrates such as reptiles and mammals), and a wide variety of complex plants. This is visible in the rock record. The evidence is fairly consistent across the rock record. Fossils usually increase in number and type as one moves up vertically through a rock column. One exception is when a catastrophic event, such an asteroid impact or major climate change, wipes out many species of animals and plants. If two different strata contain the same kinds of fossils, both rock units must be the same relative age.

Certain fossils seem to be found only during relatively short geologic periods. These fossils are called index fossils. Index fossils help geologists narrow the relative age of rock strata significantly.

Consider the Explain Question

| What is relative dating, and how can it be determined?

Go online to complete the scientific explanation.

dlc.com/ca10062s

Check Your Understanding

| Can you compare catastrophism and uniformitarianism?

dlc.com/ca10063s

in Action

Applying Relative Dating

According to the law of superposition, older sedimentary rock is found beneath younger sedimentary rock. Is there ever a time where it can actually be reversed? Could older layers of sedimentary rock be located above younger layers?

The law of superposition supports that the youngest rock layer is located on the top, while the oldest is located on the bottom. With the law of superposition in mind, geologists collect data in the field in order to support the relative age of the rocks they are studying. They know that each layer has a marker for time. For example, one layer may be made of a different material when compared to the rock layers above and below the layer. Gathering data on the makeup of a particular rock layer informs geologists about the landscape at the time that the layer was created. Perhaps the area was covered in water, or there was an active volcano. Gathering data about the formation of the rock will assist in learning about the history of that particular area.

However, forces within Earth test the principle of superposition as uplifting of Earth's materials occurs through tectonic movement. These forces inside Earth can sometimes cause older rock layers to be arranged above younger rock layers. Folding and faulting are two examples that can cause this situation to happen. At convergent plate boundaries, tectonic plates coming together can cause the rock to uplift and bend, creating a fold in the rock layer. If there is extreme uplifting and bending of the rock layers, the folding can be extreme and cause the layers to overturn. Data collected from these sites on the angle at which the rock layer was uplifted can assist geologists with information about the properties of the rock and with the type of force that caused the uplift. At seduction zones, one plate will subduct, and the other plate will go over top of that plate. This will cause a younger rock layer to be on top of an older rock layer.

Erosional forces, typically from water, also cause gaps in the rock record. As erosion occurs, the layers of rock are literally washed away, and there is no longer concrete evidence that the layer existed. However, information collected about erosion will assist with determining a time frame and the cause of the erosion.

Inconsistencies occur often when determining relative age. However, fossils found in sedimentary rock layers aid in the identification of relative age. Some fossils are able to give scientists a lot of information about the relative age of a particular rock layer.

EARLY JURASSIC FOSSIL

This is a fossil of Promicrocerasplanicosta, and scientists have confirmed that is was from the early Jurassic period. What makes some fossils better than others for marking Earth's history?

Fossils are very useful when applying relative dating principles to actual field observations. Some types of fossils, called index fossils, can be especially useful. Index fossils are the remains of organisms that typically have three characteristics. First, they lived for a relatively short span of geologic time, so when a certain specific fossil is found, the age of the rock layer is easy to determine. Second, they were very abundant and can be located in many different locations. Third, they lived over a broad geographic area. They are called index fossils (also guide fossils or indicator fossils) because they are used to define and identify specific geologic periods. Index fossils are often used as guides to help determine the age of the rock layers in which they are found. Index fossils can help identify whether rock layers have or have not been overturned by folding or tilting.

STEM and Relative Dating

Fossils are useful in determining the relative age of an area, and this information is utilized in the oil industry. The use of index fossils to determine the age of a rock layer and the environment at the time the index fossil was alive informs a scientist about the potential for a particular area to contain petroleum. Often a paleontologist (a person that studies fossilized plants and animals) is hired to locate petroleum. With their knowledge of index fossils and data they have available to them, they are able to assist in locating the most suitable place to drill. When finding a location that is best suited for the presence of hydrocarbons, a cutting is made in which the rock is broken and brought to the surface to be analyzed. In addition to bits of rocks, microscopic fossils (called microfossils) also stick to the lubricated drill and are brought to the surface. Microfossils are fossilized plants and animals that are typically less than 1 millimeter in diameter. Because they are so tiny, microfossils often survive the drilling process and may be extracted whole from the bits of rock.

But how do paleontologists use microfossils to determine if it is useful to be drilling for oil and minerals in a particular location? The paleontologist will study these fossils and create an environmental analysis of the area to determine the presence of petroleum. How? Microfossils are often good index fossils. Tiny microorganisms are typically more abundant than larger macroorganisms and can be found in many locations. Many of these species also tend to evolve more rapidly and have relatively short life spans. This enables paleontologists to quickly and easily identify specific geologic locations that might contain known resources such as oil and minerals.

OIL WORKERS LOOKING AT A GEOLOGIC CROSS SECTION

These engineers are looking over the geology of the land to determine the best location for drilling. Index fossils are often used to determine the best drill site. Why is it important to work with a geologist before drilling?

Comparing Formations

Compare the two images of the rock layers. Both images were taken in the same protected national park area in Utah; however, they have distinguishing differences. Different natural processes have occurred in order to create the differences that you see.

COMPARING ROCK LAYERS

This rock formation in Utah is called "The Wave." What do the rock layers look like in this formation?

GLEN CANYON

This rock formation is also in Utah. How is it different from "The Wave" formation?

What information can these two images give to geologists?

Both of these images were taken at Coyote Buttes in Utah. You can see formations similar to this, collectively called "The Wave," spanning the entire Coyote region from north-central Arizona to south-central Utah. What hidden details can you see in different rock layers?

Evidence for Evolution

dlc.com/ca10064s

LESSON OVERVIEW

Lesson Questions

- How are fossils used as evidence for evolution?
- How do scientists explain gaps and sudden appearances in the fossil record?
- What do anatomical and developmental homologies tell us about common ancestry?
- How do molecular sequences provide evidence for evolution?
- How does biogeography provide evidence for evolution?
- Can evolution be observed today?

Key Vocabulary

Which terms do you already know?

- [ ] antibiotic
- [ ] biogeography
- [ ] Cambrian explosion
- [ ] Charles Darwin
- [ ] comparative morphology
- [ ] convergent evolution
- [ ] convergent evolution
- [ ] directional biogeography
- [ ] evolutionary tree diagram
- [ ] fossil
- [ ] genetic variation
- [ ] homology
- [ ] homology
- [ ] macroevolution

Lesson Objectives

By the end of the lesson, you should be able to:

- Assess how the fossil record supports evolutionary theory.
- Analyze how the structure and develop of organisms provides evidence of common ancestry
- Use diagrams to interpret ancestral relationships between species
- Explain how molecular sequences may be used as evidence of common ancestry.
- Analyze biogeographical evidence for evolution.

Key Vocabulary continued

- ☐ mass extinction
- ☐ molecular sequences
- ☐ mutation
- ☐ natural selection
- ☐ paleontology
- ☐ Theory of Evolution

Everything Is a Relative

dlc.com/ca10065s

Are you related to a snail, or a shark, or an oak tree? Could you be related to now-extinct dinosaurs or fossilized worms?

A RELATIVELY CLOSE RELATIVE

This baby orangutan looks a lot like you, and yet he is also different. Why does it have these similarities and differences?

EXPLAIN QUESTION

How do scientists use evidence from a wide variety of sources to determine evolutionary relationships?

How Are Fossils Used as Evidence for Evolution?

After the publication of Darwin's book, *On the Origin of Species*, interest in evolution soared. Many fields of science began to make discoveries that provided evidence for the theory. Evidence is still being collected today.

One of the most difficult aspects of evolution research is that evolution often takes place over long periods of time. The time span is much longer than one individual could observe in his or her lifetime. Luckily, there is a record of life that began billions of years ago—the **fossil** record.

FOSSILS

Fossils, such as this trilobite, provide information about species of the past. What modern animals have bodies composed of many segments, like this trilobite?

Fossils are the preserved remains or traces of animals, plants, and other organisms that provide information about Earth's history. Using radiometric dating, scientists are able to estimate a fossil's age based on the known radioactive decay rates of various isotopes that accumulated in the organism when it was alive. Fossils are also dated by their specific presence in older or younger layers of rock in Earth's history.

The fossil record contains data that indicates that groups of organisms appeared in a sequential nature. For example, the oldest fossils seem to be those of simpler animals without backbones. Only later fossils contain organisms, such as fish, with a spinal cord. The earliest mammals are in still later fossils.

Fossils that show links between species of the past and modern-day species have been discovered. By analyzing and evaluating the fossil record, scientists are able to trace the changes in physical structures as they evolved little by little over the years.

ANALYZING FOSSILS

This prehistoric fossil shows a species similar to a modern-day lizard. What characteristics does this fossil share with a lizard?

For example, scientists have found some fossil organisms that represent intermediate steps between living mammals and their ancestors. By examining and dating these fossils, scientists have been able to document stepwise changes in the development of the mammalian skull, jaws, and teeth. A similar analysis of fossils has enabled scientists to trace the evolutionary history of the present-day horse. Scientists have also used fossils to support the hypothesis that whales evolved from land-dwelling mammals. Although the fossil record does not provide a complete record of all life on Earth, it does provide extensive and ever-increasing evidence to support **the theory of evolution**.

How Do Scientists Explain Gaps and Sudden Appearances in the Fossil Record?

Darwin thought evolutionary change occurred gradually over long periods of time. Observations of the fossil record suggest that evolution is, by human standards, a slow process. However, it also shows that evolution does not take place at a constant rate. Sometimes, there are periods of stasis (no apparent change), or very slow change. At other times, there appear to be rapid spurts of evolutionary change. In addition, as Darwin acknowledged, the fossil record appears to have gaps or to be incomplete. There are sudden appearances and disappearances of life-forms.

When analyzing and evaluating scientific explanations for gaps in the fossil record, it is important to consider all sides of the evidence. Does a sudden appearance suggest that a species or body form suddenly appeared? Was it simply not preserved in the fossil record previously? Has it not yet been discovered? In order for fossils to be preserved, certain conditions must be met. The remains of an organism must experience minimal decay and environmental disturbance. The remains must be buried in sedimentary rock without excessive heat or pressure. Catastrophic or other natural events such as erosion and subduction can affect these conditions. The difficulty in meeting these conditions might explain many gaps in the fossil record.

FOSSIL FORMATION AND PRESERVATION

Certain conditions must be present for fossils to form and be preserved. What are some of those conditions?

One of the biggest puzzles in the history of life is a period called the **Cambrian explosion**. The fossil record suggests that about 550 million years ago, during the Cambrian period, there was an "explosion" in the diversity of life. Some argue that many types of animals with different shapes and body plans appeared suddenly. How do scientists account for this evolutionary event? Many scientists think that the Cambrian explosion had a number of causes.

In evolutionary terms, the Cambrian explosion event was fast. However, this "rapid" event took place over tens of millions of years. Rare fossils of soft-bodied organisms show that complex animals existed before this time. These provided the raw material for this evolutionary spurt. Because some Precambrian and early Cambrian fossils share a few traits with today's living organisms, some scientists argue that these life-forms are ancestors of modern phyla. But at this point, the evidence for a direct ancestral link between Precambrian and Cambrian fossils is inconclusive.

The sudden disappearance of many life-forms in the fossil record just before the Cambrian suggests that a **mass extinction** occurred. For those species that survived a mass extinction, new ecological niches became available. This may have led to rapid evolution, which would appear to be a "sudden appearance" in the fossil record of many different species.

The fossils of the Precambrian are rare, but Cambrian fossils are common. The main reason for this is that most Cambrian fossils are of organisms with hard body parts—external skeletons and shells. Fossils of soft-bodied Cambrian organisms are rare. There are a number of suggestions as to why hard body parts appeared at this time. These include the availability of chemicals for mineralization (to make hard shells) and an arms race triggered by the development of the first eyes. Recent research indicates that genes that govern critical developmental processes formed a genetic tool kit that enabled a rapid burst in diversification of animal life.

One of the best fossil records of the Cambrian explosion is found in the Burgess Shale in British Columbia. This fine mudstone was laid down when the explosion had already been underway for a few million years. It contains the first appearance in the fossil record of organisms with clam-like shells, arthropods such as trilobites, echinoderms, mollusks, early vertebrate-like animals, and many strange animals that may belong to evolutionary dead-ends. These include bizarre life-forms such as opabinia. Opabinia had five eyes and a trunk-like nose.

The Cambrian explosion is not the only period of rapid evolution and diversification. Other "explosions" took place in Earth's history. One occurred about 420 million years ago when terrestrial vertebrates invaded the land.

BURGESS SHALE

This piece of the Burgess Shale contains the fossil of a trilobite. During which period of rapid evolution and diversification did this trilobite live?

Punctuated Equilibrium

Many parts of the fossil record show the gradual evolutionary change of organisms over time. However, some parts of the fossil record show long periods of stasis or equilibrium in which no or very few new species appear. These periods of equilibrium are interrupted or punctuated with short bursts of speciation. The model of punctuated equilibrium may be used to explain these observations. The following scenario provides an example of punctuated equilibrium at work.

Imagine a big lake containing a population of fish. Conditions in the lake remain fairly constant for hundreds of thousands of years. The fish live and die, and some of their remains are fossilized every few thousand years. A fossil record of the fish species builds up as a horizontal stasis. Then conditions change:

- One of the rivers feeding into the lake is captured by another stream. Less water is available. Parts of the lake dry up.
- A smaller lake, surrounded by ponds, forms.
- The smaller lake and ponds each have an isolated population of fish.
- The environmental conditions in these ponds are different. They may differ in a number of ways—depth, temperature, water quality, and oxygen availability.
- The small isolated fish populations may undergo rapid evolutionary change as a result of the genetic drift and the different selection pressures encountered in each pond.
- Over a few thousand years, they rapidly evolve into new species through the process of peripatric speciation. The process is fast, so none of the transitional forms of fish are fossilized.
- A landslide blocks the valley and a new lake forms that floods and combines most of the isolated ponds.
- The fish species mix. Those occupying the same niche compete. Some species—perhaps the original species—become extinct.
- In the new lake, the populations of the remaining fish species grow. Conditions in the lake remain stable for thousands of years. The fish die and leave behind a fossil record.
- Millions of years later a paleontologist visits the area. He finds a fossil record that shows a period of stasis in terms of fish species, followed by a period in which new species suddenly appear.

Punctuated equilibrium is a useful model for understanding how the fossil record forms. You may have noticed that it fits well with other aspects of evolutionary theory, including **natural selection**, common ancestry, and the time frame over which the fossil record has been formed.

What Do Morphological and Developmental Homologies Tell Us about Common Ancestry?

Homology is similarity in morphological features resulting from common ancestry. You can analyze and evaluate morphological homologies in the mammalian forelimbs of the human, cat, whale, and bat. As different species faced varying environmental conditions over time, characteristics that were present in an ancestral mammalian organism gradually evolved to enable each species to survive in its environment. Because these species all share a common ancestor, the bones of the forelimbs exhibit an underlying similarity. Yet each forelimb evolved differently as each organism faced different environmental conditions. For example, the forelimb of a cat has become well suited for chasing and capturing prey, while the forelimb of a whale has become a paddle-like structure enabling it to successfully swim in an ocean habitat.

FORELIMB HOMOLOGIES ON MAMMALS

The forelimbs of different vertebrates show the similar structures derived from a common ancestor. Compare the forelimb bone structures of the human, cat, whale, and bat. How are they similar?

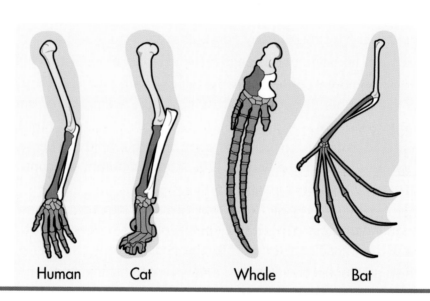

Human   Cat   Whale   Bat

Not all structures that look alike or perform the same function are homologous. Similar structures may evolve independently in different groups of unrelated organisms. This results in organisms that appear to possess homologous structures, when in fact they do not. A good example of this is found in fish, reptiles, and mammals. Sharks, ichthyosaurs (an extinct reptile), and dolphins all have streamlined body shapes and dorsal and lateral fins. All three have sharp teeth for catching prey. However, these organisms did not inherit these traits from a common ancestor. These structures are not homologous. These structures evolved independently as a result of similar selection pressures that produced similar adaptations to a marine predatory lifestyle. This coming together, or convergence, of similar adaptations is called **convergent evolution**. There are numerous examples of convergent evolution.

Developmental Homologies

Developmental homology is recognized as a common embryonic trait in different organisms. For example, as vertebrates undergo embryonic development, they share certain common traits that can be analyzed and evaluated. These shared traits are referred to as developmental homologies. For example, the early embryos of chicks, humans, and cats all have tail-like structures as well as structures called gill pouches. The presence of these common embryonic traits suggests that these different species share a long-ago common ancestor. As embryonic development proceeds, however, an embryonic trait may be lost and the organism can be structurally different when it matures. Embryos of some snake species show evidence of developing legs, for example, yet these legs are lost during the development process. This, along with fossil evidence of snake-like organisms with hind limbs, supports the hypothesis that snakes evolved from a limbed ancestor.

How Do Molecular Sequences Provide Evidence for Evolution?

Molecular (DNA or protein/amino acid) sequencing can be used to analyze the molecules of life in groups of organisms. At the molecular nucleotide or amino acid level, organisms from bacteria to pigs have many similarities. All living things carry their genetic code in DNA or RNA. These are also the molecules that pass on traits to offspring in every living organism. Many genes and proteins are also homologous across the living world. For example, one particular protein, cytochrome c, which functions in cellular respiration, is very similar in all living cells. In another example, bacteria and eukaryotes are very different kinds of organisms, yet both share the same genes that code for the ribosomal units used in protein synthesis, suggesting that bacteria and eukaryotes shared a common ancestor long ago. By comparing sequences in the proteins or DNA of different organisms, scientists can determine how closely related they are. Generally speaking, the greater the number of differences the greater the amount of time that has elapsed since they had a common ancestor. Molecular sequencing is just another piece of evidence that supports Darwin's original idea, that with modification through natural selection, life evolved from a common ancestor.

Molecular Clocks

Molecular clocks are techniques that use genetic **mutation** rates to determine historical time when divergence of species occurs. There is some evidence that some evolutionary changes take place at the molecular level in a clock-like fashion. Over millions of years, random mutations build up in any given stretch of DNA at a fairly constant rate. This makes changes in DNA a powerful tool for analyzing and evaluating the evolutionary histories of related organisms, enabling scientists to calculate the dates when evolutionary lineages split. For example, imagine that a length of DNA found in two species differs by two bases, and we know that this entire length of DNA changes at a rate of about one base per 10 million years. That means that the two DNA versions differ by 20 million years of evolution. Since each lineage experienced its own evolution, the two species must have descended from a common ancestor that lived at least 10 million years ago. When comparing different organisms, the more genes that are compared, the more accurate the dating.

How Does Biogeography Provide Evidence for Evolution?

Biogeography is the study of the distribution of organisms, species, ecosystems, and biomes around the world. Factors affecting the distribution of organisms and biological communities include habitat area, climate and soil composition, longitude, latitude and elevation, and the geological history of a region.

In Darwin's time, there were many aspects about the distribution of organisms that could not be explained. Why, for example, were there ostrich-like birds in Africa, South America, and Australia, continents that are thousands of kilometers apart? Why did many remote islands have species that were found only on those islands? How did these animals and plants get to these places? Darwin used his ideas about evolution to explain some of these observations.

Darwin considered biogeographic distributions as evidence for evolution and natural selection. On his visit to the remote Galapagos Islands Darwin noticed the presence of many unique species. He realized that island-dwelling plants and animals are often geographically isolated from other islands or the nearest mainland. Because of this geographic isolation, island organisms can breed only with other island organisms. As time passes, island plants and animals often evolve into new species that are distinctly different from the mainland species from which they descended. This is the reason islands often have many endemic species (species of plants and animals that are found nowhere else). For example, the Galapagos Islands were the home of a number of species of finches. These birds have many similarities, but all are slightly different. They all occupy different niches. One scientific explanation is that these similarities are a result of the finches evolving from a few common ancestors that managed to find their way to the islands long ago. Over time, the finches adapted to vacant niches. This is an example of adaptive radiation.

Better understanding about the movement of the continents in Earth's past has helped to unravel some of the mysteries of plant and animal distribution. For example, scientists know that the continents of Africa, Australia, and South America were once joined. This probably enabled the common ancestor of today's ostrich-like birds to colonize all three, now widely separated, continents.

EVIDENCE FOR EVOLUTION

This *Aepyornis* fossil is from an early ancestor of New Zealand's modern kiwi bird. How would this fossil provide evidence that the continents of Africa, Australia, and South America were once joined?

Can Evolution Be Observed Today?

The traditional idea that evolution is a very slow process that can only be inferred from other evidence and cannot be observed in human timescales is inaccurate. Natural selection is an ongoing process that occurs in all populations. Since natural selection is one driving force behind evolution, it makes sense that evolutionary processes are readily observable in natural and man-made systems. Evolution has been observed in wide variety of studies, perhaps the most famous of which is work conducted on the Galapagos medium ground finch. Observations of this bird, made over a few decades on one of the islands in the archipelago, has shown that, within the population, the size of its beak changes in response to competition with other bird species and fluctuates dramatically in response to changing climate.

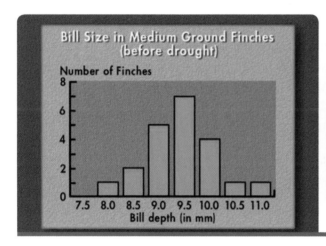

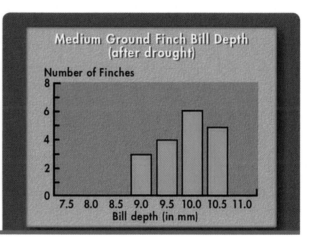

GALAPAGOS FINCHES EVOLVE IN RESPONSE TO CHANGING CLIMATE

These graphs compare the depth of beaks in ground finches before and after a period of drought. What impact has drought had on the size of beaks in the finch population?

Evolution is most rapid, and therefore most readily observed, in populations of organisms with short life cycles and high rates of reproduction. Bacteria fit this description particularly well and provide many examples of evolution in action. One of these is the evolution the bacterium *Mycobacterium tuberculosis*, which causes the disease tuberculosis (TB). Historically, TB has been a major cause of early death in people. In the middle of the last century, a new class of drugs, antibiotics, was introduced to combat this disease. These drugs were initially very effective at curing the disease, but after about 30 years, doctors began to notice that drugs that were once effective no longer worked. In many countries, the disease began to make a major comeback so that, by 1993, the World Health Organization declared TB a global health emergency.

The bacterium, *Mycobacterium tuberculosis*, had evolved; it had become resistant to a number of antibiotics. This resistance was traced to a small substitution mutation in one gene. Once the mutation had occurred, it spread quickly throughout the *Mycobacterium tuberculosis* population. In recent years, other disease organisms have shown similar resistance to what were once effective treatments.

The treatment of TB is one example as to how human activities can unintentionally create selection pressures that drive evolution. Another example is trophy hunting. Hunters deliberately select animals that are in peak condition. Deer, for example, are often selected for their magnificent antlers. Hunters select the largest and healthiest bighorn rams to shoot. In both cases, this has led to a reduction in the individual size and "headgear." In Africa, poaching for ivory has produced some populations with higher numbers of elephants with no or very small tusks. In North America, selection of the largest Kodiak Bears by hunters has produced a decline in the average size of bears within the population. Similar changes have been observed in fish stocks. Nets select fish above a certain size, so some species have evolved by reducing their size and breeding at a younger age than they used to.

Consider the Explain Question

How do scientists use evidence from a wide variety of sources to determine evolutionary relationships?

Go online to complete the scientific explanation.

dlc.com/ca10066s

Check Your Understanding

What evidence supports Darwin's idea of natural selection and the evolutionary theory?

dlc.com/ca10067s

STEM in Action

Applying Evidence for Evolution

Ideas about how life originated are varied. Recent theoretical research suggests that life could have started near a deep-sea hydrothermal vent. The porous structure of hydrothermal vents, the high temperature and pressure, plus the chemicals present could have fueled many of the chemical reactions necessary for the evolution of life. Furthermore, DNA sequences of modern organisms suggest that the most recent common ancestor for all life was a microorganism that lived in extremely high temperatures, like those found in hydrothermal vent habitats. Hydrothermal vents deep in the ocean are protected from fluctuating conditions in the atmosphere and harmful ultraviolet light from the sun, the effects of which were much stronger early in Earth's history. However, it is far from certain how or where life started.

Whatever the location, it is very likely that life originated in a series of steps. These steps probably started with the formation of simple organic molecules like nucleotides that arose before the evolution of the first cellular life forms. It is believed that the extreme heat of early Earth provided the energy needed for chemicals to react to form organic molecules. This step has been replicated in the laboratory. It is believed that these molecules could have been formed in the hot atmosphere and rained down to Earth's oceans. This formed a primordial soup of organic molecules in the early oceans. Eventually some of these molecules joined to form larger molecules. Although not yet cells but similar to RNA, these molecules acquired the ability to self-replicate, a feature of all life as we now know. Once some of these molecules began to self-replicate, they would begin to evolve through the process of **natural selection**. Later, some of these self-replicating molecules became associated with membranes and metabolic processes that were the forerunners of cells.

The first cells would have been prokaryotic, meaning they would not have had a nucleus. In essence, they were the self-replicating catalytic RNA molecules surrounded by—and perhaps embedded within—a membrane. Floating around in the primitive oceans, these protocells possibly crashed into each other, joining up. The material from each protocell could have fused and the beginnings of genetic diversity occurred. Over time, these more complicated cells would fuse with others and eventually the formation of organelles would occur.

The origins of simple organic molecules are a very difficult area for scientists to explain. Since the conditions that existed on early Earth are very hard to replicate, it is almost impossible to know for certain how these molecules formed.

BLACK SMOKER
Scientists were startled to discover abundant life, such as the shrimp that appear white in this photo, around deep-sea hydrothermal vents. Far away from sunlight, how do these organisms get the energy they need for life?

STEM and Evidence for Evolution

Piecing together the history of life on Earth is not an easy task. In the past, scientists made inferences based mostly on fossil records, which only provide snapshots of the past. However, new technologies may help solve many of the remaining mysteries.

All organisms share remarkable similarities in biochemistry. Geneticists can evaluate DNA to help determine the degree to which two types of animals are related. Using a technique called DNA sequencing, biologists closely examine the way in which an organism's DNA is structured. Through the Human Genome Project, geneticists can identify the human genetic code and compare it to another organism's DNA. Using the process of comparative genomics, researchers have been able to analyze genomes from different species to study the similarities. This has led to advances in pharmaceutical therapies and disease research, as well as further insight into evolutionary commonalities.

Mechanisms for Evolution

dlc.com/ca10068s

LESSON OVERVIEW

Lesson Questions

■ What are Charles Darwin's contributions to our understanding about evolution?

■ How does natural selection work?

■ How do natural selection and adaptation impact biodiversity?

■ How can the changes in allele frequency within a population be measured?

■ How does speciation occur?

■ What role do genetic drift, bottleneck effect and the founder effect, play in evolution?

Key Vocabulary

Which terms do you already know?

☐ allopatric speciation
☐ antibiotic
☐ artificial selection
☐ bottleneck effect
☐ Charles Darwin
☐ directional selection
☐ disruptive selection
☐ founder effect
☐ genetic drift
☐ genetic variation
☐ Hardy-Weinberg equation
☐ mutation
☐ natural selection
☐ parapatric speciation
☐ sexual selection
☐ stabilizing selection
☐ sympatric speciation
☐ Theory of Evolution

Lesson Objectives

By the end of the lesson, you should be able to:

- Understand how the theory of evolution was developed.

- Recognize the contribution of Charles Darwin to our ideas about evolution.

- Describe the mechanisms that contribute to natural selection.

- Define the unit of evolution.

- Use the Hardy-Weinberg equation to predict the frequency of genotypes in a population.

- Identify processes of evolution, including bottleneck effect, founder effect, and sexual selection.

- Distinguish among directional, disruptive, and stabilizing selection.

- Distinguish among sympatric, parapatric, and allopatric speciation.

Thinking about Evolution

dlc.com/ca10069s

Do you know what the most closely related land animal is to the humpback whale? You might think it is the elephant. However, it is actually more closely related to the hippopotamus. Why is this so?

REACH UP

Giraffes today all have long necks, but they were not always like that. How have giraffes changed over time?

EXPLAIN QUESTION

❚ **How does evolution work to create the diversity of life on Earth?**

What Are Charles Darwin's Contributions to Our Understanding about Evolution?

There are millions of species on the Earth, so many that scientists are not sure of the exact numbers. These species differ widely in their appearance, ecology and behavior, yet they also have many common characteristics. Where did all these species come from? This is a question that has occupied the minds of some scientists for hundreds of years. For a longtime people thought species were created individually over short periods of time, but by the early 19th century many scientists were beginning to think that perhaps they had evolved slowly from common ancestors. This idea of biological evolution was something of a puzzle. What was the mechanism behind it? How long would it take? Was Earth old enough for the process to produce the species that were observed?

Originally scientists thought Earth was only a few thousand years old. But new discoveries and the developing science of geology were changing these ideas. Scientists discovered Earth had been around for at least millions of years. Perhaps long enough for life to produce all the species on the planet. Into this era of exciting discoveries about deep time and an ancient Earth stepped a young naturalist. His name was **Charles Darwin**, he was an avid collector of beetles and was training to be a pastor when he was offered the opportunity for a trip around the world. He was invited to become the naturalist aboard a small British Naval survey ship called the *HMS Beagle*. His job was to make observations of natural phenomena and collect plant and animal specimens on what was to become a five-year voyage.

The *HMS Beagle* took Darwin first to islands in the Atlantic and tropical South America. Here, for the first time he saw the high biodiversity that can be found in the tropics. He began to ask himself where all the species he encountered came from. He came back to this question repeatedly as he made observations on his field trips. On his trips he found fossils of ancient organisms no longer found on Earth. He found fossils of marine organisms in rocks thousands of meters above the Pacific Ocean. On a visit to a small Pacific archipelago, the Galapagos Islands, he observed how the distribution of species differed between islands that were only a few miles apart. When he eventually returned home to England he began to realize that here was evidence of processes that could begin to account for the origin of all the world's species.

Darwin returned to England in 1836 and spent the next twenty-two years collecting evidence that eventually led to his theory of **natural selection**. He was reluctant to publish because his ideas would conflict with religious ideas that were prevalent at that time. Then in 1858, he received a letter from another naturalist, Alfred Wallace, who had come up with similar ideas about how evolution occurred. Darwin and Wallace's work was immediately presented to the scientific community. A year later, Darwin published a book that gave details of his theory. The book was called *On the Origin of Species*, and its first printing sold on the first day it was published. Although at first considered controversial, the ideas in the book eventually became accepted by the scientific community. Central to these ideas was his mechanism for evolution that he called natural selection.

CHARLES DARWIN

Charles Darwin is often called "The Father of Evolution." Why is he sometimes given this title?

How Does Natural Selection Work?

Darwin believed that organisms could change their appearance, structure, and behaviors through slow changes that occurred over many generations. What he needed was a mechanism to account for this. Darwin observed that such a process occurred when humans bred animals and plants. He called this method of producing new "man-made" varieties **artificial selection** and wondered whether a similar process could occur in nature.

Artificial Selection as a Model

During the 18th and 19th centuries, many new plant and animal varieties had been bred through a process called selective breeding. Selective breeding involved taking individual plants or animals with desired traits and crossing them. The resulting offspring would be selected for the same desired traits. This would usually take place over a number of generations until a new breed was produced. For example, plants that produced the juiciest berries might be purposely cross-pollinated with another plant that was frost resistant. Farmers understood that the resulting plants could produce juicy berries and also be resistant to low temperatures.

Darwin recognized that this process was similar to what happens in nature, but that characteristics were selected by humans, rather than by nature. Darwin argued that, for example, different types of sheep found around the world had a common wild ancestor. He also crossed different breeds of pigeon to select a wide variety of forms. However, he noticed that young often looked like the wild rock dove that lived on cliffs. He concluded that the rock dove was the common ancestor of the domestic pigeon. This research supported his ideas about all organisms being descended, through evolution from a common ancestor. Artificial selection provided Darwin with a useful model for how similar changes occurred in nature.

COMMON ANCESTORS

These different bird species have different features but are descended from a common ancestor. What process most likely caused these different species to evolve?

Natural Selection

Darwin eventually came up with an explanation as to how this natural process—he called it natural selection—could occur. His explanation was based upon four observations:

- All parents, regardless of species, can produce many more offspring than are needed to replace them. For example, an oak tree will produce hundreds of thousands of acorns during its lifespan. Each of these acorns has the potential to grow into a new oak tree. If this happened, then why isn't the surface of the Earth covered in oaks? The same applies to animals, including people. What stops the populations of all organisms from growing out of control?

- All organisms must interact with their environment in order to survive. For example, the availability of food, water, and shelter affect the individual's chances of survival. Their ability to avoid predators and disease are also important factors. Conditions in the environment affect an individual's chances of survival. Many are not successful. So, in any population, many individuals do not survive long enough to reproduce.

- With the exception of identical twins, all individuals of a species are different from one another—this is why we can tell people apart. The existence of these differences is called variation. Although sometimes they look the same to us, all individual organisms, even of the same species are different. Some organisms have features, or adaptations, that better suit them for survival.

- Many variations can be inherited. These variations can be structural or behavioral. For example, mice inherit the color of their fur and some birds inherit their urge to migrate.

Together, these four observations could account for how organisms changed over time. From these observations, he realized that most organisms that are born fail to reproduce. Only those that have characteristics that help them to survive the struggle for existence can breed and pass on their characteristics to the next generation. Their offspring that have these characteristics are better fitted for survival. Although the differences between generations could be small, over time, they could build up. The species would become better adapted to its environment. It could even change into a new species. He realized this process occurred everywhere in nature and named it natural selection.

NATURAL SELECTION IN ACTION

This emerald boa snake has evolved a green color that provides camouflage. How does camouflage benefit a predator, such as a snake?

Darwin knew nothing about genetics and how new traits arise through **mutation**. Mendel's work on genetics did not come to light until after his death and the discovery of DNA, genes, and how mutations occur was decades in the future. Today, scientists are less concerned with the survival of individuals. They think of natural selection in terms of the impact of differential reproductive success on the selection or loss of genes.

How Do Natural Selection and Adaptation Impact Biodiversity?

Natural selection is an evolutionary mechanism that results in differential reproductive success. This is when some individuals of a species leave behind more offspring than others. If this is the result of **genetic variation**, then these advantageous changes are passed on to future generations. Scientists use the word *adaptation* to describe the physical and behavioral changes that enable successful reproduction. So, what is the relationship of natural selection to adaptation and to the development of diversity within and among species?

Natural selection is most easily understood at the level of the individual. Those individuals that leave behind descendants are favored. In time, the genes of reproductively successful individuals will come to dominate a population's gene pool. This eventually results in evolutionary change at the level of a population or a species. Diversity within a species commonly arises when populations of a species are separated in some way. The genetic composition of these isolated populations may change over time as each separate population experiences different mutations and is exposed to different selection pressures.

Eventually, the gene pools of these species become so different that reproductive barriers build up. These barriers could take a variety of forms, including behavioral differences such as preferences in selecting a mate to genome incompatibility. At this point, the populations cannot interbreed and can be considered two species.

As different species compete for limited resources, differential reproduction will result in the populations of each species having traits that are different from each other. It will favor traits that make a species particularly well-suited to a niche within an ecosystem. Each species can occupy a niche that is not being contested by the other. In this way, natural selection fosters diversity among species.

Types of Natural Selection

Within the process of natural selection, there is variety as to how traits are selected. Natural selection is probably most often connected to **directional selection**. In this type of natural selection, a single beneficial phenotype is favored increasing allelic frequency to shift in the direction of that phenotype. Since individuals having this trait are more likely to survive and reproduce, the trait's allele frequency increases in the population. Throughout the generations, more and more members of the population will possess the trait. Directional selection is most often seen when there are environmental changes, or when populations move to new areas with different environmental influences. The evolution of a giraffe's neck exemplifies directional selection. As food became scarce, those individuals that could reach to higher branches were more likely to survive. The trait for long necks, then, became more prominent.

NATURAL SELECTION

Individuals with certain traits are more likely to survive in a particular environment. What trait shown here is likely to help with survival?

Disruptive selection occurs when extreme phenotypes are favored and selected instead of those with average or intermediate phenotypes. Disruptive selection increases diversity in and among species. Darwin's finches are an example of this type of selection. As midsized seeds became scarce on the Galapagos Islands, the birds were forced to rely on large or small seeds. Those birds with either unusually large or unusually small beaks were better adapted to the environment. Thus, they survived, reproduced, and passed on these extreme traits.

The opposite situation is true in **stabilizing selection**, which reduces diversity in a species. Stabilizing selection describes changes in population genetics in which intermediate forms of a trait are favored. Much like the story of Goldilocks, stabilizing selection favors those traits that are not "too much" or "too little," but "just right." The birth weight of babies is one such trait that follows a stabilizing selection pattern.

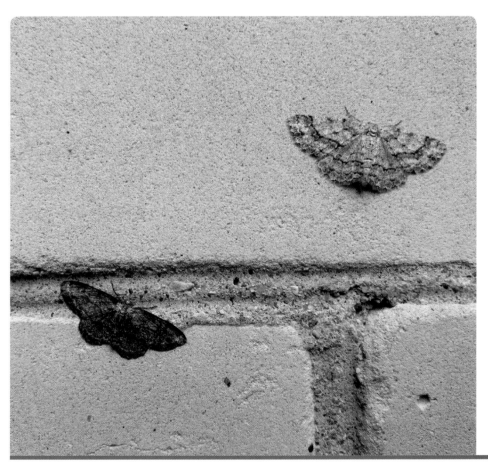

MOTHS ON A WALL
Some species of moths exist as light and dark (melanic) forms. In this particular situation, which moth is most likely to survive?

How Can the Changes in Allele Frequency within a Population Be Measured?

Evolution is the change in a population's gene pool over time. Therefore, the population is considered the unit of evolution. The Hardy-Weinberg equilibrium is a principle that can be used as a baseline against which changes in allele frequencies among a population can be measured. The principle states that, in the absence of disturbing factors, different genotype frequencies in a population will reach an equilibrium and will remain stable over generations. However, the Hardy-Weinberg equilibrium also states that evolution should be expected in all populations virtually all of the time. This is possible because populations in nature always experience disturbing factors such as mutations, selection, migrations, **genetic drift**, and changes to their environment.

ALLELE CHANGES OVER GENERATIONS

A population of flowers with two alleles, red and white, changes over time. The white allele, plotted here, decreases in frequency. How could you calculate the frequency of heterozygotes in generation 6?

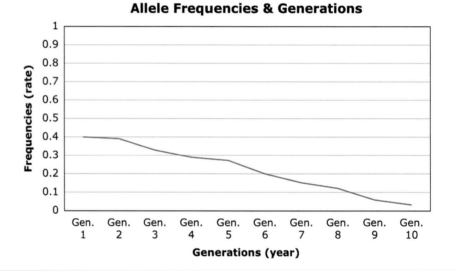

Conditions of Hardy-Weinberg Equilibrium

If the allele frequencies change, then the population is not in equilibrium. This is true of every population in nature. Hardy-Weinberg equilibrium is possible only for an idealized population that satisfies the following set of assumptions:

- no mutation
- no migration into or out of the population
- infinitely large population size
- no natural selection
- no **sexual selection** (random mating)
- organisms are diploid and allele frequencies are equal in both sexes

Clearly these requirements cannot be met in nature. Therefore, in all real populations, evolution wins over equilibrium.

Using the Hardy-Weinberg Equation

The **Hardy-Weinberg equation** can be used to make predictions about a population. The Hardy-Weinberg equation for a population in equilibrium is:

$$p^2 + 2pq + q^2 = 1$$

where p is the frequency of the dominant allele and q is the frequency of the recessive allele. So, for a gene with alleles B and b, the equation representing possible genotypes in genetic equilibrium is:

(frequency of B)^2 + 2 (frequency of B) (frequency of b) + (frequency of b)^2 = 1

The Hardy-Weinberg equation can be used to make predictions about future generation's genotypes.

Sample Problem

The allele frequencies in one generation of a population are R = 65% and r = 35%. Predict the probability of the possible genotypes (RR, Rr, and rr) in the next generation.

Solution:

Use the equation: $p^2 + 2pq + q^2 = 1$

Plug the allele frequencies into the equation:

p^2 = (frequency of RR)^2 = $(0.65)^2$ = 0.42 = 42%
$2pq$ = 2 × (frequency of RR) (frequency of rr) = 2(0.65) (0.35)
    = 0.46 = 46%
q^2 = (frequency of rr)^2 = $(0.35)^2$ = 0.12 = 12%

Check that allele frequencies add up to 1:

$$0.42 + 0.46 + 0.12 = 1$$

How Does Speciation Occur?

The formation of a new species is called speciation. Members of the same species that reproduce sexually must be able to mate and produce fertile offspring. Mating and thus gene flow might stop between two parts of a population if splitting of the population occurs. Once populations can no longer reproduce with each other, speciation can occur.

Speciation may occur for various reasons. A divergence based on behavioral, ecological, or genetic reasons is called **sympatric speciation**. This happens when two or more descendants arise from a single ancestral species and all of them are located in the same geographical region. For example, part of a population may seek out a new food source or develop a different type of mating ritual. Over time, changes due to the different behaviors of the groups can lead to speciation.

In **parapatric speciation**, a new species evolves due to changes in local habitats that cause nonrandom mating. Those individuals occupying and adapting to one habitat, although physically close to individuals in another habitat, are more likely to mate with one another. Over time the genomes of the two groups diverge. Sometimes, gene flow is restricted because of changes in mating habits of the population (e.g., time of mating). Speciation may, therefore, occur because of a reduced gene flow between the sections of the population. Parapatric speciation is another example of how natural selection increases diversity.

The most common reason for speciation is the separation of a population. Separation is most often due to geographic features such as mountains or water. This type of speciation is termed **allopatric speciation**.

Natural selection is the driving constant for most of the speciation that we see; however, sexual selection may also play a part.

Sexual Selection

Some inherited traits increase an individual's chance of attracting a mate. These traits will tend to be passed on as the attractive individual reproduces more frequently. This type of selection is called sexual selection. Sexual selection often results in sexual dimorphism, or phenotypic differences between the sexes of a species. Many animals exhibit sexual dimorphism through either structural or behavioral differences. This is evident in the differences between a male peacock and a female peahen. The male has a colorful plumage that, coupled with a display, is intended to encourage the female to mate. Strangely, sexual selection may result in phenotypes that are harmful to an individual's survival. For example, long decorative tail feathers possessed by birds may attract predators and make escape flight more difficult. In such cases, the benefits of obtaining mates and breeding, outweigh these additional risks of death from predation. Many scientists think that sexual selection often occurs in conjunction with natural selection and some consider it a specific form of sympatric selection.

SEXUAL DIMORPHISM
Mallard ducks show sexual dimorphism with the male (left) exhibiting much more colorful plumage than the female (right). Why might a male mallard have evolved colorful feathers?

What Role Do Genetic Drift, Bottleneck Effect, and the Founder Effect Play in Evolution?

Populations can be changed by factors other than natural selection. For example, a natural disaster—such as a volcanic eruption—may randomly eliminate part of a population. Random changes can produce evolutionary change. These types of changes include gene flow, genetic drift, founder effects, and bottleneck effects.

Gene flow describes the movement of alleles into and out of a gene pool. For example, a bird may migrate from one area to another. In doing so, it may move and transfer its alleles from one population to another. It may introduce new alleles into a population. Gene flow can therefore change the genetic variety and/or frequency within a population. Gene flow can also make genetically dissimilar populations more alike. This will reduce the chance of these populations evolving into separate species. Populations, isolated from others, will experience little or no gene flow. They are more likely to evolve into separate species.

MIGRATING BIRDS

Many birds migrate in autumn and spring to avoid extreme winter or summer weather. How could bird migration increase gene flow into a population?

From one generation to the next, the number of individuals carrying particular alleles in a population at equilibrium fluctuates randomly around a mean. This change in allelic frequency within a given population is called genetic drift. In a large population, random genetic drift has a small impact on gene frequency. In smaller populations, the gene frequency may fluctuate more widely. In a small population, it is possible that, through random genetic drift, a gene may be lost altogether. Unlike natural selection, this is a random process. Forms of genetic drift include the founder and bottleneck effects.

What happens when a few individuals from a population leave and find a new population elsewhere? By chance, the small colonizing population may have a different allele frequency than the original population. As the new population grows, its gene pool will represent that of the founding individuals. This phenomenon is called the **founder effect**. For example, Dutch settlers in Southern Africa are mainly descended from an original small group of colonists. Purely by chance, this small population of colonists had an unusually high frequency of the gene that causes Huntington's disease. Today, the descendants of this group exhibit a similar high frequency of the disease.

When the size of a population is quickly and dramatically reduced, because of a factor like a natural disaster, a **bottleneck effect** can occur. The smaller surviving population may have a different allele frequency than the larger population—the number of alleles are usually reduced. Even if the new, smaller population were to grow in number again, the population's allele frequency would match that of the survivors, rather than the original population. The bottleneck effect can greatly reduce the genetic variation of a population. For example, the African cheetah is a species that has a low genetic diversity. Using DNA analysis, scientists have determined that the species almost became extinct and went through a bottleneck around 10,000 years ago. All of today's African cheetahs are descendants of a few survivors of this event.

RUNNING CHEETAH

All of today's African cheetahs are descendants of a few survivors of the bottleneck effect. How is the genetic variation in today's cheetahs different from the variation in cheetahs over 10,000 year ago?

Consider the Explain Question

How does evolution work to create the diversity of life on Earth?

Go online to complete the scientific explanation.

dlc.com/ca10070s

Check Your Understanding

What evidence supports Darwin's idea of natural selection and the evolutionary theory?

dlc.com/ca10071s

STEM in Action

Applying Mechanisms for Evolution

How can the spread of bacterial diseases be stopped? Antibiotics are medicines that are designed specifically to kill bacteria. They provide doctors with a class of drugs to fight a wide variety of bacterial infections. At one time, doctors thought **antibiotics** would become available that would stop all bacterial infections in their tracks. What they did not count on was that the process of evolution would make that far more difficult. By using antibiotics on a large scale, doctors unknowingly "selected" in an evolutionary sense for bacteria that were resistant to the drugs. We tend to think of evolution as a slow process, but it only took a few decades for many bacterial infections to evolve resistance to the drugs.

Given a process of heredity, variation in a population, and time, all living organisms will evolve when a selective pressure is introduced. In bacteria, the process was particularly fast because of the large number of individual organisms involved, their rapid reproduction rate and short generation time, and the widespread and often misuse of antibiotics in medicine and agriculture. However, by applying the theory of evolution, doctors and patients can use specific strategies to reduce the likelihood of antibiotic resistance. These strategies include:

- Not treating viral infections with antibiotics. It is not helpful Togo to the doctor with a cold or influenza and ask the doctors to prescribe an antibiotic, because antibiotics do not work against viral diseases. Most doctors refuse to prescribe antibiotics under these circumstances. However, in some parts of the world, people can buy antibiotics at any pharmacy without a prescription. The result is that even though bacteria are not causing the illness, they may be exposed to the antibiotic, which can influence which strains of the virus remain viable. When this happens, antibiotic-resistant forms are inadvertently selected.

- Always take the full course of medication. If you are prescribed antibiotics, you get a course that usually takes about a week to complete. Sometimes, when a patient feels better, they stop taking the pills. By doing this, some of the disease-causing bacteria may survive in an adapted, disease-resistant strain. The next time this strain is encountered, it will be resistant to the antibiotic.

■ Take the correct dose. Doctors prescribe a dose that is designed to kill all of the infecting bacteria. If you take an incorrect or lower dose, some bacteria may survive and show some resistance. These may reinfect you or another person, but the next time around they will be less likely to respond to the same antibiotic.

■ Use more than one drug to treat a bacterial infection. When a doctor encounters an infection that does not respond to the usual antibiotic treatment, chances are that the patient may have an antibiotic-resistant strain. Giving a stronger dose will not help. By increasing the dose, the resistant strain will be selected for. This could lead to the evolution of a super-resistant strain, a so-called "superbug." One solution to this problem is to prescribe a combination of drugs. There is a much smaller chance of the patient having an infection that is resistant to two antibiotics that act in different ways on the bacterium.

Have you ever seen milk that was labeled "antibiotic-free"? Antibiotic resistance in humans is not the only situation in which it can occur. The most common other place is in the use of antibiotics as a preventative measure in livestock production. Cows in particular are given antibiotics in hopes of keeping them healthy, even if they are not sick. Such widespread, long-term use provides an ideal opportunity for antibiotic resistance to evolve. Over time, the antibiotics are released at low levels in waste products into the environment or into the bodies of the people who consume the animal products (e.g., milk).

Understanding the process of evolution has helped scientists to predict how bacteria will evolve when they are exposed to antibiotics. It has also provided them with strategies to combat the development of antibiotic-resistant bacterial pathogens.

ANTIBIOTIC-FREE MILK

Do you drink organic milk? Products labeled "organic" are produced without the use of additional hormones or antibiotics.

STEM and Mechanisms for Evolution

Have you ever been walking through the woods and brushed up against a plant, only to have its burrs stick to your clothing? The seeds of the plant are protected by the burrs. The purpose of the burr is to disperse the seeds by attaching themselves to passing animals. These give the plant a better chance of increasing its range and genetic success. One day, a Swiss engineer noticed the burrs attached to his dog's fur, and that gave him an idea. After some study and experimentation, he invented Velcro. Velcro is just one of the many products that have been adapted from the traits of living things.

THE INVENTION OF THE HOOK AND LOOP FASTENER

How did a little burr lead to a popular invention? Many natural traits like the burr's are being used by scientists to develop better inventions and technologies.

Of what other inventions can you think? Military weapon designers used the narrow elongated shape of dolphins and sharks to serve as a model for torpedoes. This streamlined shape makes moving through the water much easier (and faster). Aviation engineers have adapted the shape of bird wings to design more aerodynamic airplanes. By studying the motion of air above and below the wing, these scientists can develop ways to make planes that fly more efficiently.

Nature is the greatest inventor around. The traits developed by living organisms over billions of years of evolution are, in many ways, the pinnacle of natural technology. Scientists use nature's hard work by applying the desired traits found in organisms to design and build better technologies.

The scientists who work on these problems are called biotechnicians. They use nature to inspire designs in computer technology, medicine, manufacturing, aviation, and many other areas. Evolution has been shown to be very beneficial, not just to the organisms of Earth, but also to moving traits into the future through technology.

Calculating a Hardy-Weinberg Equation

Use the Hardy-Weinberg equation to solve the problems below.

1. Suppose the frequency of the dominant allele in a population is 75%. What is the frequency of the recessive allele?

2. A population of salamanders has two colors, blue and white. Blue is the dominant color and white is recessive. The frequency of the white allele is 36%. What percentage of the salamander population is white?

3. A population of 100 individuals has 49 individuals that are homozygous dominant for a certain trait. How many individuals are heterozygous for the trait? How many are homozygous recessive for the trait?

RR	49 out of 100, or 0.49
Rr	?
rr	?

4. The frequency of a dominant allele (P) in a population is 60% and the frequency of the recessive allele (p) is 40%. Predict the probability of the possible genotypes in this population.

5. A population has two alleles *A* and *a* for a gene, with phenotypic frequencies: 20:60:20. Is this population in Hardy-Weinberg equilibrium? Explain your answer.

Genetics

dlc.com/ca10072s

LESSON OVERVIEW

Lesson Questions

■ What is Mendelian inheritance?

■ What is the difference between dominant and recessive alleles?

■ What are the definitions of homozygous, heterozygous, genotype, and phenotype?

■ What are Mendel's laws of inheritance?

■ How are the results of monohybrid and dihybrid crosses diagrammed?

■ What are the effects of multiple alleles, codominance, and incomplete dominance on phenotype?

Key Vocabulary

Which terms do you already know?

☐ allele
☐ asexual reproduction
☐ autosomal dominant disorder
☐ autosomal recessive disorder
☐ chromosomal abnormalities
☐ chromosome
☐ codominant allele
☐ dihybrid cross
☐ diploid cell
☐ dominant allele
☐ double helix
☐ gene expression
☐ gene therapy
☐ genetic disorder
☐ genetic testing

Lesson Objectives

By the end of the lesson, you should be able to:

- Describe Mendelian inheritance.
- Differentiate between dominant and recessive alleles.
- Distinguish between the terms *homozygous*, *heterozygous*, *genotype*, and *phenotype*.
- Discuss Mendel's laws of inheritance.
- Diagram and predict the results of monohybrid and dihybrid crosses.
- Identify and describe the patterns of multiple alleles, codominance, and incomplete dominance on phenotype.
- Differentiate the role of DNA and chromosomes in coding for hereditary traits.

Key Vocabulary continued

- ☐ genotype
- ☐ Gregor Mendel
- ☐ haploid cell
- ☐ heterozygous
- ☐ homozygous
- ☐ incomplete dominance
- ☐ Law of Independent Assortment
- ☐ Law of Segregation
- ☐ meiosis
- ☐ mitosis
- ☐ monohybrid cross
- ☐ multiple allele
- ☐ nondisjunction
- ☐ phenotype
- ☐ recessive allele
- ☐ sex-linked disorders
- ☐ sexual reproduction
- ☐ single-gene disorders

Similar but Different

dlc.com/ca10073s

What descriptions would you use to describe yourself? What characteristics do you have in common with your parents, siblings, or other relatives?

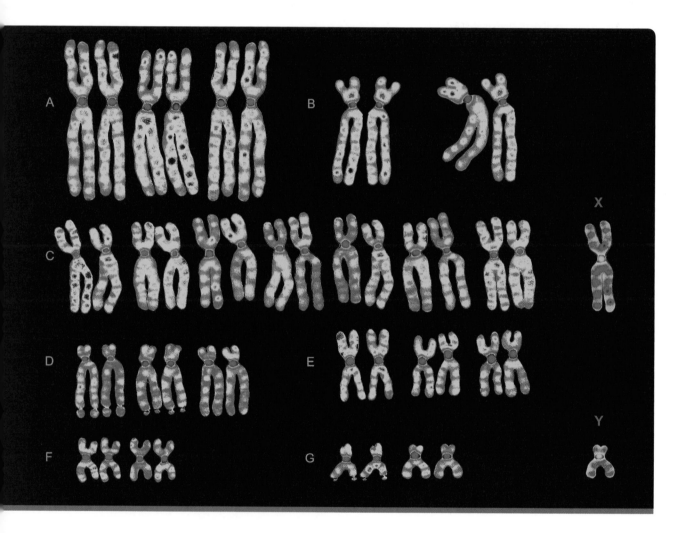

CHROMOSOMES

How are an organism's inherited chromosomes related to its non-observable traits?

EXPLAIN QUESTION

How does the genetic information inherited from an organism's parents affect its characteristics?

What Is Mendelian Inheritance?

Gregor Mendel's Pea Plant Experiments

All organisms of the same species have common characteristics, colored eyes or hair, for example. However, members of the same species exhibit variations in these characteristics. For example, eyes or hair may exist in a variety of colors. These differences in an organism's characteristics are called traits. Blue-eye color is one trait for eye color. Some other traits for this characteristic include brown or green eyes. To investigate how organisms inherit traits from their parents, **Gregor Mendel** bred pea plants. He observed particular traits that appeared from one generation to the next. To keep things simple, he chose to track only those characteristics that came in just two forms. He studied the traits of white or purple flower color, for example.

Mendel also made sure to use parent plants that were "true-breeding" for each trait. If after many generations of self-pollination, a purple-flowered plant produces only purple flower offspring, it is considered true-breeding for purple flowers.

Mendel's scientific method included crossing two contrasting, true-breeding plants for two different traits for a particular characteristic. A classic example is the cross between a white-flowered plant and a purple-flowered plant. These plants are the *P* generation, or parental generation. He carefully observed the flower color exhibited by a large number of offspring. These offspring are called the F1 generation, for first filial generation. He then cross-bred plants of the F1 generation with each other. The offspring are called the F2 generation, for second filial. What were the resulting flower colors of the F1 and F2 generations?

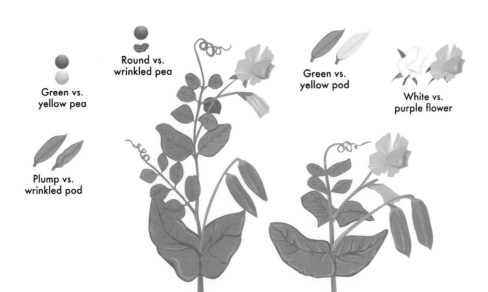

Green vs. yellow pea

Round vs. wrinkled pea

Plump vs. wrinkled pod

Green vs. yellow pod

White vs. purple flower

TRAITS MENDEL OBSERVED

Mendel observed pea plant traits that varied between two versions. Why was the limitation of his study to traits with only two possibilities for expression crucial?

The Results of Mendel's Experiment

Surprisingly, Mendel found that all of the F1 generation plants had purple flowers, even though one of the parent plants had white flowers. Mendel wondered whether the trait of white flower color somehow disappeared during the breeding process.

This turned out not to be true. When Mendel crossed purple-flower F1 generation plants with one another, approximately 25 percent of the F2 generation had white flowers. In other words, there was a 3:1 ratio of purple-flowered plants to white-flowered plants. Mendel obtained these same results when he studied the traits for other characters such as pea shape and pod color.

Mendel concluded that differences in inherited traits result from alternative versions of genes (which Mendel called "factors"). We now refer to these differing versions of the same genes as alleles. Mendel also realized that organisms inherit two copies of each **allele**, one from each parent. He noticed that of the two inherited alleles, one would be expressed and the other one would have no effect.

What Is the Difference between Dominant and Recessive Alleles?

Mendel Draws Conclusions about Alleles

Based on his experiments, Mendel concluded that if an organism inherited two different alleles for a given character, one **allele** would fully control the appearance of that character and the other would not have any effect. In the case of the traits purple and white pea plant flowers, the purple allele was fully expressed and the white allele was not expressed at all. Only when members of the F1 generation were crossed did white flowers reappear in the F2 generation. These white-flowered plants did not inherit any purple flower alleles, but inherited two copies of the white allele.

Alleles that always appear when they are present (such as the purple flower allele) are called **dominant alleles**. Alleles that are not manifested when a dominant allele is present (such as the white flower allele) are called **recessive alleles**. Recessive alleles only show in the **phenotype** when there is no dominant allele.

Alleles are often represented by single italicized letters. Dominant alleles are represented by capital letters. The recessive versions of the alleles are represented by the lowercase version of the same letter. (In this case, *P* represents purple flower color, and *p* represents white flower color).

What Are the Definitions of Homozygous, Heterozygous, Genotype, and Phenotype?

Homozygous vs. Heterozygous

One of Mendel's conclusions was that organisms inherit two alleles for each character, one from each parent. In the case of flower color in the F1 generation, the pea plant offspring inherited an **allele** for white flowers from one parent, and an allele for purple flowers from the other parent. An organism that contains two different alleles for a given character is **heterozygous** for that character.

In the F2 generation, the white-flowered plants contained two alleles for white flowers. When an organism contains two identical alleles, it is **homozygous** for that trait. An organism can be homozygous recessive (if both alleles are recessive) or homozygous dominant (if both alleles are dominant).

Consider the genetic character of eye color. The allele for the trait brown eyes is dominant. If you have brown eyes, you might have one brown-eye allele and one blue-eye allele. In this case, you'd be heterozygous for eye color. Alternatively, you might have two brown-eye alleles, making you homozygous for eye color.

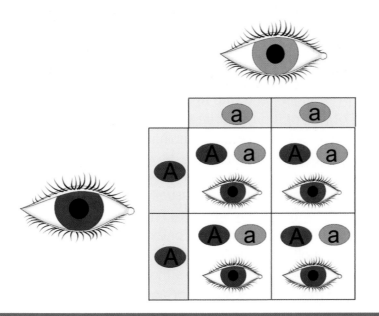

HOMOZYGOUS AND HETEROZYGOUS

An individual with two copies of the same allele is homozygous for that gene. Heterozygous individuals contain two different versions of an allele. How could you tell from eye color whether someone has a homozygous or heterozygous genotype?

Genotype vs. Phenotype

How many physical characters such as eye color can you think of? There are a vast number! They include characters such as nose size and shape, earlobe attachment or detachment, and the presence or absence of a widow's peak on the forehead. They even include eye shape and length of the second toe. An organism's **phenotype** refers to its observable traits such as blue eyes or curly hair.

HORNED LIZARD

An organism's phenotype refers to its appearance, or observable characteristics. What are examples of this horned lizard's phenotype characteristics?

In contrast, an organism's **genotype** describes precisely which alleles are present. Consider the case of human ear-wax—a characteristic controlled by a single gene with two alleles. This person has the phenotype of wet, or runny, ear-wax. However, his or her genotype may include one of two possible combinations. Either two wet ear wax alleles or one wet and one recessive dry ear wax allele may be present.

An organism's phenotype does not usually give enough information to determine its genotype. Only when we know the genetics behind a trait can we be certain of the genotype. For example, if we know that white flowers on a pea plant are the results of a recessive allele. If we see a pea plant with white flowers, we know that it is homozygous for white flower color. In this case, the organism's genotype for flower color can be inferred from its phenotype.

Genes	Alleles	Genotype	Phenotype
Shape	R	RR	Round
		Rr	Round
	r	rr	Wrinkled
Height	T	TT	Tall
		Tt	Tall
	t	tt	Short
Color	P	PP	Purple
		Pp	Purple
	p	pp	White

Recessive phenotype: Results from genotype with two recessive alleles

GENOTYPES AND PHENOTYPES

An individual pea plant's phenotype is determined by the alleles present (genotype). What experiments could be done to investigate which genotypes produce specific phenotypes?

What Are Mendel's Laws of Inheritance?

The Law of Segregation

Mendel was able to discover a great deal about inheritance from the results of his pea plant studies. He formulated two laws of inheritance. The first, the **law of segregation**, deals with what happens to alleles during the formation of gamete cells. Mendel believed that the two alleles for a given character must separate when gametes are produced. Each **allele** ends up in one gamete (egg or sperm), and thus each gamete only contains one allele. In this way, when gametes combine during fertilization, an offspring will inherit one allele from each parent.

We now know that this is precisely what happens during **meiosis**. Two partner chromosomes in each pair separate. Each gamete receives one **chromosome** and thus one allele for each gene.

The Law of Independent Assortment

Mendel also wondered whether the expression of certain characters, such as flower color, might affect the expression of other characters, such as pod color. This is similar to asking the question of whether tall people are more likely to have the traits brown or blond hair. What do you think the answer is?

Mendel investigated this question by observing the appearance of two or more characters during some of his breeding experiments. He found that the inheritance of one character did not influence the inheritance of other characters.

Today, this law is called the **law of independent assortment**. This is due to the segregation of alleles during gamete formation. Each pair of alleles segregates independently of other pairs of alleles. Alleles are randomly distributed into gametes. This law holds true except when the alleles for two different characters are located on the same chromosome.

TRAITS IN PEAPODS

Mendel's law of independent assortment explains that alleles are distributed independently of one another. How does this mechanism lead to multiple genotypes, and why do these genotypes produce organisms with varying phenotypes?

How Are the Results of Monohybrid and Dihybrid Crosses Diagrammed?

Monohybrid Cross

When the genotype for a given trait is known for two breeding individuals, a diagram called a Punnett square can be constructed. A Punnett square is used to predict the ratio of genotypes of the offspring. For example, crossing a homozygous dominant trait (green pod color, allele denoted here *G*) with a homozygous recessive trait (yellow pod color, allele denoted *g*), we can predict the ratios of genotypes and phenotypes of the F1 and F2 generations. Remember that a homozygous individual has two identical alleles.

The results of this cross between a *GG* individual and a *gg* individual are shown in the Punnett square shown below. The genotype of one parent appears across the top of the Punnett square. The genotype of the other parent appears down the left side of the Punnett square. The four predicted genotypes of the offspring are shaded blue:

Genotypes of Parents

	G	*G*
g	*Gg*	*Gg*
g	*Gg*	*Gg*

What is the phenotype of these four *Gg* offspring? Because the allele *G* (for green pods) is dominant to the allele *g* (for yellow pods), these heterozygous offspring exhibit the dominant phenotype. (All of these plants would produce green pods.)

These heterozygotes are also known as monohybrids. Further crossing them with each other is called a **monohybrid cross**. Do you remember the phenotypic ratio of Mendel's monohybrid F2 cross? Can you predict it with a Punnett square?

Genotypes of Parents

	G	*g*
G	*GG*	*Gg*
g	*Gg*	*gg*

Again, the four possible genotypes of the offspring are shaded blue.

As you can see, of four offspring produced by the monohybrid cross, there are two heterozygotes, one homozygous dominant, and one homozygous recessive. Just as Mendel noted in his experiments with flower color, there is a 3:1 ratio of the dominant to the recessive phenotype. There will be, on the average, three plants with green pods for every one that has yellow pods.

The results of this cross between a *GG* individual and a *gg* individual are shown in the Punnett square shown below. The genotype of one parent appears across the top of the Punnett square. The genotype of the other parent appears down the left side of the Punnett square. The four predicted genotypes of the offspring are shaded blue:

Genotypes of Parents

	G	*G*
g	*Gg*	*Gg*
g	*Gg*	*Gg*

What is the phenotype of these four *Gg* offspring? Because the allele *G* (for green pods) is dominant to the allele *g* (for yellow pods), these heterozygous offspring exhibit the dominant phenotype. (All of these plants would produce green pods.)

These heterozygotes are also known as monohybrids. Further crossing them with each other is called a **monohybrid cross**. Do you remember the phenotypic ratio of Mendel's monohybrid F2 cross? Can you predict it with a Punnett square?

Genotypes of Parents

	G	*g*
G	*GG*	*Gg*
g	*Gg*	*gg*

Again, the four possible genotypes of the offspring are shaded blue.

As you can see, of four offspring produced by the monohybrid cross, there are two heterozygotes, one homozygous dominant, and one homozygous recessive. Just as Mendel noted in his experiments with flower color, there is a 3:1 ratio of the dominant to the recessive phenotype. There will be, on the average, three plants with green pods for every one that has yellow pods.

© Discovery Education | www.discoveryeducation.com

Imagine that you had an individual that expressed a dominant phenotype, such as brown eyes, and you wanted to know her or his genotype. Are they brown homozygous, *BB*, or brown heterozygous, *Bb*? Knowing that brown eyes is dominant and blue eyes is recessive, can you determine the genotype of the brown-eyed individual by "crossing" her or him with another individual (assuming that it was both ethical and feasible to do so)?

A testcross is designed to test this very scenario. In a testcross, an individual with an unknown genotype (in our example, brown eyes) is crossed with an individual with a homozygous recessive genotype *(bb)*. The first step is to complete two Punnett squares, one in which the unknown individual is homozygous for the dominant trait, and one in which the unknown individual is heterozygous for the dominant trait. In each square, the unknown individual is crossed with a homozygous recessive individual. What would be the phenotypic ratios of the offspring in each case? In the first case, the phenotypic ratio of the offspring should be 100 percent dominant. In the offspring of the second case there should be a 1:1 ratio of dominant and recessive phenotypes.

Using testcrosses, scientists can determine the genotype of unknown individuals by modeling the cross of each possible unknown genotype with individuals having a known homozygous recessive genoype.

PUNNETT SQUARE

A Punnett square is used to predict the genotype and phenotype ratios resulting from the crossing of two parents of known genotypes. When is it possible to predict accurate ratios from two parents if only the phenotypes are known?

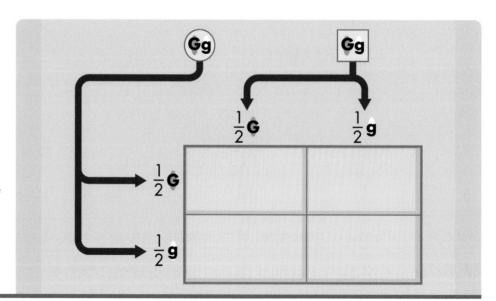

Dihybrid Cross

Until now, we have dealt with crosses that involve only one character. How can we diagram a cross observing two characters at the same time? Let's take both flower color (purple dominant, *P*, and white recessive, *p*) and pod color (green dominant, *G*, and yellow recessive, *g*). The following Punnett square crosses an individual that is homozygous dominant for both characters with an individual that is homozygous recessive for both characters.

Genotype	PG	PG
pg	PpGg	PpGg
pg	PpGg	PpGg

As you can see, all of the offspring from this cross are heterozygous for both traits. They are called dihybrids.

Can we predict the F2 generation outcome of crossing these dihybrids? This **dihybrid cross** chart must be somewhat more complex to display each possible combination of alleles:

Genotype	PG	Pg	pG	pg
PG	PPGG	PPGg	PpGG	PpGg
Pg	PPGg	PPgg	PpGg	Ppgg
pG	PpGG	PpGg	ppGG	ppGg
pg	PpGg	Ppgg	ppGg	ppgg

What are the phenotypic ratios of the F2 offspring? Looking closely, we find that of the 16 individuals, 9 are purple-flowered and have green pods (both dominant traits). In addition, 3 are purple-flowered with yellow pods (one dominant trait is expressed and the other recessive trait is expressed). Another 3 are white-flowered with green pods (the alternative dominant trait is expressed and the other recessive trait is expressed). Finally, 1 individual is white-flowered with yellow pods (both recessive traits are expressed). Thus, a 9:3:3:1 ratio is the outcome of a dihybrid cross.

Constructing Punnett squares for the crossing of known genotypes allows us to make predictions about the probability of obtaining offspring with particular phenotypes. We can also use simple addition and multiplication rules to determine this probability.

Dihybrid Cross: Sample Problem

In the dihybrid cross above, what is the probability that the first offspring of the heterozygous parents will be either purple-flowered with yellow pods or white-flowered with yellow pods?

Solution:

Those chances would be

$$\frac{3}{16} + \frac{1}{16} = \frac{4}{16} = \frac{1}{4}, \text{ or } 25\%.$$

What about the probability that the first two offspring born will be purple-flowered with yellow pods and white-flowered with yellow pods? Now we use multiplication:

$$\frac{3}{16} \times \frac{1}{16} = \frac{4}{256}, \text{ or } 1.6\%.$$

What Are the Effects of Multiple Alleles, Codominance, and Incomplete Dominance on Phenotype?

Multiple Alleles

In his pea plant experiments, Mendel worked with characters that involved only two alleles. He considered traits such as white or purple flower color, smooth or wrinkled pea shape, yellow or green pod color, for example. However, many characters involve three or more different forms. For these characteristics, there exist multiple alleles. A classic example of multiple alleles is human blood type. Your blood type might be A, B, AB, or O. Three alleles exist for this gene: IA, IB, and i. Receiving two IA alleles results in A blood type, two IB alleles results in B blood type, and two i alleles results in O blood type.

If an individual has a genotype of one I^A and one I^B allele, a different form of dominance occurs.

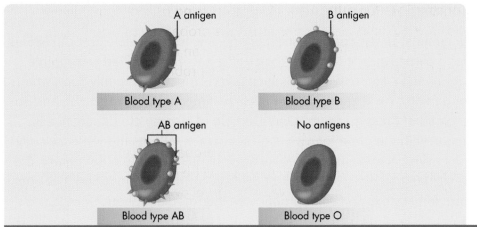

Blood type A — A antigen

Blood type B — B antigen

Blood type AB — AB antigen

Blood type O — No antigens

BLOOD TYPES

Human blood type is determined by three alleles. What distinguishes these alleles, in terms of what they code for?

Codominance

Completely dominant and recessive alleles were the types of traits studied by Mendel. However, there are other forms of dominance. In some cases, two alleles for a given character are both fully expressed. They will equally affect the phenotype of the organism. These alleles are said to be codominant.

As with multiple alleles, an example of codominance is also found with human blood type. If a person inherits one *IA* and one *IB* allele, they will have a blood type of AB because both alleles are completely codominant. What does this mean on a molecular level? The letters A and B refer to two specific types of sugars that are expressed on the surface of red blood cells. A person may have the A sugar expressed (blood type A), the B sugar expressed (blood type B), both sugars expressed (type AB), or neither (*ii*, type O).

ROAN HORSE

This roan horse is a product of a cross between a white horse and a grey horse. How is this horse an example of codominance?

Incomplete Dominance

In contrast to the codominant scenario, it is also possible for both alleles for a particular trait to be partially dominant. This is called **incomplete dominance**. Here, two alleles for a given character are only somewhat, or partially, expressed. Neither allele is dominant over the other, and so a blend of the two results. One example of incomplete dominance is found with the gene for curly hair. If a person inherits the allele for curly hair from one parent and one for straight hair from the other parent, the result may be wavy hair. Neither allele is completely dominant, but both are partially expressed to produce an intermediate phenotype.

INCOMPLETE DOMINANCE

Incomplete dominance occurs when neither allele is dominant over the other. How can the F1 flowers' phenotypes be used to determine incomplete dominance among pairs of alleles?

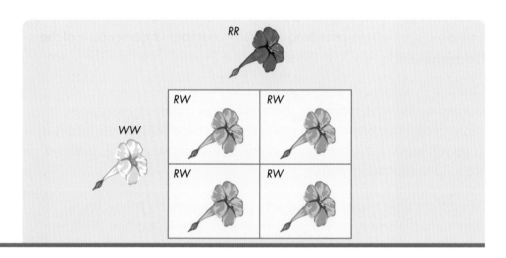

Sex Determination

Most organisms that reproduce sexually come in two forms—male and female. The chances of a child being born a boy or a girl are about 50 percent or 1:1. What determines the sex of a child?

Human cells contain 23 pairs of **chromosomes**. In females, the chromosomes in each pair look identical, but in males, 22 are similar but one pair is different. In males, this 23rd pair consists of one large chromosome (X) and one small chromosome (Y). In females the 23rd pair consists of two similar XX chromosomes. These chromosomes are called sex chromosomes.

During meiosis, males produce sperm that contain either an X chromosome or a Y chromosome. Females produce eggs containing X chromosomes. When a sperm fertilizes an egg the probability the zygote containing two X chromosomes is 50 percent (one X from the mother and another X from the father). The chance of it containing an X and Y chromosome is also 50 percent (the X from the mother and the Y from the father). There is therefore an equal probability of the child that develops being either a boy or a girl.

Polygenic Inheritance

When Mendel selected traits to study in his pea plants, he chose ones that, unknown to him, were controlled by single genes. This greatly simplified his work, but does not give a complete picture as to how most phenotypes are determined. Most phenotypes are controlled by more than one gene. Because of this they are referred to as being controlled by multiple genes or polygenic. These polygenic traits, such as height, hair color, or skin color, show continuous variation. For this reason, they do not follow the simple phenotypic ratios of Mendelian inheritance.

For example, human skin color depends upon the amount of melanin, a dark pigment that it contains. The genetics of skin color are quite complex, but it goes something like this: A number of genes control the manufacture of melanin in the skin. For each of these genes, there are two possible alleles, one allele that contributes to melanin production, and one allele for non-melanin production. The more alleles for melanin production you have, the darker your skin. Parents will have different combinations of these alleles, which they will contribute randomly their offspring. The skin color of a child depends upon which alleles it gets from each parent. Their skin may well be a different shade than either parent.

Height is another example of polygenic inheritance. People are not just tall or short, they show a continuous variation in height. Scientists have identified over 400 genes that may be involved in determining height. These genes contribute to the many processes that determine height, from cell growth to bone shape. Of course, these multiple genes are not the only factor that determines height. The environment, particularly diet, also plays a part.

Consider the Explain Question

| How does the genetic information inherited from an organism's parents affect its characteristics?

Go online to complete the scientific explanation.

dlc.com/ca10074s

Check Your Understanding

| Two plants are being crossed, each heterozygous for blue flower color (*B*), with white (*b*) as the recessive color. What is the possibility that the offspring will have white flowers?

dlc.com/ca10075s

S T E M in Action

Applying Genetics

Do you notice anything unusual about this building? What do you think the green panels on the building are?

This is a design for construction of the future. The green panels contain algae growing for biofuel. What does this have to do with genetics? Why grow algae, and how is this done?

This is just one application of genetic engineering, which is direct manipulation of an organism's genotype. People have been genetically engineering organisms for centuries, for example by selectively breeding livestock or pets. Modern methods of genetic engineering involve manipulating an organism's genes for a desired result.

GENETICALLY ENGINEERED ALGAE

The Algae House in Hamburg is the first algae-powered building in the world equipped with an algae bioreactor facade. Why grow algae on a building?

How would you like to live in an apartment that grows algae? Or drive a car that runs on algae? Photosynthetic microorganisms, including algae, are attracting considerable interest for use in biofuels. Many plants can be used as biofuels, but certain traits that algae possess—including their relatively high photosynthetic conversion efficiencies, diverse metabolic capabilities, superior growth rates, and ability to store or secrete energy-rich hydrocarbons—make them attractive candidates. Algae biofuels emit less carbon than traditional petroleum fuels, and are a renewable resource.

Microbiologists have identified several strains of algae that show promise for use in biofuel production. By essentially wringing out the natural oils in the algae and then refining it, biodiesel fuel can be produced. But powerful new genetic techniques enable targeting of locations of specific genes and redesigning the genetics for rapid growth and tolerance to extreme conditions. Molecular geneticists have also figured out ways to curb the production of an enzyme within the bacteria that breaks down the lipid within algae that is used in making biofuel. Because we can control the genetics, algae can be programmed to produce certain molecules quickly and in greater quantities than they do naturally, turning them into fancy biofuel molecular machines.

STEM and Genetics

Genetic engineers can use transgenic techniques to modify an organism's traits. A transgene is described as a segment of DNA that has been isolated and removed from one organism and incorporated into the genetic material of another organism. These new organisms are called genetically modified organisms, or GMOs. Although this technology has many applications, the term GMO is most commonly used to refer to agricultural crops.

Transgenic techniques are used by molecular biologists to modify products from organisms, change the characteristics of plants or animals, and develop microorganisms—commonly bacteria—for specific use. Food crops are modified for pest and disease resistance, or to produce fruits and vegetables that can withstand traveling over long distances.

A new potentially game-changing technology called CRISPR has recently been developed. This technology uses a virus as a vehicle containing enzymes that edit specific genes rapidly, easily, and efficiently. It can be used on a wide variety of cell types and organisms. It is expected that this powerful new technology will revolutionize genetic research, drug development, agriculture, and treatments for genetic diseases.

Dihybrid Cross

Use dihybrid cross to solve the problems below.

Dihybrid Cross for Hair Type and Eye Color

Genotype	HA	Ha	hA	ha
HA	HHAA	HHAa	HhAA	HhAa
Ha	HHAa	HHaa	HhAa	Hhaa
hA	HhAA	HhAa	hhAA	hhAa
ha	HhAa	Hhaa	hhAa	hhaa

H = long hair
h = short hair
A = brown
a = green

1. What is the probability of having offspring that are homozygous dominant for both traits?

2. What is the probability that the first offspring will be either long-haired and brown-eyed or long-haired and green-eyed?

3. What is the probability that among the first two offspring, one will be short-haired and green-eyed and the other will be short-haired and brown-eyed?

DNA

LESSON OVERVIEW

dlc.com/ca10076s

Lesson Questions

- What are the components of DNA and RNA?
- How are the structures of DNA and RNA related to their functions?
- How do cells make copies of DNA?

Key Vocabulary

Which terms do you already know?

- ☐ adenine
- ☐ amino acid
- ☐ chromosome
- ☐ codon
- ☐ cytosine
- ☐ DNA
- ☐ double helix
- ☐ gene expression
- ☐ guanine
- ☐ hydrogen bond
- ☐ induced mutation
- ☐ meiosis
- ☐ mitosis
- ☐ mRNA
- ☐ nucleic acid
- ☐ protein
- ☐ replication fork
- ☐ ribosome

Lesson Objectives

By the end of the lesson, you should be able to:

- Distinguish the various components of DNA and RNA.
- Relate the structures of DNA and RNA to their functions.
- Summarize key steps in the process of DNA replication.
- Relate the role of the DNA code and chromosomes to the inheritance of specific traits.

Key Vocabulary continued

- ☐ RNA
- ☐ RNA polymerase
- ☐ rRNA
- ☐ thymine
- ☐ transcription
- ☐ translation
- ☐ tRNA
- ☐ uracil

Glowing Fish

dlc.com/ca10077s

Why is it that when you go into an aquarium store, you will most likely encounter glowing freshwater fish? Also, in the same store you will most likely find fish of the same species that do not glow. What is going on here?

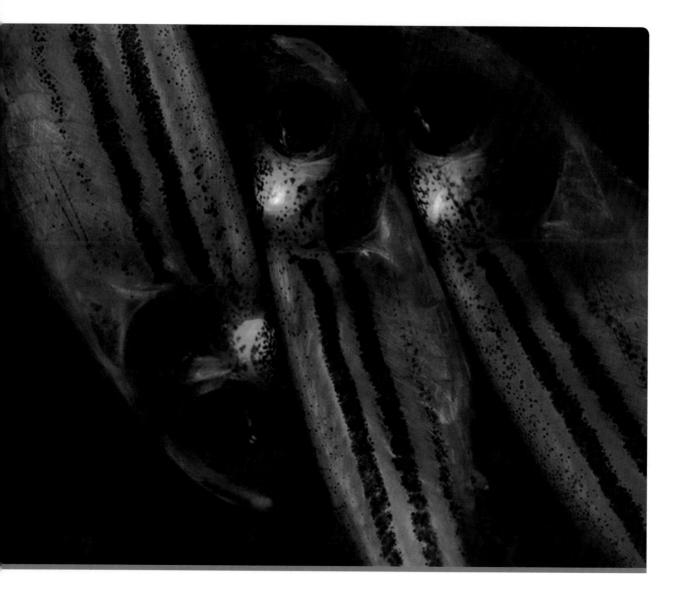

GLOWING FISH

These aquarium fish glow, but their wild counterparts do not. Why?

EXPLAIN QUESTION

▎ **How does DNA carry the code for a specific protein?**

What Are the Components of DNA and RNA?

DNA and RNA

Like other biological molecules, **nucleic acids** are large polymers made up of smaller repeating units, or monomers. Nucleic acid monomers are called nucleotides. **DNA** contains four different nucleotides, each with a different chemical base: **adenine** (A), **guanine** (G), **thymine** (T), and **cytosine** (C). The bases can form hydrogen bonds with each other, but only complementary bases can bond. Guanine bonds only with cytosine, while adenine bonds only with thymine.

Nucleic Acid Structure

DNA STRUCTURE

DNA has a double helix structure that, if untwisted, looks like two parallel strands. How can the order of the letters in one strand be used to determine the sequence in the other strand?

RNA also contains four different nucleotides, three of which are identical to DNA bases. In RNA, the base **uracil** (U) replaces thymine. Uracil is complementary to adenine.

In addition to the bases, nucleotides also contain a 5-carbon sugar (deoxyribose in DNA and ribose in RNA) and a phosphate group. The sugar and phosphate groups of adjacent nucleotides bond together to form a backbone. Scientists label the carbons in the sugar from 1' to 5' based on their position in the molecule. The phosphate group is attached to the sugar at the 5' carbon. The 5' end of one nucleotide bonds to the 3' carbon of the adjacent nucleotide to form the sugar-phosphate backbones. The two backbones of the DNA molecule run in opposite directions. One sugar-phosphate chain runs in the 5' to 3' direction and the other runs in the 3' to 5' direction.

DNA contains two separate, complementary strands of deoxyribonucleotides held together by hydrogen bonds. The two strands wind together to form a spiral shape called a **double helix**. In contrast, RNA is made up of a single strand of ribonucleotides. Although RNA is single stranded, some RNA molecules form folded structures, and, like **proteins**, these folded RNA molecules perform various functions like catalyzing reactions and transporting molecules.

DNA and RNA are very large molecules, but they follow the same chemical rules that apply to smaller molecules. For example, the charge on DNA's phosphate backbone is negative. This makes DNA a polar molecule, and it behaves like other, smaller polar molecules such as water. Because DNA is polar, it dissolves easily in water, and it does not dissolve in nonpolar solvents such as alcohol.

DNA AND RNA

DNA and RNA are both nucleic acids. What are the differences between DNA and RNA molecules?

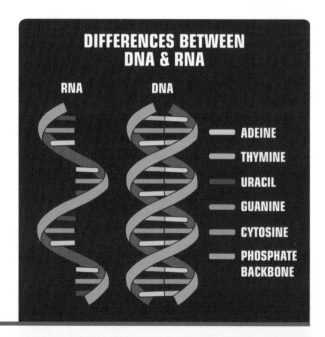

DIFFERENCES BETWEEN DNA & RNA

RNA   DNA

— ADEINE
— THYMINE
— URACIL
— GUANINE
— CYTOSINE
— PHOSPHATE BACKBONE

DNA in Eukaryotes and Prokaryotes

In eukaryotic organisms, DNA is contained inside the cell nucleus. DNA is tightly coiled around proteins to form structures called chromosomes. This packaging enables the long, delicate strands of DNA to be compacted into a tiny space. It also provides a way for cells to control **gene expression**. The chromosomes of eukaryotes are typically rod-shaped. By contrast, the DNA of prokaryotes is usually arranged in a single circular **chromosome** that is located in an area called the nucleoid and may be loosely tethered to the cell membrane.

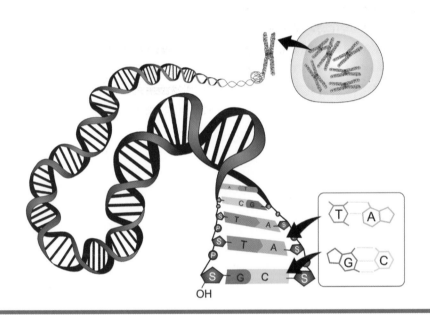

CHROMOSOMES

A eukaryotic chromosome is composed of DNA coiled tightly around proteins. What is the shape of a eukaryotic chromosome?

Each eukaryotic species contains a certain number of chromosomes, each with a characteristic shape. Chromosome number does not directly relate to the complexity of organisms. Chromosomes of sexually reproducing species come in pairs, one inherited from each parent. Humans have 23 pairs of chromosomes, or 46 total; a dog has a total of 78, and the adder's-tongue fern a total of 1,260!

How Are the Structures of DNA and RNA Related to Their Functions?

Coding for Traits

Genetic information is encoded in the order of nucleotide bases in DNA. The order of bases in DNA is analogous to the order of letters in written text. Just as the English language uses 26 letters arranged in patterns to form words that convey meaning, DNA uses a four-letter alphabet to carry genetic information.

DNA is a very long molecule that contains intermittent "coding" segments called genes. In general, each gene codes for a different protein. An organism's DNA contains the genes to code for all of the proteins that the organism needs to produce structures and carry out life processes.

Genes are made up of sequences with three-base segments called codons. Different codons code for unique amino acids. However, some amino acids may be coded for by more than one **codon**. For example, the **amino acid** leucine is coded for by six different codons. Other codons signal the stop or start of the gene. Amino acids are the monomers that make up proteins. There are 20 different amino acids. Proteins can contain hundreds of amino acids. The order of amino acids in a protein determines the protein's structure and function. To make a protein the gene containing the DNA, coding for that protein must first be converted into an RNA molecule.

Transcription and Translation

The cell copies the information in a gene by making complementary messenger RNA strands—a process called **transcription**. These messenger RNA (**mRNA**) strands are then used as the code to assemble amino acids in the correct order to form a protein. This second part of the process is called **translation**.

During transcription, the enzyme **RNA polymerase** catalyzes the copying of base codes in a gene from DNA to a complementary strand of mRNA. This complementary mRNA strand then travels through the cytoplasm to structures called ribosomes. Ribosomes are made of another kind of RNA called ribosomal RNA (**rRNA**). Protein synthesis occurs at the ribosomes.

A third type of RNA, transfer RNA (**tRNA**), carries amino acids to the ribosomes and attaches them in the order coded on the mRNA molecule. The amino acids are linked together with peptide bonds to form a protein. At this point, the original DNA code has been translated by the RNA into a protein sequence. This is why this second part of the process is called translation. Transcription and translation are covered in more detail in the Concept *Transcription and Translation*.

How Do Cells Make Copies of DNA?

Cell Division

Cells pass along their genetic information each time they divide. This ensures that every non-reproductive cell in an organism contains a complete copy of the organism's genetic code. In asexual reproduction, an organism passes its complete genetic code to offspring. In sexual reproduction, half of each parents' genes are passed to its offspring. To pass genetic information, the cell copies its DNA in the process of replication. DNA replication is a biological process that occurs in every living organism.

Replication

DNA replication begins when the enzyme helicase unwinds a segment of DNA and separates the two strands of the double helix, forming a structure called a **replication fork**. Each strand of the double helix serves as a template for duplicating the sequence of bases found in the original molecule of DNA.

A different enzyme, DNA polymerase, catalyzes the synthesis of complementary strands of DNA by attaching the correct deoxyribonucleotide having the correct complementary base (A if the template reads T, G if the template reads C) to the new strand of DNA being made.

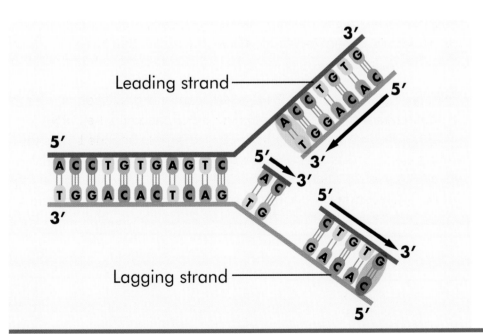

DNA REPLICATION

In contrast to the leading strand, which proceeds continuously, assembly of a complementary strand proceeds in small segments on the lagging strand. Why can't both strands be assembled simultaneously?

The synthesis of new DNA proceeds differently on each complementary strand. DNA polymerase can add nucleotides only to a free 3' end of a growing segment, never to a 5' end, so DNA synthesis can occur in the 5' to 3' direction only. As a result, only one strand—the leading strand—can be continuously assembled. Synthesis of the other strand—the lagging strand—occurs in segments. The enzyme DNA ligase joins these segments, called Okazaki fragments, by their sugar-phosphate backbones to form a continuous strand of DNA.

Consider the Explain Question

▌ **How does DNA carry the code for a specific protein?**

Go online to complete the scientific explanation.

dlc.com/ca10078s

Check Your Understanding

▌ **How do the components that make up RNA nucleotides differ from the components that make up DNA nucleotides?**

dlc.com/ca10079s

STEM in Action

Applying DNA

How can knowing about the structure of DNA and RNA lead to the development of new understandings of how living things operate? The study of DNA has revolutionized many areas of biology, including evolutionary biology, taxonomy, medicine, and criminology. Scientists have developed methods for analyzing the vast sequences of nucleotide bases that make up an organism's complete genetic code, or genome. Knowing how to do this has allowed scientists to analyze and publish completed genomes for many organisms, including humans. This effort was called the Human Genome Project and was an international effort to map all of the genes on every chromosome in the human body. It started in 1990 and took 13 years to complete.

Genome sequencing is an area of active research as scientists map out Earth's great diversity of species. Scientists have found that much of the DNA found in the genomes of organisms does not appear to code for anything. This is sometimes incorrectly referred to as junk DNA but is more accurately called noncoding DNA. About 98% of the human genome is noncoding DNA. This noncoding DNA is highly conserved during replication. This suggests that it has an important role to play within the cell. Recently, scientists have determined that these functions include the regulation of genes, including which genes are "turned on," or activated, and which are not. This is very important in determining how cells develop and what type of cell they become. Not only does noncoding DNA have important functions, it also provides useful information about the process of evolution.

GENOME SEQUENCING
Dark and light bands in the image represent different DNA sequences in the human genome. How long did it take scientists to map all of the genes in the human genome?

The genetic code is universal among all living things, meaning it always has the same nitrogen bases regardless of the organism. Comparing and contrasting the DNA of different organisms has helped scientists determine evolutionary relationships. In general, the more DNA code that species have in common, the species are more closely related. Classification systems are in flux as scientists analyze great volumes of genetic data from thousands of species.

DNA sequencing has practical applications for people as well. Genetic research is helping medical scientists to develop new treatments for genetic disorders and diseases related to changes in genetic code, such as cancer. DNA sequencing of infectious agents, such as bacteria and viruses, holds potential for preventing or treating resistant infections.

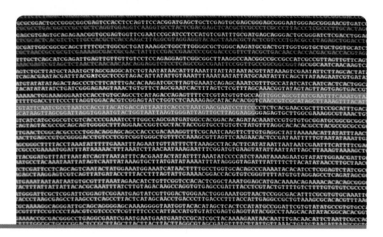

THE HUMAN GENOME

What is the purpose of all the letters seen here? How did knowing the structure of a DNA molecule help with the research into the human genome?

Criminology has also benefited greatly from DNA sequencing research. Every individual has a slightly different genetic code. Therefore, DNA sequences (or "DNA fingerprints") from materials such as hair, blood, or saliva can be used to confirm or cast doubt upon a suspect's presence at a crime scene. DNA fingerprinting of suspects and crime scenes is common police practice. DNA analysis of old evidence has also been used to solve previously unsolved cases and free people wrongly convicted of crimes.

Another place where knowledge of DNA is essential is in the production of genetically modified foods. Have you ever eaten corn on the cob? Had a drink of soy milk? If you have, you have most likely consumed a genetically modified food. For food to be considered genetically modified, scientists must have somehow changed the genome of the food item to enhance or remove a particular trait. For example, scientists have been able to transfer a gene from a deep-water fish into tomatoes. Why would this be beneficial? The gene enables the fish to prevent freezing in the icy water of the deep ocean. By putting that gene into the tomato, it prevents the fruits from freezing if their environment gets too cold.

There are many other examples of genetically modified foods, but they are not without controversy. While there is no scientific evidence that GMOs (genetically modified organisms), as they are called, are dangerous to humans, many people do not like the idea of consuming things that have been modified or untested. Critics of GMO foods have stated that just because problems have not yet been found does not mean there won't be some in the future. However, scientific research has not shown this to be a concern.

STEM and DNA

The technology used for DNA sequencing has greatly enhanced biology and the study of genetics. Chemical methods of replicating and analyzing DNA samples are the foundation of sequencing. Computer technology is also necessary to analyze large amounts of data. Modern computerized sequencing methods allow scientists to quickly find new genes among data for whole ecosystems.

Picture yourself as a forensic scientist at a crime scene. All of the fingerprints and other evidence have been wiped clean. Buried within the carpet, you find a single piece of human hair. How can DNA science and technology be used to determine whose hair it is?

The key to this mystery is a technology called polymerase chain reaction (PCR). PCR is a molecular copying process that can be used to duplicate DNA many times. It amplifies even the smallest pieces of DNA and allows them to be copied, so they can be studied. DNA from a sample as small as a single cell can be amplified, producing millions of copies in a few hours and allowing the copies to form the basis of a genetic analysis and comparison. The hair you found at the crime scene would provide sufficient DNA for researchers to use PCR to create a complete picture of its owner's genome.

PCR uses a series of cycles of heating and cooling to break up and then copy the DNA. At the start of the process, the sample is heated to separate the double-stranded DNA into its two strands. This process is called denaturation. Next, the mix is cooled, and a type of enzyme called DNA polymerase is used to synthesize complimentary copies of the DNA using segments (about 20 nucleotides long) called primers that are added to the mix. This makes two DNA molecules. The process is then repeated, and this cycle of denaturing and synthesizing is continued. Each time the cycle is run, the number of DNA molecules is doubled (2, 4, 8, 16, 32, 64, 128, 256, etc.). Soon, there are millions of copies of the original DNA molecule. This entire cycle has been automated using machines called thermocyclers that alter the temperature every few minutes. Once amplified, the DNA can be used in biochemical research or in medical and forensic applications.

CONCEPT

4.3

Transcription and Translation

dlc.com/ca10080s

LESSON OVERVIEW

Lesson Questions

- What is transcription?
- What are the steps involved in RNA processing?
- What are the functions of messenger RNA (mRNA), transfer RNA (tRNA), and ribosomal RNA (rRNA)?
- What is translation?
- How do cells control gene expression?
- What are the causes, types, and effects of mutations?

Key Vocabulary

Which terms do you already know?

- [ ] allele
- [ ] anticodon
- [ ] chromosome
- [ ] codon
- [ ] DNA
- [ ] gene expression
- [ ] genome
- [ ] mRNA
- [ ] mutation
- [ ] phenotype
- [ ] polypeptide
- [ ] ribosome
- [ ] RNA
- [ ] RNA polymerase
- [ ] rRNA
- [ ] transcription
- [ ] translation
- [ ] tRNA

Lesson Objectives

By the end of the lesson, you should be able to:

- Distinguish the processes of transcription and translation.
- Summarize the steps involved in RNA processing.
- Distinguish among messenger RNA (mRNA), transfer RNA (tRNA), and ribosomal RNA (rRNA).
- Summarize how cells control gene expression.
- Compare the various causes, types, and effects of mutations.
- Cite evidence for how DNA determines protein structure.
- Relate the role of the DNA code and chromosomes to the inheritance of specific traits.
- Cite evidence that genetic variation may arise by meiosis, replication errors, and mutations due to environmental factors.
- Explain the variation and distribution of observed traits in a population in terms of statistics and probability concepts.

Organism Instructions

dlc.com/ca10081s

Some people are good at building models, but others find it difficult. Remember those plastic building blocks that clip together? The key to successfully building the intended model was to carefully read and follow the instructions.

BUILDING AN ORGANISM

Building an organism is a complex process. Building a much simpler model, like this one, requires careful adherence to the instructions. How is this accomplished in a cell?

EXPLAIN QUESTION

How is transcription related to translation by the steps in which different types of RNA are processed, thereby allowing cells to control gene expression, and how is gene expression affected by various types of mutations?

What Is Transcription?

Transcription

The discovery of **DNA**'s structure and function was the first step toward understanding the information held within the molecule. The discovery of **RNA**, or ribonucleic acid, revealed the way in which DNA code is unraveled.

DNA and RNA are similar and different. Enzymes synthesize RNA from DNA. Think of RNA as a disposable copy of the original DNA molecule. RNA reads the DNA code and controls the production of proteins. Different types of RNA are responsible for various aspects of protein production.

Protein synthesis occurs in the cytoplasm of a cell. RNA travels from the nucleus to the cytoplasm, carrying the instructions for forming proteins. The original DNA molecule stays inside the nucleus. It remains enclosed within the nuclear membrane. In growing tissue, it replicates and divides to produce new cells.

Before RNA can be used in protein synthesis, it must be made from DNA in a process called **transcription**. During transcription, segments of the DNA molecule serve as a template. The template is used to produce a complementary RNA strand. In eukaryotes, transcription takes place in the nucleus. The completed RNA molecule (called a transcript) then moves to the cytoplasm. Here protein synthesis takes place. In prokaryotes, RNA synthesis and protein synthesis occur in the cytoplasm.

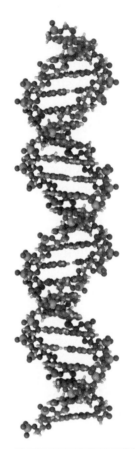

DNA DOUBLE HELIX
Rosalind Franklin and Raymond Gosling's X-ray images of DNA led to the discovery of the double helix structure by James Watson, Francis Crick, and Maurice Wilkins. How does this structure relate to how DNA and RNA facilitate the production of proteins?

Transcription begins when the enzyme **RNA polymerase** binds to DNA. The enzyme separates the DNA strands. Using one of the DNA strands as a template, RNA polymerase adds complementary base pairs to form a strand of RNA. Recall that one of the base pairs differs between RNA and DNA. In an RNA molecule, adenine pairs with uracil instead of the adenine-thymine base pair in DNA.

How does RNA polymerase determine where it should begin to make the RNA molecule? Regions along the DNA template with specific sequences act as signals to RNA polymerase to begin transcription. Other sequences signal RNA polymerase where to stop building the new RNA molecule.

What Are the Steps Involved in RNA Processing?

RNA Processing

After the **mRNA** molecule has been synthesized by **RNA polymerase**, it is not quite ready to be used for protein synthesis. Three main steps must occur to process the mRNA molecule in preparation for protein synthesis:

1. Extra sequences at one or both ends of the primary transcript are trimmed off. Specialized enzymes called exoribonucleases cut the RNA strand at specified locations.
2. Sections of sequences in the middle of RNA are edited out. Enzymes join, or splice, the remaining sequences to form the complete RNA.
3. RNA nucleotides can be modified at either end or within the body of the strand. Modification on the ends, which caps the molecule, prevents further degradation by exoribonucleases. Other modifications specialize RNA for different functions it will perform during protein synthesis.

SYNTHESIS OF mRNA

During transcription, DNA is unwound, while mRNA is transcribed from the template strand, after which DNA is rewound. What steps are necessary before the mRNA can then proceed to complete the process of protein synthesis?

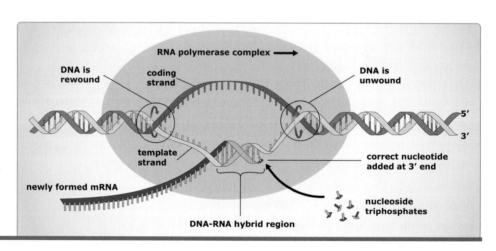

What Are the Functions of Messenger RNA (mRNA), Transfer RNA (tRNA), and Ribosomal RNA (rRNA)?

Types and Functions of RNA

Since RNA carries out so many jobs for protein synthesis, there are several different types of RNA, each with a specific role. The table describes the three main types of RNA and their functions.

Type	Function
Messenger RNA (mRNA)	It contains a sequence of nucleotides that direct the assembly of amino acids into proteins. Messenger RNA carries this information from the cell nucleus to ribosomes in the cytoplasm.
Transfer RNA (tRNA)	It transfers amino acids to the ribosome as the protein is built. Transfer RNA connects each three-letter genetic code carried in mRNA to a corresponding amino acid. There are 64 different three-letter codes for 20 amino acids.
Ribosomal RNA (rRNA)	It is present in the sub units of a ribosome that allow for decoding of mRNA. Ribosomal RNA also interacts with tRNA during protein synthesis to help form peptide bonds between amino acids.

What Is Translation?

Translation

Once mRNA has been transcribed in the nucleus, the job of deciphering the genetic message can begin. Decoding the message carried by mRNA into the proteins needed to carry out life processes is called **translation**. Translation plays a major role in **gene expression**.

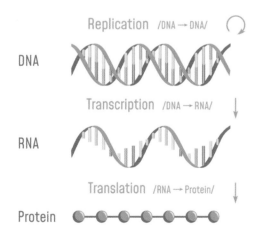

TRANSCRIPTION AND TRANSLATION

During transcription, the DNA of a gene is used as a template to produce a complementary mRNA strand. During translation, the code on the mRNA strand is used to produce a protein. What happens during the process of replication?

Recall that the code carried by RNA is made up of just four nucleotides represented by the letters: A, U, G, and C. The code is read in three-letter increments, called **codons**, one at a time. Each codon corresponds to an amino acid. There are more codons than amino acids (64 codons, only 20 amino acids) so most amino acids have more than one codon specific to them. For example, four different codons—ACG, ACA, ACC, ACU—specify the amino acid threonine. Some codons code necessary signals, such as "start" or "stop," for building the amino acid chain, or **polypeptide**. A table of the genetic code shows which codons specify each amino acid or the start or stop signals. Sequences along DNA that signal the RNA polymerase to begin transcription are called promoter sequences.

1st Base (5' end)	Middle Base				3rd Base (3' end)
	U	**C**	**A**	**G**	
U	Phenylalanine Phenylalanine Leucine Leucine	Serine	Tyrosine Tyrosine STOP STOP	Cysteine Cysteine STOP Tryptophan	U C A G
C	Leucine	Proline	Histidine Histidine Glutamine Glutamine	Arginine	U C A G
A	Isoleucine Isoleucine Isoleucine Methionine	Threonine	Asparagine Asparagine Lysine Lysine	Serine Serine Arginine Arginine	U C A G
G	Valine	Alanine	Aspartic Acid Aspartic Acid Glutamic Acid Glutamic Acid	Glycine	U C A G

mRNA CODONS

DNA codons are converted into mRNA codons during transcription. What changes in a codon could lead to a different amino acid being used in the protein?

Following transcription, the mRNA transcripts are transported from the nucleus to the endoplasmic reticulum (ER), specifically the rough ER. The rough ER is studded with ribosomes where translation takes place. Translation occurs in sequence and only in one direction, known as the 5' to 3' direction. The following steps outline the process of translation:

1. A ribosome attaches to the 5' end of mRNA at a specific sequence that is located upstream from the "start" codon.

2. Once the start codon is read, construction of the polypeptide begins. The ribosome moves along the mRNA strand "reading" each codon. tRNAs with corresponding anticodon bring the correct amino acid to the ribosome. Anticodons are a complementary set of three nucleotides in the anticodon region of tRNA.

3. One at a time, the ribosome attaches an amino acid from each tRNA to the next amino acid with a peptide bond. Simultaneously, the ribosome breaks the bond between tRNA and its amino acid. The tRNA is released and the ribosome is available to bind the next tRNA dictated by the mRNA code.

4. The ribosome continues to move from the 5' end of mRNA toward the 3' end, reading each codon as it moves along. Construction of the protein continues until the ribosome reaches a "stop" codon. At that point, both the protein and mRNA strand are released from the ribosome.

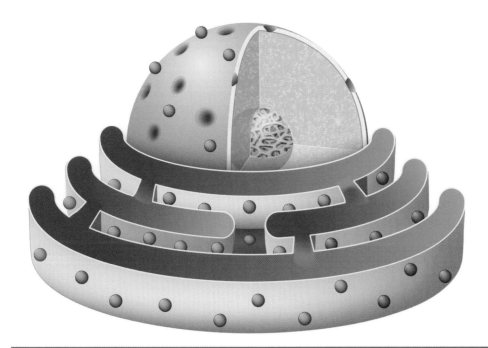

ROUGH ENDOPLASMIC RETICULUM

The rough endoplasmic reticulum is studded with protein-producing ribosomes. Why does rough endoplasmic reticulum have its distinctive folded membrane structure?

How Do Cells Control Gene Expression?

Gene Expression

The identity, physical appearance, and performance of every organism is determined by the genetic information stored in its DNA, which determines the fate and function of each cell. But how do proteins result in blue eye color or yellow plant flowers? Recall that many proteins are enzymes. Enzymes catalyze a wide range of biochemical reactions in an organism's cells. The cellular instructions to make the enzymes that produce a flower's yellow pigment are encoded, or stored, in the information of the organism's DNA. The flower cells then follow these instructions to make the enzymes responsible for yellow pigmentation in a multi-step process called gene expression.

The total set of genes of a cell or of an organism is called its **genome**, arranged in structures called chromosomes made of double-stranded DNA spooled around special proteins. The smallest unit of information stored in DNA is called a gene.

The size of a genome, the number of chromosomes, and the total number of genes is specific to the organism. Most normal human cells (except eggs and sperm) contain two sets of 23 chromosomes (46 total), one set from one's mother and one set from one's father. Therefore, each cell has two copies of each gene, one from each parent. This totals around six billion base pairs of DNA per cell, packed to all fit within the cell nucleus.

Some genes code for RNA only. Most genes code for proteins, including some proteins that make up cell structures and other proteins that are enzymes. In humans, there are an estimated 19,000 genes that code for proteins. Gene expression is the process of using the information stored in each gene to instruct the synthesis of each gene product. However, protein is not expressed directly from DNA; there are multiple steps involved in getting from the starting information (DNA) to the end product (protein).

In biology, there is a widely-accepted idea about how the DNA gets expressed as traits in an organism. This is called the Central Dogma. The Central Dogma states that DNA provides the template of instructions for the synthesis of RNA (by a process called transcription), and messenger RNA (mRNA) provides the template of instructions for the synthesis of proteins (by a process called translation). All cells, whether they are bacterial cells or human cells, share these two basic steps of gene expression; transcription and translation. The end products produced, usually proteins, determine the traits of an organism. A visible or measurable trait of an organism, for example eye color, is called a **phenotype**.

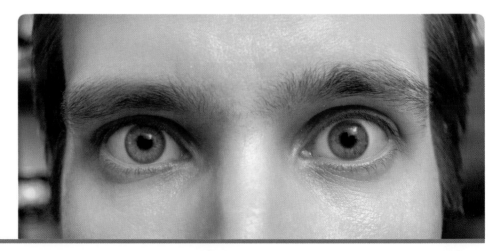

HETEROCHROMIA

Heterochromia is caused by the uneven distribution of melanin. How did heterochromia affect the person shown in this photo?

Some genes are expressed by transcription into transfer RNA (tRNA) or ribosomal RNA (rRNA), not mRNA. These tRNA and rRNA molecules are not the template of instructions for the synthesis of protein, but they serve other essential roles during the process.

In addition to the basic steps of transcription and translation common that are common to all cells, additional steps exist in eukaryotic cells that are not present in bacteria. These include removing non-coding information from the mRNA of higher cells in a process called splicing, and making other modifications to mRNA that alter its stability and ability to be translated.

All cells have ways to regulate or adjust the level of gene expression. No cell expresses all of its genes all of the time; genes are expressed when they are needed. Every step involved in the expression of a gene is a step that can be regulated. DNA itself can undergo changes in the level and pattern of methylation at CpG sites, altering the level of its transcription into RNA.

Activity of enzymes involved in each step of gene expression can be regulated. For example, RNA polymerase transcribes DNA into mRNA; its activity can be blocked by DNA-binding proteins that repress transcription or enhanced by DNA-binding proteins that assist **RNA polymerase** function. In eukaryotes, mRNA carries the genetic information out of the nucleus to the ribosomes. The passage of the mRNA through the membrane can be controlled by proteins that enable this process. The level of gene expression also can be controlled by the stability or concentration of reactants; for example, some mRNA molecules are more stable than others so are more likely to be translated into their protein products than if they were unstable.

Although technically not regulation of "gene expression," once a protein is made by translation, protein function can be altered by modifications that activate it, inactivate it, or reduce its level in the cell by degradation.

All of these mechanisms contribute to controlling which genes are expressed and the amounts of functional gene product. Although life is incredibly diverse, the cellular mechanisms controlling gene expression are remarkably similar.

DNA Structure Determines Protein Structure

The DNA molecule has a double-helix shape. The two helices wind around each other, making a structure that looks like a twisted ladder. Each rail of the ladder forms the backbone of each helix, made from sugar (called deoxyribose) and phosphate groups, while the rungs consist of nitrogen bases. The sequence of these nitrogen bases codes for the proteins that are made from the DNA template.

The four nitrogen bases are adenine, thymine, cytosine, and guanine. Due to its shape, each base can pair with only one other base. Adenine pairs only with thymine, while cytosine pairs only with guanine. When DNA replicates or during transcription, the two strands of the double helix split apart. This unzipping exposes the nitrogen bases. During replication, complementary bases pair with the original molecule, forming two duplicate DNA molecules. Each duplicate has an identical order of bases as the original molecule.

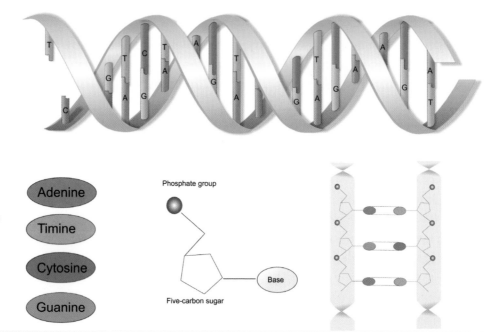

NUCLEIC ACID STRUCTURE

Pairs of nitrogen bases connected by hydrogen bonds form the rungs of the DNA "ladder." How do changes in the structure of DNA contribute to genetic variation in organisms?

Adenine

Timine

Cytosine

Guanine

Phosphate group

Five-carbon sugar

Base

Transcription involves another molecule called RNA, which also consists of a string of bases attached to a sugar-phosphate backbone. The RNA bases attach to the exposed bases of DNA. The order of bases in the DNA determines the order of bases in the RNA molecule. Transcription is the first step in protein synthesis.

Genes in an organism only become active when protein synthesis is needed. Some genes lie dormant for most of the organism's life, while others are active from the time the organism starts its existence. Tadpoles develop into frogs, which look and behave very differently. Yet the tadpole and the frog have the exact same genetic code. The difference is that in the tadpole, the genes are activated that cause a tail and gills to grow. When the tadpole becomes a frog, these genes are turned off, and genes that cause legs and lungs to grow are turned on. The proteins responsible for the developmental process that produces these traits directly result from the sequence of DNA in the animal's body cells.

SAME CODE, DIFFERENT EXPRESSION

A tadpole develops into a frog, which looks and behaves very differently. Yet both the tadpole and frog have the same genetic code. How can the same DNA cause different traits?

The sequence of bases in the DNA molecule governs the process of protein synthesis. Studying the structure of DNA and its sequence of nitrogen bases enables scientists to better understand the processes of transcription and translation, and how proteins give rise to the traits of living things.

What Are the Causes, Types, and Effects of Mutations?

Mutations

With the myriad steps that occur in transcription and translation, mistakes can arise. These mistakes may lead to **mutations**. Mutations are heritable, abrupt changes in the type, structure, sequence, or number of the nucleotides of DNA. They may benefit or have no effect on the organism. But more often, they are detrimental in some way.

Mutations fall into two main categories: gene mutations and chromosomal mutations. Gene mutations are errors that affect only a single gene. The error is usually at a single point of the DNA molecule so these are referred to as point mutations. These errors include substitutions, insertions, or deletions of the DNA nucleotides. Point mutations usually occur during DNA replication.

© Discovery Education | www.discoveryeducation.com ● Image: Eric Isselee / Shutterstock

Large-scale chromosomal mutations produce changes in the structure of chromosomes. Chromosomal mutations include amplifications (such as duplications), deletions, and translocation. The table describes the two main classes of mutations, the types of errors that occur, and their common effects.

	Type of Mutation	Error	Effect
Gene Mutations	substitution	One nucleotide is switched for a different nucleotide.	Usually affects only one amino acid and often has no effect on the organism.
	insertion	An extra nucleotide is added to the mRNA strand.	Can be dramatic because the three-nucleotide codons are shifted, resulting in a string of incorrect amino acids. This may completely disable the protein.
	deletion	A nucleotide is deleted from the mRNA strand.	
Chromosomal Mutations	amplification	An extra copy or copies of part or all of a chromosome is made.	May lead to over-expression of the gene(s).
	deletion	Part of a chromosome is lost.	Loss of genetic material may result in genetic disease.
	translocation	Part of one chromosome breaks off and attaches to another.	Can lead to several genetic diseases, including certain cancers.

Causes and Results of Mutation

Natural or environmental factors, or both, may cause mutations. On the molecular level, spontaneous mutations can occur due to:

- Tautomerism: A base is altered by a change in the hydrogen bonding pattern of a base. This results in incorrect base pairing during replication.
- Depurination: Loss of a purine base (A or G).
- Deamination: A base loses an amine group.

- Slipped strand mispairing: the breakdown of the new DNA strand during replication, followed by re-synthesis in a different spot that leads to insertions or deletions.

Mutations may be caused by exposure to certain chemicals, radiation, or viruses. Chemicals such as those in tobacco smoke or pollutants can interact with DNA, causing multiple mutations. These mutations may lead to cancer or other diseases. Harmful substances can interfere with nucleotide pairing, cause breaks in nucleic acid strands, and produce inversions and deletions. If cells are unable to repair the mutations, the base sequence can be permanently changed. If this happens, the mutation will be copied during replication and inherited by daughter cells.

The damage caused by mutations varies greatly. Many mutations have no effect at all on the organism. Some are even beneficial. Mutations are one of the key mechanisms in the production of new phenotypes and thus play an important role in evolution.

Environmental Factors Affecting Gene Expression

Gene expression can be influenced by the environment. The "environment" includes the world in which the organism lives, as well as its internal environment. This internal world may include factors such as metabolism or gender. External influences could include factors such as food, substances in the environment, light, and temperature. Some of these factors will influence which genes are switched on or off, and may alter how an organism functions and develops.

Different genders express autosomal traits (those not carried on the sex chromosomes) in different ways. One example of this is baldness in men. Usually this type of baldness only occurs when levels of testosterone and dihydrotestosterone—male sex hormones—are high. This is because the allele for baldness is only expressed at these high concentrations. Women carry this gene, but it is not usually expressed because they have very low levels of these hormones.

Food availability can influence gene expression. Certain gut bacteria in mammals produce specific enzymes only when certain types of food are present. The bacteria can alter the types of enzymes according to the nutrients present in the food. Imagine that you had cereal and milk for breakfast. The bacteria produce enzymes specifically to digest carbohydrates and fats from this meal. Imagine that you then have a hamburger and salad for lunch. The bacteria now produce enzymes to digest fats and fiber. These bacteria produce different enzymes by turning on and off certain genes due to changes in the food substances in their environment. This helps the bacterium and its host.

Chemicals or drugs in the environment can also change gene expression. One such example involved a drug called thalidomide. Thalidomide was a sedative drug that was used in the 1950 and 1960s. In adults, it was shown to have no measurable effect on gene expression and was widely prescribed. However, it was later discovered that it altered gene expression in fetuses. Many pregnant women who had been prescribed the drug gave birth to infants with missing or malformed arms and legs. About 10,000 infants were impacted in this way.

Temperature can also alter gene expression. One example of the influence of temperature is the Himalayan rabbit. Himalayan rabbits carry a gene which is needed for pigment production. The expression of this gene depends upon the temperature. Those parts of the rabbit that are cold generally express the gene, whereas those that are not have no pigment and are white. This gives rise to the characteristic black ears and noses of this breed of rabbit.

Light may also alter gene expression. For example, exposure of some caterpillar species to different colors of light will change the color of the wings they develop when they become butterflies. Those exposed to green light had dark wings, whereas those raised under red light had very brightly colored wings.

There are many examples of the environment influencing gene expression. Genes that are influenced by internal and external environmental factors may provide certain adaptive advantages and will be selected for through the process of natural selection.

Consider the Explain Question

How is transcription related to translation by the steps in which different types of RNA are processed, thereby allowing cells to control gene expression, and how is gene expression affected by various types of mutations?

dlc.com/ca10082s

Go online to complete the scientific explanation.

Check for Understanding

What is the main function of each of the three types of RNA?

dlc.com/ca10083s

STEM in Action

Applying Transcription and Translation

Can you name any genetic diseases? You may have heard of diseases such as cystic fibrosis or sickle-cell anemia. You may even know someone who has one of these diseases. What is the underlying cause of such diseases? Since genes are responsible for creating the correct instructions to make proteins, any error in the genes, or in the translation or transcription of genes, can result in genetic disease.

Mutations are heritable changes in the nucleotide sequence that can cause changes in protein structure, which are observed as changes in normal characteristics. Many mutations have no effect, while others are fatal or can cause enough change to result in disease.

Doctors have long realized that understanding the expression of the genetic code in cells could help to prevent or treat these diseases. Studies of transcription and translation also show promise in treatment of a common disease that we don't normally think of as being a genetic disease: cancer. Following the discovery of DNA's structure in the 1950s, scientists soon came to understand that cancer had a genetic basis. Before long, scientists grasped the basic idea that cancer resulted from genetic mutations.

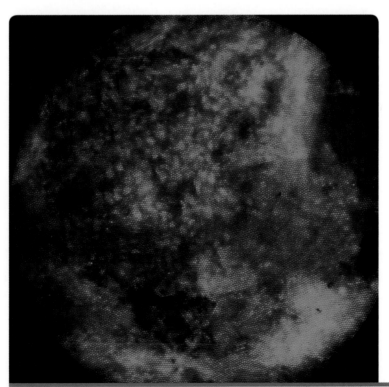

GLOWING CANCER CELLS

Scientists use powerful microscopes to identify cancer cells in the body. How does knowing about the transcription of genetic material in these cells help with the development of treatments?

Scientists know that mutations to the genetic code will be transcribed and translated. However, some conditions can also arise through mistakes during transcription and translation. By studying errors that occur during these processes, scientists can better understand how the diseases express themselves at a genetic level, spurring preventive measures and treatments. For example, scientists have discovered that many, if not all, cancer-causing molecules that promote transcription are poorly regulated. These molecules stimulate the production of molecules such as growth hormones, which in turn stimulate cell proliferation, leading to tumors. Therefore, some cancer treatments can focus on drugs that restore the regulation of these transcription factor molecules.

When you go outside in the sun, what is the most important thing to do before you leave? You need to put on sunscreen to protect you from the ultraviolet rays of the sun. Through research into gene expression, scientists discovered that excessive exposure to this type of radiation could cause the DNA of skin cells to mutate. These mutations are inherited by replacement skin cells, and, given time, skin cancer can develop. To prevent this cause of cancer, medical researchers invented sunscreen with differing levels of protection. These sunscreens provide a barrier against the sun's harmful rays.

MELANOMA

Melanoma is a skin cancer that can be caused by exposure to the sun. How can sunscreen help to prevent melanoma?

STEM and Transcription and Translation

Shows about forensic science are hugely popular. A forensic scientist requires a strong background in gene expression and DNA. This career involves work with law enforcement agencies to help solve crimes. How would a crime scene provide DNA that could be used as evidence? Let's say a hair was found at the scene. The forensic scientist would take that hair and isolate the DNA present. If there were just fragments of DNA present, the scientist would use a technique called polymerase chain reaction (PCR) to enhance the amount of DNA found. Prosecutors would then use a DNA match as evidence in their indictment.

Genetic engineers use their knowledge of gene expression to modify the traits of organisms. They use genetic engineering technology to change the genetic code. The aim is to improve desirable characters or to eliminate undesirable ones. Depending on the specific trait, the scientists may modify an existing gene's expression or introduce a new gene. The new genome thereby expresses proteins that control specific cellular activities. This approach is used to treat diseases, make pharmaceutical drugs, and to boost crop and livestock production.

Agriculture is increasingly making use of genetic engineering. Farmers routinely plant crops engineered with higher yields than before or to use fertilizer more efficiently or resist disease or pests. For example, scientists have created a genetically altered corn plant that produces a naturally- occurring pesticide. The new strain produces higher yields and more profits for farmers. However, recent studies indicate that insects are becoming resistant to these varieties. Efforts are currently underway to further modify the corn genome to counter the insects' adaptations.

CONCEPT
4.4

Genetic Disorders and Technology

dlc.com/ca10084s

LESSON OVERVIEW

Lesson Questions

- What are the causes and symptoms of various genetic disorders?
- What are the definitions and some examples of autosomal dominant, autosomal recessive, and sex-linked disorders?
- What are the uses, benefits, and risks of genetic testing and gene therapy?

Lesson Objectives

By the end of the lesson, you should be able to:

- Distinguish various genetic disorders by their causes and symptoms.
- Differentiate examples of autosomal dominant, autosomal recessive and sex-linked disorders in humans.
- Summarize the uses, benefits, and risks of genetic testing and gene therapy.
- Analyze statistics to explain patterns of genetic disorders in a population.

Key Vocabulary

Which terms do you already know?

- ☐ aneuploidy
- ☐ autosomal dominant disorder
- ☐ autosomal recessive disorder
- ☐ gene therapy
- ☐ genetic disorder
- ☐ genetic testing
- ☐ genome
- ☐ monosomy
- ☐ nondisjunction
- ☐ sex-linked disorders
- ☐ single-gene disorders
- ☐ spontaneous mutation
- ☐ trisomy

Understanding Genetic Disorders

The people in the photo are from one family. The children have many characteristics in common with their parents but the young boy has certain facial features that are different. He has a genetic disorder called Down syndrome. How can this boy have a genetic disorder, when his parents and sister do not?

dlc.com/ca10085s

EXPLAIN QUESTION

▌ **Explain how a person's genes affect his or her health.**

DOWN SYNDROME

How can you tell that the people in the photo are from the same family? Which child has Down syndrome, a genetic disorder? How can you tell?

What Are the Causes and Symptoms of Various Genetic Disorders?

Small-scale Mutations

Genetic disorders are caused by DNA abnormalities. These abnormalities can arise in a number of different ways. Some of these irregularities are small in scale, affecting only single genes. Others are large-scale, affecting entire chromosomes.

Small-scale irregularities, also called **single-gene disorders**, can occur during DNA replication when new complementary strands of DNA are synthesized. When DNA is copied, it is supposed to be identical to the parental DNA, like a copy machine with an original document. However, mistakes can occur during the assembly of new DNA strands. Occasionally, a mismatched nucleotide might be added to the growing strand. Sometimes an extra base is accidentally added, and other times a base may accidentally be removed. While there are proofreading mechanisms to correct such mistakes, they may not be 100 percent effective. An error that arises naturally during DNA assembly is called a **spontaneous mutation**. Toxic chemicals and substances, such as free radicals in the body can also cause DNA mutations.

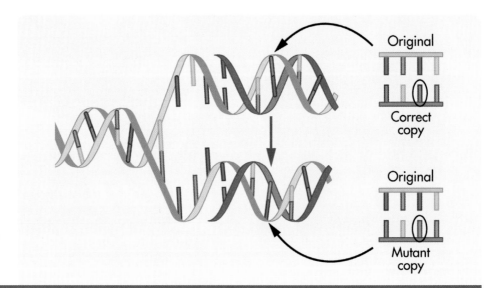

MUTATION DURING REPLICATION

Mutations within DNA can arise from mistakes made during replication. How are such mistakes classified?

Sometimes a mutation does not change the function of the protein the gene codes. This type of mutation is called a neutral mutation. A mutation may improve protein function. In this unlikely event, the outcome for the affected individual is positive. However, most mutations cause the protein to malfunction. In these cases, the negative consequences can be severe. You may know someone who has a genetic disease caused by a single gene. Some well-known single-gene disorders include:

Cystic fibrosis: This is the most common lethal genetic disease in the United States. In cystic fibrosis the gene for a chloride channel is mutated. The channel normally allows chloride ions to pass across the cell membrane. When this channel does not function properly, chloride ions build up inside the cell and do not pass outside the cell. This causes mucus to become thick and sticky, preventing debris from being cleared from the body. Since all of the cells in the body have the same mutated chloride channel, the mucus builds up all over the body, causing chronic bronchitis, malnutrition, and bacterial infections.

Sickle-cell anemia: This is caused by a mutation in the hemoglobin gene. When oxygen levels are low, the mutant hemoglobin proteins clump up into long structures that deform red blood cells. These deformed red blood cells can clog small blood vessels. Symptoms that may arise include pain, weakness, and tissue damage.

Normal
Red Blood Cell

Sickled
Red Blood Cell

NORMAL AND SICKLED BLOOD CELLS

Sickle-cell anemia occurs when red blood cells with abnormal hemoglobin become crescent-shaped, and do not pass through blood vessels smoothly. Why could this disorder provide some protection against malaria, a disease that infects blood cells?

Huntington's disease: This affects the nervous system, causing certain nerve cells in the brain to waste away. A protein called huntingtin is mutated in such a way that it contains excess repeats of the DNA nucleotides CAG. Scientists still know little about the natural function of the protein and why the mutation causes a disease. The resulting degeneration is very severe. Huntington's disease is marked by cognitive decline, psychiatric problems, and difficulty with muscular movements.

HUNTINGTON'S GENE MUTATION

Huntington's disease is caused by excess repeats of the sequence CAG on the gene that codes for a protein called huntingtin. What happens to the structure of the protein coded for by the huntingtin gene because of these repeats?

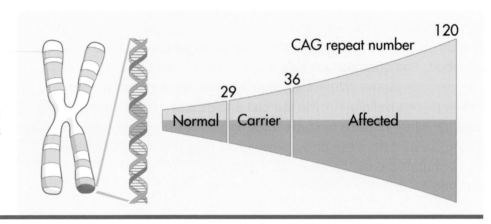

Phenylketonuria (PKU): PKU is a **genetic disorder** caused by a mutation in the liver enzyme phenylalanine hydroxylase. This enzyme is required to metabolize the amino acid phenylalanine. However, the mutated enzyme does not properly metabolize phenylalanine. As a result, blood levels of phenylalanine rise. Symptoms of PKU are largely brain-related. Improper brain development, brain damage, and seizures can result if the disease is left untreated. However, living by a strict, low phenylalanine diet can prevent symptoms.

Large-scale Mutations

Large-scale mutations cause abnormalities in chromosomal structure. For instance, extra copies of chromosomes or portions of chromosomes may result due to errors in meiosis, called **nondisjunction**. This results in too many copies of the genes found on these chromosomes. Alternatively, large portions of chromosomes may fail to copy or may be removed altogether. These portions are said to be deleted. This loss of large numbers of genes can have devastating results.

One common multi-gene disorder is Down syndrome. It affects approximately 1 out of 700 children born in the United States. The typical cause of this disorder is called **trisomy** 21. Humans normally have two copies of every chromosome. Trisomy refers to cases in which three copies of a chromosome are present. Down syndrome results when a person has three copies of chromosome 21. This condition can occur when homologous chromosomes fail to separate during meiosis. It can also occur when genetic material is rearranged between chromosome 21 and another chromosome. Individuals affected by Down syndrome commonly have mental retardation, heart and respiratory defects, and other physical abnormalities. These symptoms generally lead to a shortened life span.

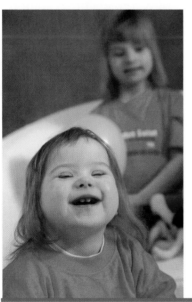

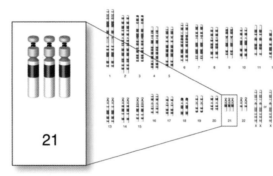

21

DOWN SYNDROME AND TRISOMY 21

Down syndrome is caused by an extra chromosome 21, leading to three chromosomes, and hence the name, trisomy 21. Why does an extra copy of a chromosome have negative effects?

Aneuploidy results when an individual's chromosome number is abnormal, usually by one more or one less. Turner syndrome is an example of **monosomy**, a form of aneuploidy caused by the absence of a chromosome as a result of nondisjunction. Normal females have two X chromosomes. In the case of Turner syndrome, one of the X chromosomes is partially or entirely missing. Symptoms in an affected female may include physical abnormalities such as a broad chest, a low hairline, low set ears, swelling, and reproductive sterility. Turner syndrome can also lead to various autoimmune disorders and poor development of certain organ tissues.

A condition called Williams syndrome arises from the deletion of about 25 genes from chromosome 7. One of the proteins affected by this deletion is the connective tissue protein elastin. Cognitive disability, developmental delays, cardiac defects, and physical abnormalities all can result from Williams syndrome. Remarkably, despite cognitive impairments, one of the hallmark traits of individuals with Williams syndrome is strong social behavior. Patients lack social inhibition, and thus communicate surprisingly well socially and emotionally. They tend to be extremely friendly and empathic.

Similar to Turner syndrome in females, Klinefelter syndrome is a sex chromosome disorder that affects males. Males normally have one X and one Y chromosome. Individuals with Klinefelter syndrome have two X chromosomes and one Y chromosome. It is a relatively common disorder, affecting approximately 1 in every 500 to 600 males. The primary symptoms include reduced male hormonal function, leading to reduced fertility, and some delay in learning and motor developmental. More serious symptoms, such as the development of certain cancers, also can occur.

Multifactorial Disorders

The most difficult disorders to understand are those arising from environmental factors combined with mutations in multiple genes. Scientists are finding many disorders that fall under this category.

One example of a multifactorial disorder is Alzheimer's disease, which results in cognitive dementia and memory decline. Research neuroscientists have discovered multiple factors that may contribute to the onset of Alzheimer's disease. In fact, several genes have been linked to the disease. Alzheimer's is also associated with environmental risk factors such as head trauma and high blood pressure. Additionally, the nutrients in many healthy foods are likely to reduce the occurrence of Alzheimer's disease.

Many types of cancers are considered multifactorial diseases as well. Someone who smokes cigarettes during his or her lifetime might never develop lung cancer, while another who never smokes might develop lung cancer. However, smokers do have a much higher risk of developing cancer than non-smokers. Certainly, many different alleles have been implicated in breast, ovarian, lung, and colon cancers. However, scientists are discovering ways in which environmental factors may determine the risk of these and other cancers. Some of these factors are lifestyle choices such as diet and exercise, while others are environmental factors such as the presence of certain toxins.

What Are the Definitions and Some Examples of Autosomal Dominant, Autosomal Recessive, and Sex-Linked Disorders?

Autosomal Dominant Disorders

Remember that humans carry two alleles for each gene and these alleles may be dominant or recessive. An **autosomal dominant disorder** is one that arises if even just one allele is mutated. This means that a child would only have to inherit a diseased allele from one parent in order to contract the illness. Huntington's disease is an example of an autosomal dominant disorder. If only one allele contains the repeated nucleotide, the disease will manifest.

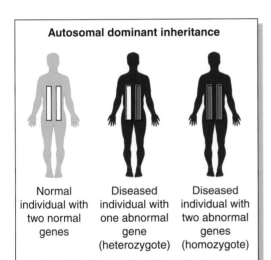

Autosomal dominant inheritance

| Normal individual with two normal genes | Diseased individual with one abnormal gene (heterozygote) | Diseased individual with two abnormal genes (homozygote) |

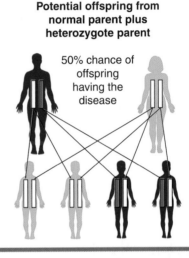

Potential offspring from normal parent plus heterozygote parent

50% chance of offspring having the disease

AUTOSOMAL DOMINANT INHERITANCE

Autosomal dominant disorders can be inherited even if only one mutated gene is passed down from a parent. Why are half the children born to an affected parent likely to be normal when the other parent is unaffected?

Another example of an autosomal dominant disorder is neurofibromatosis type 1. In this relatively common disease, a mutation occurs in the gene responsible for producing neurofibromin. The neurofibromin protein is important in determining cell division cycles. The mutation ultimately causes non-cancerous growths and skin malformations. Symptoms vary widely and may be mild or severe.

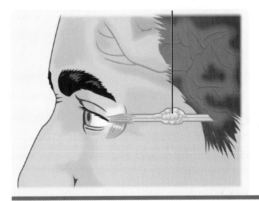

NEUROFIBROMA ON THE OPTIC NERVE

Neurofibromatosis type 1 can lead to blindness if a tumor, or neurofibroma, grows near the optic nerve. What problems may arise if a neurofibroma grows near the spinal cord?

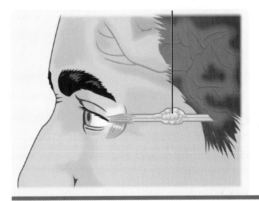

Marfan syndrome is an autosomal dominant disorder caused by a mutation in a gene called fibrillin 1. This gene plays an important role in the development of connective tissues all over the body. Symptoms of Marfan syndrome include various physiological defects, such as cardiac and respiratory problems, physical abnormalities, visual problems, and learning disability. Individuals tend to have long limbs and fingers.

The autosomal dominant disorder called hereditary non-polyposis colorectal cancer syndrome is also known as Lynch syndrome. This disorder involves mutations in genes that are important for DNA mismatch repair. Mismatch repair is a process that naturally happens in humans that helps to correct malfunctioning DNA. Lynch syndrome commonly leads to a high risk of colorectal cancer.

Hereditary multiple exostoses is an autosomal dominant disease characterized by multiple bone tumors. The growths extend from bones throughout the body. There have been at least three mutated genes linked to this disorder. However, it is not yet clear exactly how the mutations lead to bony tumors.

Autosomal Recessive Disorders

An individual must have two copies of dysfunctional, or mutant, alleles in order to have an autosomal recessive disorder. If they have one normal copy of the gene, they will remain healthy. Two examples of autosomal recessive disorders are sickle-cell disease and cystic fibrosis.

Tay-Sachs disease also is an autosomal recessive disorder. This disease is caused by a mutation in a gene that codes for an important enzyme. The enzyme hexosaminidase A normally breaks down phospholipids. Without the properly functioning enzyme, phospholipids build up in nerve cells. This disease typically begins in the fetus by damaging nerve tissue. It progresses until death, which usually occurs between the ages of three and five. The disease is particularly common among the Eastern European Jewish population. It is estimated that 1 in 27 members of this population carries the mutated allele. However, since two mutated alleles are required to cause disease, carriers having only one mutated allele will not be symptomatic.

Another example of an autosomal recessive disorder is Niemann-Pick disease. There are multiple forms of the disorder; however, all forms involve mutations that ultimately cause problems with metabolizing lipids. These lipids collect in various organ tissues throughout the body. Symptoms include motor impairments, seizures, and other physiological abnormalities. A diet low in cholesterol can help some patients manage the illness.

Spinal muscular atrophy is another group of autosomal recessive disorders. It is characterized by muscular degeneration. The onset of symptoms occurs at different ages. For early onset cases, respiratory and digestive problems are common in infants. Progressive muscle weakness occurs until eventual death between the ages of two and three.

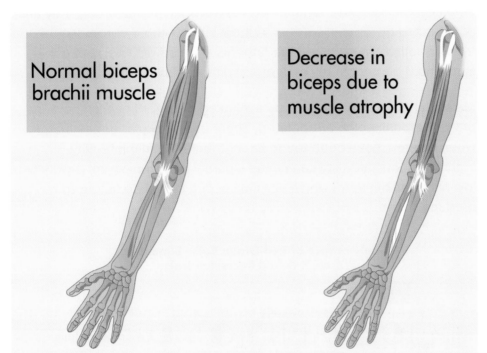

Normal biceps brachii muscle

Decrease in biceps due to muscle atrophy

MUSCULAR ATROPHY
Spinal muscular atrophy has a degenerative effect on muscles, including large superficial muscles. Why would muscle weakness lead to respiratory and digestive problems?

Sex-linked Disorders

Sex-linked disorders are caused by mutations in genes on the X or Y chromosome. Thus, they affect males and females differently. There are both X-linked and Y-linked disorders.

Rett syndrome is an X-linked disease that affects approximately 1 in 10,000 births. Receiving one affected X chromosome causes mild or moderate symptoms. An unborn female with two mutant X chromosomes typically does not survive to birth. Males who receive an affected X chromosome do not have a healthy X chromosome to offset it. Thus, most die before birth or early in life. As a result, Rett syndrome affects females almost exclusively. It involves impairments in hand use, language development, and social engagement. The disease also causes respiratory and muscular movement problems.

Incontinentia pigmenti is another X-linked disorder. Like Rett syndrome, this disease is most common among females, and lethal to most males. It affects skin, hair, teeth, nails, and the nervous system. It is often characterized by discoloration of the skin. More severe symptoms include slow motor development, loss of brain cells, and seizures.

Y-linked disorders are caused by mutations found on the Y chromosome. Because females do not have Y chromosomes, they are not affected by these disorders. A male inherits the Y chromosome from his father. Therefore, if the father is affected, 100 percent of his sons and 0 percent of his daughters will be affected.

Male infertility can be caused by a Y-linked disorder in which portions of the Y chromosome are deleted. There are particular genes that, when deleted, have been found to contribute to male infertility. Y chromosome infertility can cause a partial defect in sperm production, low numbers of sperm which are motile, or a complete failure to produce sperm.

SEX-LINKED COLOR BLINDNESS

Red-green color-blindness is more common among males than females. What explains this statistic, given that red-green colorblindness is a recessive trait coded on the X chromosome?

**Inheritance of Red-Green Color Blindness:
an X-linked Recessive Trait**

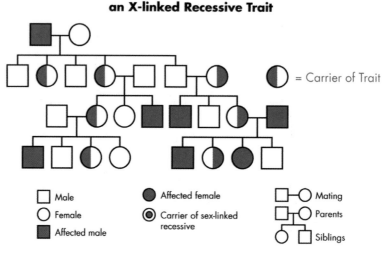

What Are the Uses, Benefits, and Risks of Genetic Testing and Gene Therapy?

Genetic Testing

Suppose a couple is thinking about having a child. The couple knows that there is a history of an autosomal recessive disease in both of their families. However, it is not known if either parent is a carrier of the diseased alleles. With this lack of knowledge, it is impossible to predict the probability that their future children will inherit the illness.

Fortunately, many types of **genetic testing** are now available that can determine whether or not individuals carry alleles for genetic diseases. For instance, the alleles for Tay-Sachs, sickle-cell, and cystic fibrosis can all be revealed with genetic tests. For Tay-Sach's disease, there are two common tests that can be done. One is an enzyme analysis. If the enzyme hexosaminidase A is found to be functioning at normal levels, the individual is probably not a carrier. In an alternative test, mutation analysis, scientists can test for genetic markers of the mutation in the person's genotype. In diseases where entire chromosomes are missing or deformed, it is relatively simple to look at the chromosomes of dividing cells. Gross abnormalities can typically be seen under a microscope.

It is also possible to test an unborn fetus for the presence of some disease-causing alleles. Amniocentesis and chorionic villus sampling are two methods during which samples are taken from different parts of the womb. The samples are then tested for markers of various genetic diseases. There are also tests for newborn babies that can screen for markers of some genetic illnesses such as PKU. It is important to remember that many genetic tests are not 100 percent accurate. Results can occasionally yield false information.

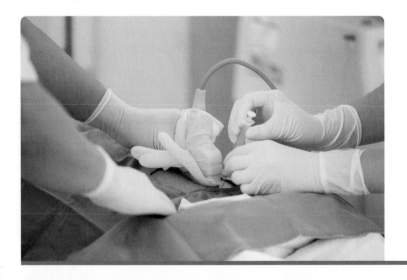

AMNIOCENTESIS TEST

Amniocentesis is one method of screening a fetus for genetic diseases. What are the benefits of this kind of test?

© Discovery Education | www.discoveryeducation.com • Image: Soda_O2 / Shutterstock.com

These technologies are very informative. However, they can also be very confusing to the general public. It can be extremely difficult for parents to make decisions about their unborn child based upon genetic testing. Trained genetic counselors are responsible for discussing the various benefits and drawbacks of genetic technologies with patients. They describe the risks and probabilities of having ill children. They also explain the consequences of caring for them. Individuals must decide for themselves whether to receive genetic counseling and how the test results will impact them.

Gene Therapy

Genetic testing reveals information about whether or not patients carry diseased alleles. Imagine the power of being able to actually replace a diseased allele within a person's **genome** with a normal allele. It may sound like science fiction, but gene therapy can do exactly that. Genetic therapy uses an experimental technique by replacing diseased genes with healthy ones, or inactivating or knocking out the diseased genes altogether.

Many diseases caused by single gene mutations can be treated with gene therapy. In order for gene therapy to work, the healthy gene must be inserted into diseased cells that will continue to multiply. As a result, the healthy gene will have a chance to propagate more and more cells.

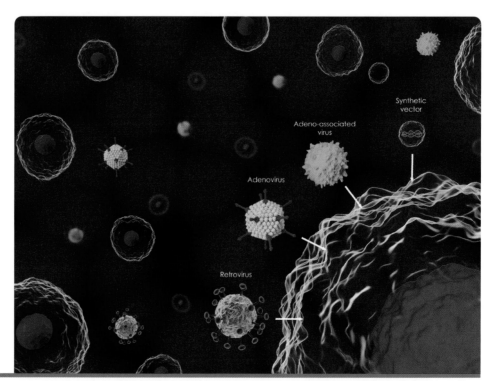

Synthetic vector

Adeno-associated virus

Adenovirus

Retrovirus

GENE THERAPY USING VIRUSES

Healthy genes can be inserted into cells using a genetically-engineered virus. What challenges might arise from this type of procedure?

Scientists can make use of viruses, rendered harmless, to carry the healthy allele into the DNA of diseased cells. These newly healthy cells then can be injected into the patient's tissue. Of course, there are still diseased cells in the tissue. However, the healthy injected cells can multiply and produce the healthy protein that is missing from the diseased tissue.

Gene therapy can involve the replacement of a mutated gene with a healthy one, the introduction of a healthy gene, or the deletion of a mutated gene. However, there are risks in gene therapy. For example, the healthy gene might accidently be inserted into the patient's DNA in a location where it interferes with another important gene. Furthermore, scientists must determine how a healthy inserted gene can be controlled to produce the correct amount of protein in the proper location.

The Human Genome Project

The Human Genome Project was an international research program aimed at creating a complete map and understanding of all the genes of human being—the complete human genome. The Human Genome Project has discovered that there about 20,500 human genes. It has also identified their nucleotide sequences and their locations on human chromosomes. The project has provided detailed information about the structure, organization and function of all human genes. This genetic information represents the instructions needed to build and maintain the entire body of a person.

The Human Genome Project was started in 1990 with funds provided by the United States government. However other countries and private organizations soon joined the effort. Thousands of scientists were involved. Improvements in the technologies of gene sequencing led to the project being completed well ahead of schedule. It took about ten years to get a rough draft of the human genome. By 2003, the sequencing was complete. The results of the project are used by scientists for continuing research and analysis. The results are available to anyone through the Internet. There is so much data that special computer programs have been developed to analyze it. Like the American space program, the Human Genome Project has produced many useful technological spin-offs.

The sequencing of the human genome has many benefits. The Human Genome Project can help us understand diseases, including identifying genes and mutations that cause cancer. The results can be used to help design better medicines. A more complete knowledge of the human genome can improve forensic investigation. It also has helped researchers in fields such as archaeology and human evolution. The project has provided techniques for the genome sequencing of numerous other organisms including pathogens, livestock, and crop plants. A multibillion dollar industry has built up around the discoveries and advances provided by the project.

Consider the Explain Question

| **Explain how a person's genes affect his or her health.**

Go online to complete the scientific explanation.

dlc.com/ca10086s

Check Your Understanding

| **What are the causes of single-gene disorders, chromosomal disorders, and multifactorial disorders?**

dlc.com/ca10087s

 **in Action**

Applying Genetic Disorders and Technology

How can gene therapy be used to treat or prevent genetic illnesses? What kinds of risks are involved?

What do you think of when you hear the term *gene therapy*? Gene therapy can involve replacing an abnormal or mutated gene that causes a disease with a healthy one, repairing a damaged gene, or altering a particular gene's function or deactivating it. There have been many recent advances in gene therapy techniques. Cells that have unhealthy genes can be extracted, altered to have the unhealthy genes replaced, grown in the laboratory, and then placed in an individual to replace cells with unhealthy genes. Sometimes an individual's genetic code can be stimulated to correct itself.

There are many important questions surrounding the use of gene therapy for the treatment of disease. What are potential negative consequences to changing an individual's genetics? What about changing the genetics of an entire population? What happens if gene therapy is performed on a gamete, or germ line, cell? We could theoretically eliminate certain disease-causing alleles permanently. Or we could add genes known for preventing disease into new generations. What are the limits of how we should manipulate human genetics? As these questions and more arise with advances in genetic engineering, there is a need for careful consideration about how this technology relates to human life.

Currently, some approaches to gene therapy are in the trial phase to treat certain types of cancer. Scientists are working hard to reduce the risks of gene therapy and improve its success.

STEM and Genetic Disorders and Technology

One successful technology for diagnosing genetic diseases involves testing for genetic markers of a mutated gene. A genetic marker is a DNA sequence with a specific known location on a chromosome. A genetic marker can help link agenetic disorder with the responsible gene, since DNA segments that are close to one another are usually inherited together. Scientists can identify inheritance patterns of nearby unidentified genes if they know their approximate location.

The majority of human DNA does not code for proteins. Some has a regulatory function that controls gene expression. Other parts appear to have no known function. These regions contain certain nucleotides that vary within the human population. These varying nucleotides are called polymorphisms. A polymorphism of only one nucleotide is called a single nucleotide polymorphism (SNP).

While researching genetic markers, scientists have found certain SNPs that are linked to diseased alleles in the human population. They may not be able to detect the diseased allele itself. However, if they detect the presence of the SNP, they can infer the presence of the diseased allele. The genes for many diseases, such as Huntington's disease, were first detected using this type of genetic marker.

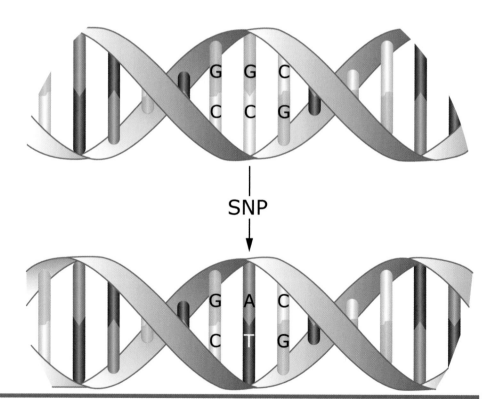

SINGLE NUCLEOTIDE POLYMORPHISM

A single nucleotide polymorphism (SNP) is a variation in only one nucleotide of a gene within a population. How are SNPs used to detect diseases?

Single base nucleotide variations are considered SNPs if they occur in greater than one percent of the population. For most SNPs discovered, there is only one variation at a specific location. Our differences in susceptibility to disease are linked to SNPs, and they serve as markers for disease-causing genes. Genetic variations are also related to how our body responds to treatment for disease and susceptibility to environmental factors. SNPs can be used to track the inheritance of disease genes within families. Future studies will work to identify SNPs associated with complex diseases such as heart disease, diabetes, and cancer.

An oncogenomist, an oncologist who applies technology to analyze a very large number of samples to characterize genes associated with cancer, may use a technique involving artificial neural networks, or ANN. The data collected help them make inferences about genetic diseases.

An ANN is a computer-based mathematical model that mimics the structure and function of neurons in the brain. Oncologists can artificially insert codes for SNPs to see how the neurons theoretically respond. Understanding how the brain responds to SNPs helps provide a better understanding of how and why the body is affected with what are often devastating symptoms.

These are examples of technologies that hold promise for new ways to treat and prevent many diseases. Instead of focusing on drugs and surgeries, we may consider altering our genetics.

The Chemistry of Life

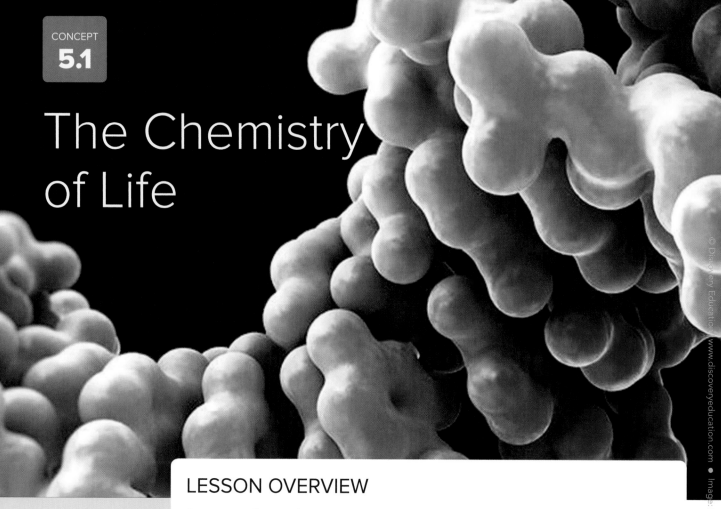

dlc.com/ca10088s

LESSON OVERVIEW

Lesson Questions

- What are the differences between inorganic and organic molecules?
- What are the characteristics of carbohydrates, lipids, proteins, and nucleic acids?
- What are the characteristics of enzymes?
- What is the role of adenosine triphosphate (ATP) in cells?

Key Vocabulary

Which terms do you already know?

- ☐ activation energy
- ☐ adenine
- ☐ adenosine triphosphate (ATP)
- ☐ amino acid
- ☐ carbohydrate
- ☐ catalyst
- ☐ cellular respiration
- ☐ chromosome
- ☐ coenzyme
- ☐ cytosine
- ☐ DNA
- ☐ enzyme
- ☐ fat
- ☐ fructose
- ☐ gene expression
- ☐ glucose
- ☐ glycolysis
- ☐ guanine

Lesson Objectives

By the end of the lesson, you should be able to:

- Distinguish between inorganic and organic molecules.
- Compare four main groups of organic molecules: carbohydrates, lipids, proteins, and nucleic acids.
- Relate the structure and diversity of enzymes to their biological functions.
- Summarize the role of adenosine triphosphate (ATP) in cells.
- Construct and revise evidence-based explanations for how carbon, hydrogen, and oxygen form amino acids and large organic molecules.

Key Vocabulary continued

- ☐ hormone
- ☐ inorganic molecule
- ☐ lactose
- ☐ lipid
- ☐ liquid
- ☐ methane
- ☐ nucleic acid
- ☐ organic molecule
- ☐ phospholipid bilayer (phospholipid membrane)
- ☐ photosynthesis
- ☐ polypeptide
- ☐ protein
- ☐ RNA
- ☐ saccharide
- ☐ starch
- ☐ steroid
- ☐ sterol
- ☐ substrate
- ☐ substrate (biochemistry)
- ☐ sucrose
- ☐ thymine

Assessing Carbon for Life

dlc.com/ca10089s

In science fiction movies, alien characters sometimes refer to people as "carbon-based life forms." Yes, you are a carbon-based life form. Life as we know it is built using carbon combined with other elements. Could non-carbon-based life forms exist?

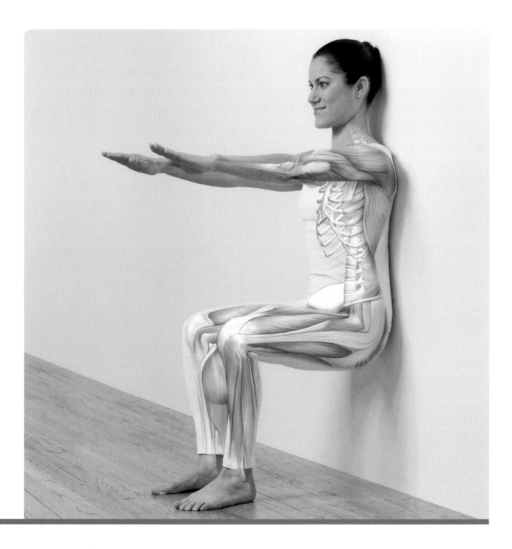

VERSATILITY OF CARBON

From the strength and hardness of bone, to the suppleness of skin, your body owes its form to the versatility of carbon bonding. What functional capabilities of living organisms are dependent on carbon bonds?

EXPLAIN QUESTION

What are some ways in which the structure of a compound influences its function?

What Are the Differences between Inorganic and Organic Molecules?

Organic Versus Inorganic Molecules

An **organic molecule** is a molecule that contains carbon atoms. Ethanol (C_2H_5OH) is an example of an organic molecule. The carbon atoms are bound to atoms of other elements, typically through covalent bonds. Commonly these elements include hydrogen. An **inorganic molecule** is generally a molecule that is not composed of carbon. Instead, they are composed of noncarbon elements. Water (H_2O) is an example of an inorganic molecule. Note that inorganic molecules are also called inorganic compounds when they contain two or more elements. All organic molecules are organic compounds, as they contain carbon and at least one other element. Furthermore, many inorganic molecules, such as carbon dioxide (CO_2), do contain carbon.

The arrangement of electrons within a carbon atom is unique, giving carbon the ability to bind to different atoms in a variety of ways. A carbon atom can also form bonds with other carbon atoms. This enables it to form complex structures such as rings and chains, which allows for a huge variety of organic compounds. This variety of organic compounds has enabled the complexity of chemical compounds and reactions that is life.

ORGANIC CONSTRUCTION

What is the value of multiple binding capabilities when thinking about living things?

© Discovery Education | www.discoveryeducation.com ● Image: Coneyl Jay / Stone / Getty Images

Some organic compounds are not directly associated with living things. However, living things have synthesized most of the organic molecules that exist on Earth today. Though living organisms naturally synthesize most organic compounds, scientists can also artificially synthesize many organic compounds in the lab.

Organic compounds exist as gases, liquids, and solids. **Methane** (CH_4) is an example of an organic gas. A common but very hazardous solvent, benzene (C_6H_6), is an example of an organic **liquid**. Sugars such as **glucose** ($C_6H_{12}O_6$) are organic solids.

CARBON JEWELRY

Diamonds are made up of carbon atoms joined together in a specific arrangement. Is diamond classified as organic or inorganic?

In nature, many things interact to form new products. Inorganic atoms and molecules react to form new substances. Organic molecules also undergo chemical reactions. Through complex chemical reactions that take place within organisms, they become rearranged into new substances that are essential for life on Earth. Living organisms can make organic compounds from inorganic ones. For example, plants use a complex series of chemical reactions called **photosynthesis** to make the organic compound glucose from the inorganic molecules carbon dioxide and water. Carbon dioxide and water are the reactants of this reaction. Glucose is the product. In a chemical equation, the reactants appear on the left of the equation. The products appear on the right. The overall chemical equation for photosynthesis is:

$$6CO_2 + 6H_2O + \text{light energy} \rightarrow C_6H_{12}O_6 + 6O_2$$

Most of the glucose that is produced during photosynthesis does not remain in the plant as glucose. Instead, minerals from the ground provide nitrogen, phosphorus, and sulfur that combine with the glucose to form other organic molecules such as carbohydrates, amino acids (the building blocks of proteins), **lipids**, and **nucleic acids**.

A process that is the reverse of photosynthesis also occurs. In **cellular respiration**, organisms turn glucose into the inorganic substances carbon dioxide and water.

$$C_6H_{12}O_6 + 6O_2 \rightarrow 6CO_2 + 6H_2O + Energy$$

In this case, the reactants are glucose and oxygen on the left and the products are the carbon dioxide, water, and energy on the right.

What Are the Characteristics of Carbohydrates, Lipids, Proteins, and Nucleic Acids?

Carbohydrates

All living things are made up of cells, which contain water plus the four main types of organic molecules: carbohydrates, lipids, proteins, and nucleic acids. These organic molecules are essential components of life.

Carbohydrates consist of the elements carbon, hydrogen, and oxygen. These molecules serve many functions in living things, including storing energy used by cells. Carbohydrates are also an important structural component of living things. Cellulose is a **carbohydrate** that gives plants their structure; chitin is a carbohydrate that makes up the exoskeleton of insects.

COMMON CARBOHYDRATES

Breads and pastas are carbohydrates commonly consumed by people. What chemical feature of carbohydrates makes them a necessary food?

Simple carbohydrates are known as sugars, and the simplest form of sugar is called a monosaccharide. Monosaccharides are single basic sugar units. One example of a monosaccharide is **glucose**. Disaccharides such as table sugar (**sucrose**) and milk sugar (**lactose**) are two units of sugar (two monosaccharides) combined. For example, sucrose is the combination of the monosaccharides glucose and **fructose**.

More complex carbohydrates contain many sugar units and are known as oligosaccharides and polysaccharides. **Starch** and glycogen are two examples of polysaccharides.

When sugars form, carbon atoms create a chain to which hydrogen and oxygen atoms attach. The type of sugar that forms depends on two things: the number of hydrogen and oxygen atoms that attach and where they attach. Other elements, such as nitrogen or phosphorus, can also combine with the carbon chain and form different organic molecules. Large carbon-based structures such as lipids, proteins, and nucleic acids can result, which are necessary for life.

Lipids

Lipids are another important type of organic molecule found in living organisms. Like carbohydrates, lipids are made up of carbon, hydrogen, and oxygen. Lipids serve many functions inside living things. They include fats, phospholipids, **sterols**, triglycerides, and more. Unlike sugars, lipids are hydrophobic, meaning that they do not dissolve well in water. Fatty acids are one of the simplest and most basic types of lipids. They sometimes serve as building blocks for more complex lipids.

Triglycerides are a primary component of human **fat** tissue (called adipose tissue). Triglycerides are important energy storage molecules. They can be broken down into carbon dioxide and water to yield a great deal of energy. Adipose tissue containing triglycerides is also important for insulation and protective cushioning. Lipids contain more energy per unit mass than carbohydrates.

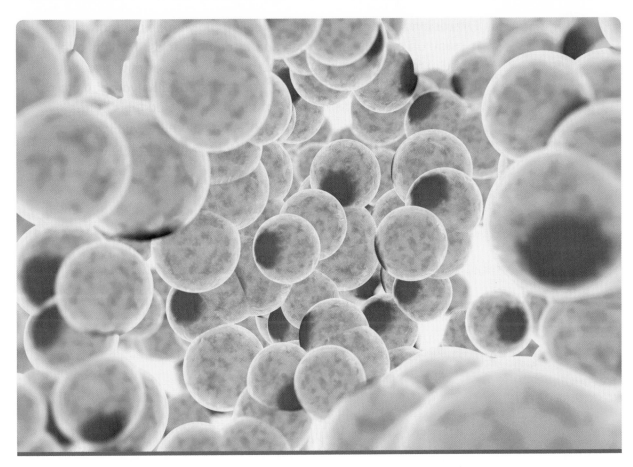

Phospholipids comprise the membranes of all cells. Most phospholipids contain a diglyceride combined with a phosphate group, and an organic molecule such as choline. These molecules form the **phospholipid bilayer membrane** that, with the help of proteins, controls the entry and exit of substances into the cell.

Steroids are a group of lipids that contain four cycloalkane rings joined to each other. The most important group of steroids is the sterols. Sterols include cholesterol and many **hormones** such as estrogen and testosterone. Hormones serve a major role in cell signaling and communication.

ADIPOSE TISSUE

Adipose tissue is made up of specialized cells that consist mostly of a lipid droplet. What are the functions of adipose tissue in the human body?

Fats belong to the group of lipids called triglycerides. A triglyceride is made up of a glycerol group and three fatty acids. The fats often found in foods, such as butter and oil, are examples of triglycerides. Triglycerides with fatty acids that are saturated with hydrogen atoms are called saturated fats. An example of a saturated fat is butter. Vegetable oils, on the other hand, are not saturated with hydrogen atoms. These oils are called unsaturated fats and are healthier than saturated fats.

Saturated

Unsaturated

MOLECULAR STRUCTURE OF FATS

Unsaturated fats are structurally different from saturated fats. How does this structural difference explain why saturated fats are less healthy?

Proteins

Proteins are perhaps the most diverse group of major organic molecules. All proteins are made up of building block molecules called amino acids. There are 20 naturally occurring amino acids. Amino acids, like carbohydrates and lipids, contain carbon, hydrogen, and oxygen. They also contain nitrogen.

A **protein** is a collection of multiple amino acids bonded together in a chain. Living cells take in amino acids and use them to make their own proteins. Proteins vary in size, from tens to thousands of amino acids. They carry out countless functions within all living cells. The sequence of amino acids determines the shape and structure of the protein, which in turn determines the function it will have.

Some proteins serve as channels through which charged molecules and other materials can pass in and out of cells. Other proteins make up the muscle fibers we need for movement. Proteins are also used for transporting materials within cells. Structural proteins give cells their shape. A special class of proteins called enzymes are involved in chemical reactions.

Nucleic Acids

Nucleic acids are a group of organic molecules that serve as the information carriers for living cells. **DNA** and **RNA** are types of nucleic acids and are the blueprints for all of life. As with carbohydrates and proteins, nucleic acids are made up of many subunits. Any kind of repeating molecular subunit is called a monomer. A molecule of many monomers put together is called a polymer.

In the case of nucleic acids, the monomers are called nucleotides. A single nucleotide is made up of a simple sugar molecule (either ribose or deoxyribose) plus a phosphate group and another molecular group called a "base," which contains a ring-shaped organic structure including nitrogen and carbon in the ring. The difference between ribose and deoxyribose is the presence or absence of a hydroxyl (−OH) group attached to a particular carbon of the sugar. Together, many nucleotides make up large polymers. Polymers of ribonucleotides are RNA molecules. Polymers of deoxyribonucleotides are DNA molecules.

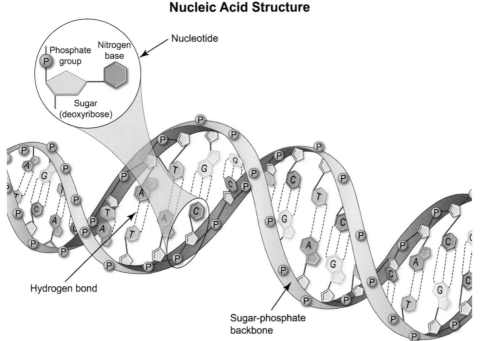

Nucleic Acid Structure

Nucleotide

Phosphate group

Nitrogen base

Sugar (deoxyribose)

Hydrogen bond

Sugar-phosphate backbone

DNA STRUCTURE

Many nucleotides bind together to form a nucleic acid such as DNA, which twists and winds into a helical structure. How is DNA packaged so that the 3 meters of DNA in a human cell fit into a nucleus?

The four types of deoxyribonucleotides that make up DNA each contain a different nitrogenous base: **adenine**, **guanine**, **cytosine**, or **thymine**. In RNA, the four types of ribonucleotides contain the bases: adenine, guanine, cytosine, or uracil. Adenine and guanine are both purines, which form flat structures containing two rings. Cytosine, thymine, and uracil are pyrimidines that form single flat rings.

DNA in cells is made up of two strands of deoxyribonucleotides that wrap around each other, so it is called doublestranded. If the two DNA strands are separated from each other and stretched out, each DNA molecule begins with a 5´ phosphate-containing end and ends with a 3´ hydroxyl-containing end. However, the two DNA strands are not identical. They interact with each other while lined up in opposite directions, so the 5´ end of one DNA strand is lined up with the 3´ end of the second DNA strand, and vice versa; this arrangement is called antiparallel.

Plus, the sequence of nucleotides in each strand is not the same, but instead complementary. This means that if the two DNA molecules are stretched out and stacked on top of each other but in opposite (antiparallel) directions, where there is an adenine-containing nucleotide in one DNA strand, there is a thymine-containing nucleotide in the complementary strand; where there is a guanine-containing nucleotide in one, there is a cytosine-containing nucleotide in the other. In fact, the two DNA strands that make up double-stranded DNA interact with each other and are held together by the force of the hydrogen bonds of these G-C base pairs and A-T base pairs. The two DNA strands twist around each other to form a helical structure like a twisted ladder. Since the pairs of bases are flat, they form the rungs of the ladder. The two DNA strands each contribute a backbone of alternating sugar and phosphate groups to the two opposite sides of the ladder.

BASE PAIRS

In double-stranded DNA, an adenine-containing nucleotide always pairs with a thymine-containing nucleotide. What does a guanine-containing nucleotide always pair with?

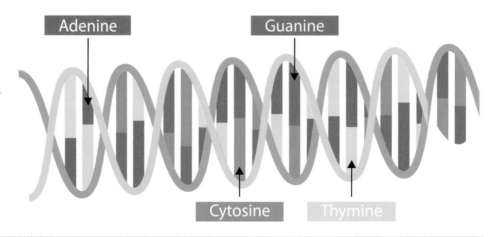

RNA is made up of a single strand of ribonucleotides. Although RNA is singlestranded, some RNA molecules can form a folded structures due to G-C and A-U base pairs within itself. Folded RNA molecules perform various functions like catalyzing reactions and transporting molecules.

Within cells, the helical double-stranded DNA is then coiled around specific DNA-binding proteins into structures that are again folded several times over to form chromosomes. A particular section of DNA that codes for an end product is called a gene. Genes store information in the particular order, or sequence, of the four types of nucleotides that make up DNA. Genes store the information for the cell to make gene products. The final products of some genes are RNA. The final products of many other genes are proteins. In most cases, the particular sequence of nucleotides in a gene includes instructions for the synthesis of a particular protein (after the gene is first copied into RNA), including the number and order of the protein's amino acids. Thus, a single protein-coding gene is a "recipe" for a specific protein. Essentially, the purpose of DNA is to code for all the proteins and RNAs that an organism needs.

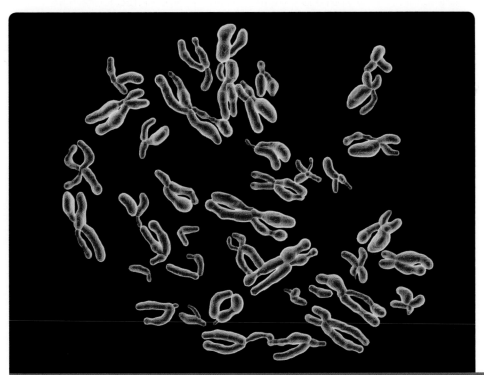

CHROMOSOMES

Chromosomes are found inside every cell of every organism. What is their function?

What Are the Characteristics of Enzymes?

Enzymes

Enzymes are biological **catalysts** that speed up biochemical reactions. Most enzymes are proteins, but some are made of RNA. Catalysts make chemical reactions take place at faster rates than they would without the **enzyme**.

There are hundreds of different kinds of enzymes. Enzymes are specific to a chemical reaction or group of chemical reactions. Different enzymes are responsible for each step of metabolism. For example, there are 10 distinct steps involved in the **glycolysis** of glucose to pyruvate, each step catalyzed by its own dedicated enzyme. The **amino acid** chain of each enzyme is different. Each is folded into its own unique shape. The composition and shape of each enzyme determine its activity.

The reactants of an enzymatic reaction are called substrates. The substrates bind to the enzyme, which provides a shaped spot for the substrates to fit into. This spot is called the active site of the enzyme. This can be thought of as being like a key that perfectly fits a lock. This model of enzyme action is sometimes referred to as the "lock and key" model. For this reason, an enzyme makes it easier for the reaction to occur by bringing the reactants together in just the right way to promote the reaction. In reactions during which a **substrate** is broken down into multiple products, the enzyme helps the substrate break apart. The enzyme might do this by helping to weaken certain bonds. Once the reaction is complete, the enzyme releases the products and can then repeat the process on a new set of reactants.

An important thing to remember is that an enzyme alone will not make a reaction occur. Enzymes simply make it easier for reactions to occur, dramatically speeding them up. Scientists have discovered that some reactions that take milliseconds with an enzyme would take millions of years for the products of that reaction to reach equilibrium on their own. By adding an enzyme into the reaction, the reactants might reach equilibrium with their products in less than a second. In fact, some enzymes speed up reactions many billions of times! Like all catalysts, enzymes speed up reactions by lowering the amount of energy needed to get them going. They lower the **activation energy** required for the reaction.

Enzyme action is impacted by factors that include substrate concentration, temperature, and pH. Most enzymes will only work in a narrow range of temperature or pH. Some enzymes require the presence of other substances in order to work. These substances are called cofactors or **coenzymes**. Cofactors are inorganic substances. For example, some metal ions, such as zinc or iron, are often important cofactors. Some enzymes required for aerobic cellular respiration have iron/sulfur cofactors that help the enzyme carry electrons during redox reactions. Coenzymes are usually nonprotein organic chemicals. Many vitamins are coenzymes. The presence of other chemicals also affects enzyme activity. Some chemicals may compete for or bind to the active site of an enzyme. This can inhibit or prevent the action of the enzyme.

The importance of enzymes for all biological processes cannot be overstated. Enzymes catalyze all the steps of metabolism including glycolysis, respiration, and photosynthesis. They also catalyze the biosynthesis of macromolecules within cells. There is a unique enzyme for each step. Sometimes there are slightly different versions of the same enzyme, for example, one that works with high oxygen and the other under low-oxygen conditions. Enzymes are also involved in the extracellular digestion of food in the digestive tracts of animals. Other enzymes break down cellular waste, bacteria, harmful chemicals, and toxins.

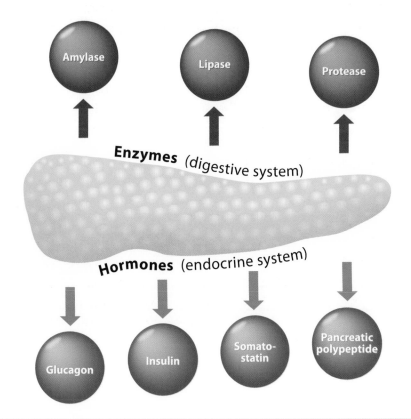

PANCREAS

The pancreas is an organ that produces hormones and digestive enzymes. What would a digestive enzyme do in the body?

What Is the Role of Adenosine Triphosphate (ATP) in Cells?

The Role of Adenosine Triphosphate (ATP)

Adenosine triphosphate (ATP) is the energy currency of living cells. Energy released when molecules of ATP react provides the energy for many chemical reactions. Such reactions enable substances to be transported within and between cells, proteins to perform their functions, and muscle cells to contract and produce movement.

A molecule of ATP is similar to a nucleotide. However, a molecule of ATP contains three phosphate groups instead of one. Therefore, a sugar group, a nitrogen-containing base group, and three phosphate groups combine to make ATP.

The bonds between the phosphate groups are involved in energy release. When one phosphate group is removed from ATP, energy is released. The resulting molecule is called ADP, or adenosine diphosphate, which has only two phosphate groups. Some free energy is again required to convert ADP back to ATP with the addition of a phosphate group.

ENERGY FROM ATP

Energy is released when the bond between the second and third phosphate group of ATP is broken. How is ATP regenerated after its conversion to ADP?

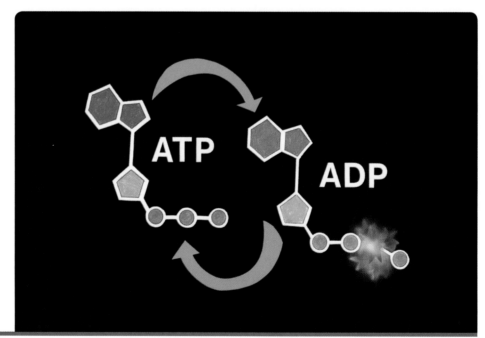

Chemical reactions may be energy releasing (exergonic) or energy requiring (endergonic). Enzymes will catalyze either type of reaction. However, endergonic reactions require energy input regardless of whether an enzyme is present or not. This input of energy usually comes from ATP. Breaking the third phosphate off of ATP releases the energy needed to make an endergonic reaction occur.

A common endergonic reaction that requires ATP is the synthesis of larger molecules from smaller subunits. An example of this is the formation of proteins from amino acids. This process requires ATP to add each new amino acid to the chain.

Another example of ATP's role in cellular processes is the maintenance of cell structure. ATP is necessary for putting together and taking apart cytoskeletal components that give cells their structure.

Consider the Explain Question

What are some ways in which the structure of a compound influences its function?

Go online to complete the scientific explanation.

dlc.com/ca10090s

Check Your Understanding

Can you describe the four main macromolecules of life?

dlc.com/ca10091s

STEM in Action

Applying Chemistry of Life

Enzymes are indispensable to living organisms. Enzymes at work in your cells make the variety of chemical reactions necessary for life processes possible. A particular group of enzymes have also revolutionized two fields of science: molecular biology and genetics. These enzymes are called restriction enzymes, and they make it possible to analyze and manipulate DNA.

Restriction enzymes were isolated from bacteria beginning in the late 1960s. They are thought to have evolved as a mechanism of bacterial defense against viruses. Like all enzymes, restriction enzymes catalyze certain chemical reactions. Specifically, they catalyze the breaking of bonds between nucleotides within a DNA molecule. Each restriction **enzyme** cleaves DNA at a specific location within a unique 4-8 base pair sequence. To date, over 4,000 restriction enzymes that recognize over 360 different DNA sequences have been isolated.

Why are restriction enzymes so useful for scientists? Even a small genome is made up of millions of bases, and the human genome is three billion base pairs. The ability to break up DNA into smaller pieces means it can be studied more easily. The sequences of these smaller pieces can be determined and manipulated. There are potential applications for this technology in a variety of different fields from medicine to agriculture.

Restriction enzymes were used to sequence the entire human genome, a feat that took 13 years and 2.7 billion dollars. Individual differences in DNA sequences, called polymorphisms, have allowed researchers to learn a great deal about genetic diseases. Currently, restriction enzymes are being used to study how factors such as nutrition and environmental exposure to chemicals alter **gene expression**, a field called epigenetics.

Restriction enzymes are also critical tools for genetic engineering. Genetic engineering, also called recombinant DNA technology, refers to the human manipulation of a living organism's genetic makeup. This technology has created new ways of producing medications and vaccines. Application of gene manipulations is behind the creation of genetically modified organisms, such as corn, that are intended to increase the efficiency of agriculture. Recombinant DNA technology also has the potential to provide a cure for genetic diseases through an exciting technique called gene therapy, wherein a healthy gene would be isolated and inserted into the DNA of a patient who has an unhealthy version of that gene.

GENETIC ENGINEERING

Genetic engineering has been used to add traits to agricultural crops. What kinds of traits would help to improve an agricultural crop?

GLOWING FISH

These fish are currently the only genetically modified animals licensed for release to the public. What features of a plant or animal do you think should be targeted?

What purpose for genetic engineering can you imagine? The growth of molecular biology research and applications in the last two decades has been staggering, all stemming from the discovery of restriction enzymes from bacteria.

STEM and Chemistry of Life

Do you know what a protein actually looks like? Most people are only familiar with proteins as the globular shapes drawn in their science books. What if you could see a protein from the inside out? Biochemist James Hinton has made it possible through the use of virtual reality.

Why would the ability to see a protein aid biochemists? Remember how closely structure and function of proteins are related. The ability to see the structural components of a protein, and how they interact with other molecules, would be helpful in determining their function. Some biophysical chemists do not stop at identifying function; they want to be able to change certain characteristics of proteins.

Researchers are interested in developing new or better drugs and vaccines for a variety of diseases. There are a variety of constraints for the successful development of a drug. Drugs must fit into the binding pocket of the target protein, but also must be absorbed and transported to the right location in the body. Additionally, it is also desirable that drugs are stable, nontoxic, and free of side effects.

Before the advent of protein structure identification techniques, new drugs were discovered or altered by the trial and error modification of compounds with known biological activity. This method was very time consuming and expensive. The ability to determine the structure of proteins has greatly changed the drug development process. Ultimately this may result in more drugs for devastating illnesses.

Cell Structure and Function

LESSON OVERVIEW

Lesson Questions

- What are the three parts of the cell theory?
- What are the differences between prokaryotic and eukaryotic cells?
- What structures make up cells?
- What are the differences between plant and animal cells?
- What is the role of mitochondria in eukaryotic cells?
- What is the structure and function of the cell membrane?

Lesson Objectives

By the end of the lesson, you should be able to:

- Describe cell theory.
- Distinguish between prokaryotic and eukaryotic cells.
- Distinguish between plant and animal cells.
- Identify subcellular structures, including organelles and cytoskeletal components.
- Discuss the mitochondrion's importance in eukaryotic cells.
- Identify the structure and properties of the cell membrane.

Key Vocabulary

Which terms do you already know?

- [ ] animal cell
- [ ] cell membrane
- [ ] cell theory
- [ ] cellulose
- [ ] chromatin
- [ ] cytoskeleton
- [ ] cytosol
- [ ] eukaryotic cell
- [ ] ion channel
- [ ] ion pump
- [ ] mitochondria
- [ ] nucleus (cell)
- [ ] organelle
- [ ] phospholipid bilayer (phospholipid membrane)
- [ ] plant cell
- [ ] prokaryotic cell
- [ ] ribosome

dlc.com/ca10092s

Grizzly Fat Cells

dlc.com/ca10093s

A grizzly bear, like many other animals, prepares to hibernate in late fall. Unlike you and other humans, the bear will not eat or drink anything for a few months, so it must have a sufficient amount of energy stored up so that it can survive. How is it able to survive for this time period with no food or water?

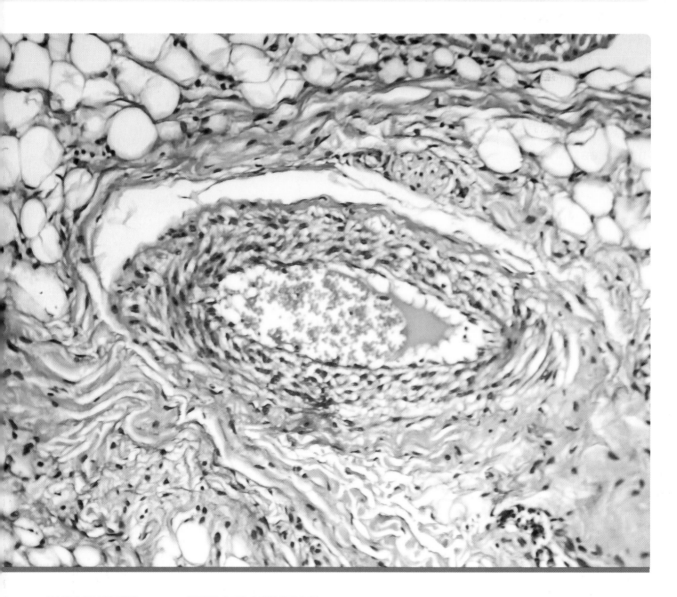

ADIPOSE TISSUE UNDER THE MICROSCOPE

How can a grizzly bear survive through a long winter?

EXPLAIN QUESTION

What kind of structures must a cell have that would be analogous to a modern business?

What Are the Three Parts of the Cell Theory?

The Cell Theory

Cells were discovered in 1665 when a scientist, Robert Hooke, observed cork through a microscope. As he examined the cork, he saw tiny sections that looked like small rooms, or cells. To this day we use the term *cell* to refer to these basic units of life. Other scientists went on to study living cells and to improve the microscope so that cells could be more closely examined. Based on their work, the concepts underlying **cell theory** were developed. Cell theory has three main parts:

- All living things are made of one or more cells.
- The cell is the basic unit of structure, physiology, organization, and function in living things.
- Every cell arises from a preexisting cell.

Living Things Are Made of Cells

Although organisms vary widely in their appearance, all living things are composed of one or more cells. These cells are the basic units, or building blocks, of life on Earth. Just as building blocks can be used to create many different structures from cars to castles, cells are units that form many different living things. Most cells are very small. The unaided human eye can see objects that are about 0.1 mm long; therefore, you may be able to see larger cells, like a human egg. To see smaller cells, you will need a microscope. Generally, plant and **animal cells** are between 0.1 and 0.005 mm long. Bacterial cells are usually smaller and *Mycoplasma spp* are known to be the smallest cells. Some cells are unusually large, like an ostrich egg cell.

OSTRICH EGG

An unfertilized ostrich egg is considered the world's largest cell. Why would this cell need to be so large?

Cells Are Basic Units of Life

The structure and physiology, or function, of living things can be analyzed at the cellular level. The different types of cells in an organism determine how the organism as a whole appears and behaves. Although the various cells carry out different tasks, the cells within an organism do not function independently. Cells are organized into tissues. Tissues are groups of cells that work together for a particular purpose. Different tissues are organized into larger components—the organs—and many of these organs function together as organ systems. Humans have many different organ systems, including the circulatory, respiratory, and nervous systems. Together these systems regulate how the body functions and responds to its environment.

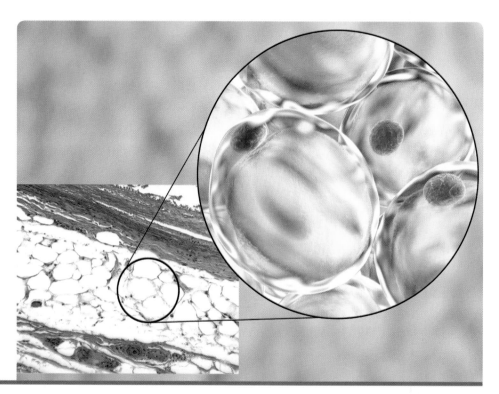

ADIPOSE TISSUE

Adipose tissue is made of the same type of cells that together store fat. Where do you think these cells are found in the human body?

Cells Arise from Preexisting Cells

All cells arise from preexisting cells. For unicellular (or one-celled) organisms, the production of a new cell results in a new organism or its progeny. For example, bacterial cell division results in an increase of the single-celled population. In multicellular organisms however, new cells increase the size of tissues and replace old or damaged cells. The process of making new cells (regeneration) allows organisms to grow and to recover from sickness and injuries by the formation of new cells and tissues. Studying this process helps doctors and scientists understand how organisms develop and how to treat damage or disease.

What Are the Differences between Prokaryotic and Eukaryotic Cells?

Prokaryotic and Eukaryotic Cells

Cells are categorized as either prokaryotic or eukaryotic. Prokaryotic cells without nuclei are found in bacteria and in archaea. Most multicellular organisms have eukaryotic cells. The root of these terms, *karyose*, comes from the Greek word for "kernel." In biology, this root refers to the **nucleus** of a cell, which is the cellular structure containing genetic material, or DNA. One of the main differences between prokaryotic cells and eukaryotic cells relates to the nucleus.

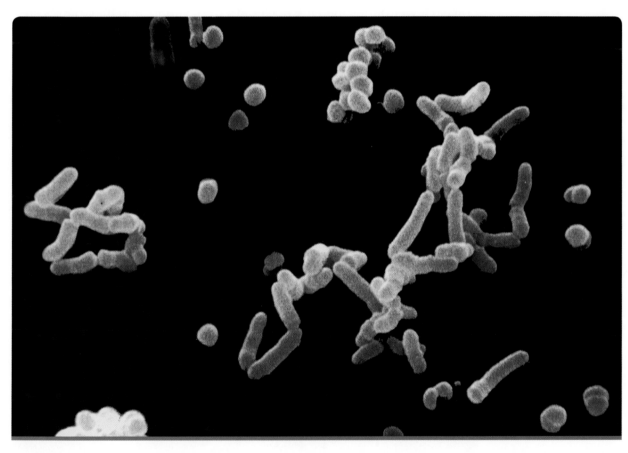

A **prokaryotic cell** lacks a membrane-bound nucleus. In contrast, a **eukaryotic cell** has a distinct membrane-bound nucleus. This nucleus contains linear strands of DNA. In prokaryotic cells the DNA is not enclosed and usually is organized as a circular **chromosome**. Furthermore, prokaryotic cells lack other membrane-bound organelles. Eukaryotic cells contain well-defined organelles that are enclosed in membranes.

BACTERIA

Bacteria are microscopic and unicellular, and some can cause disease in humans. What are some bacterial diseases?

What Structures Make Up Cells?

Components of Prokaryotic Cells

The prokaryotic cells of bacteria and archaea have simple organization and lack membrane-bound organelles, but they have distinct components that carry out important functions within the cell. In prokaryotic cells, DNA is coiled up in a region within the cytoplasm called the nucleoid. This DNA usually consists of a single, circular chromosome. Unlike the nucleus of eukaryotic cells, a membrane does not enclose the nucleoid. Prokaryotic DNA is in direct contact with the cytoplasm, a gel-like component that contains subcellular structures. Prokaryotic cells may also contain plasmids, which are relatively small, circular DNA molecules. Plasmids contain fewer genes than the nucleoid's DNA strand, and their genes are not needed for normal cell functions. However, plasmids confer useful properties, such as antibiotic resistance in some bacteria. Structures called **ribosomes** are also found in prokaryotic cells. Ribosomes are small bodies within the cell. Ribosomes are involved in protein synthesis. In prokaryotic cells, the ribosomes are suspended in the cytoplasm.

Prokaryotic cells are enclosed by a **cell membrane**. The cell membrane serves as a barrier to unwanted chemicals and allows cells to recognize one another. A key function of the cell membrane is to control which substances move into and out of the cell. Photosynthetic prokaryotic cells may also have inner membranes called thylakoids, which facilitate photosynthesis. Outside the cell membrane, most prokaryotic cells have a cell wall that protects the cell and gives it a specific shape. Some bacteria have an outer covering called a capsule. The capsule is a hard coat that retains moisture and prevents the bacteria from being engulfed and destroyed by other cells.

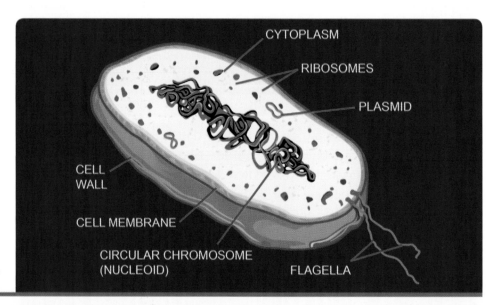

BACTERIAL CELL

This bacterial cell has a nucleoid that is not surrounded by a membrane. What is the purpose of the nucleoid?

CYTOPLASM
RIBOSOMES
PLASMID
CELL WALL
CELL MEMBRANE
CIRCULAR CHROMOSOME (NUCLEOID)
FLAGELLA

Components of Eukaryotic Cells

Eukaryotic cells are larger and more complex than prokaryotic cells and are found in plants, animals, fungi, and protists. The membrane-bound subcellular structures in eukaryotic cells are highly specialized and called organelles. These subcellular structures are present in the cytoplasm or **cytosol**. The membrane surrounding an **organelle** isolates it from rest of the cellular components, thereby allowing it to carry out specific functions. A cell or plasma membrane also encloses the entire cell, containing the cytoplasm and separating the cell from its environment. Some eukaryotic cells also have a tough cell wall surrounding the cell membrane.

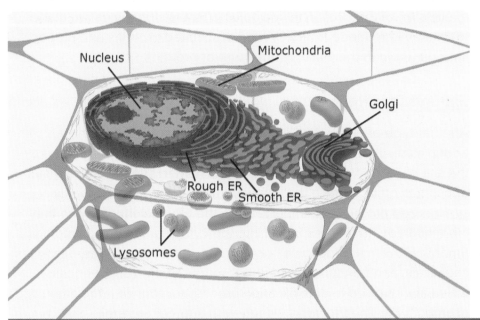

ANIMAL CELL

Animal cells, like other eukaryotic cells, have subcellular parts called organelles. How would you describe the structure of the different organelles?

Nucleus

Not all eukaryotic cells are the same, but they do share many of the same organelles. One organelle that is present in all eukaryotic cells is the nucleus. Most of the cell's genetic information, in the form of deoxyribonucleic acid (DNA), resides within the nucleus. Like other organelles, a membrane encloses the nucleus. It serves as the control center of the cell, carrying genetic material and instructions for making proteins and other important molecules.

The nucleus can occupy up to 20 percent of the volume of a typical **eukaryotic cell**. The nucleus is surrounded by a double-layered membrane called the nuclear envelope. This membrane is connected to the endoplasmic reticulum. The membrane has tiny nuclear pores. Nuclear pores provide a route for the movement of large molecules, like proteins and RNA, into and out of the nucleus. Most of the cell's DNA is found inside the nucleus. The DNA is organized on structures called chromosomes. Chromosomes consist of DNA, proteins, and some RNA. This granular complex is called **chromatin**. The nucleus also contains filaments that organize its contents. A spherical structure, called the nucleolus, can be seen inside the nucleus. The nucleolus is rich in ribonucleic acid (RNA).

The functions of the nucleus include the organization, protection, and expression of the DNA. The nucleolus is where ribosomes are made. Ribosomes are made from RNA and associated proteins and play an important role in the cell's manufacture of proteins.

Endoplasmic Reticulum

Another type of organelle found in most eukaryotic cells is the endoplasmic reticulum (ER). There are two kinds of ER: rough ER is the site of protein synthesis. Rough ER is named such because it has ribosomes on its surface that manufacture proteins. These newly synthesized proteins are imported into the ER machinery where they are modified and then exported into the cytoplasm or cell membrane. Smooth ER with no ribosomes on its surface produces lipids, detoxifies chemicals, and transports materials throughout the cell. Liver cells, which are involved in detoxification processes, contain large amounts of smooth ER. The ER works closely with another organelle called the Golgi apparatus, or Golgi body. The Golgi apparatus modifies and packages proteins from the ER and sends them to other parts of the cell. Proteins processed by the Golgi apparatus may be transported to the cell membrane to be released from the cell.

Other Organelles

Other structures found in eukaryotic cells include **mitochondria**, lysosomes, vacuoles, and chloroplasts.

- Mitochondria are oblong or ovoid organelles that serve as the power packs of the cell. The mitochondria convert chemical energy obtained from food into energy-rich compounds, which are released as the cell's stored energy.
- Lysosomes are structures that contain digestive enzymes. These enzymes break down food like lipids, carbohydrates, proteins, and waste material into simpler molecules.

- Vacuoles are fluid-filled, sac-like structures enclosed within a membrane. Some eukaryotic cells store nutrients, water, and waste products in vacuoles. The size and function of vacuoles differ for plant cells and animal cells. Plant cells have big vacuoles that help support its structures and help maintain the cell's homeostasis.
- Chloroplasts, found in some plant cells, contain the green pigment, chlorophyll. These organelles produce sugars and starches via the process of photosynthesis.
- Centrosomes are small cylindrical structures found in animal cells. They are involved in the regulation of cell division.
- Peroxisomes are small, membrane-enclosed organelles. They contain enzymes involved in metabolic reactions, like the breakdown of long-chain fatty acids.

The Cytoskeleton

Both prokaryotic and eukaryotic cells have an internal system of network fibers called a **cytoskeleton**. The cytoskeleton helps the cell maintain its shape and helps to transport materials. It is also important for cell division.

The cytoskeleton of eukaryotic cells is comprised of three types of protein fibers: microfilaments, intermediate filaments, and microtubules. Microfilaments, which are the thinnest of these structures, function in cellular movements, such as gliding and contracting, as seen in amoeba when they crawl on surfaces. Intermediate filaments provide mechanical support and are also involved in cell adhesion—sticking the cells to other cells and surfaces. Microtubules are hollow tubes that maintain cell shape and provide connections to transport organelles and large molecules within the cell. Microtubules also play an important role in cell division.

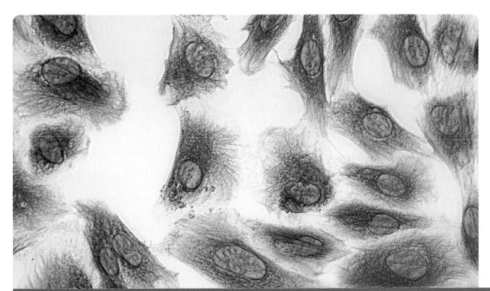

MICROTUBULES

Microtubules, shown in brown, are an important part of a cell's cytoskeleton. What is the function of the cytoskeleton?

Cilia and Flagella

Some cells have organelles that extend from the main body of the cell. There are two main types—cilia and flagella. Cilia can be used for moving the cell, for moving substances outside the cell, or can be used as sensory devices. Those cilia that move cells are usually present in large numbers. Some small organisms use them to move around. Most of these belong to a group of protists called the ciliates. Multicellular eukaryotes use cilia in large numbers. The cilia of adjacent cells often work together. For example, cells lining the windpipe use cilia to sweep mucus and dirt away from the lungs. Other cilia are adapted to sense the environment around the cell.

Flagella, on the other hand, are longer than cilia. They are usually present in fewer numbers. They have a whip-like movement that can propel a cell along. They are mostly found in protists and simple organisms, like sponges.

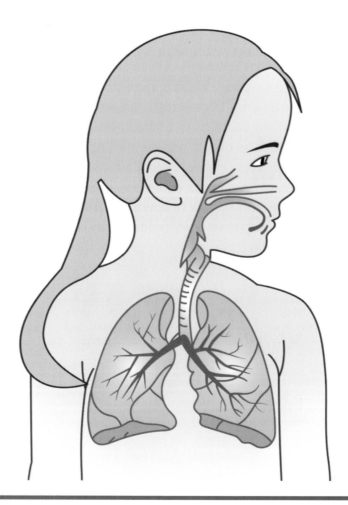

CILIA

Cilia are in the trachea, or windpipe of humans. What is their function?

What Are the Differences between Plant and Animal Cells?

Plant and Animal Cells

Plants and animals are both composed of eukaryotic cells, but their cellular structures differ in important ways. Plant cells have cell walls, while animal cells do not. The **plant cell** wall is made of **cellulose**. The cellulose is organized in a matrix comprising a tough outer layer that supports the plant and allows pressure from liquid to build up inside the cell. The cell wall also provides protection against mechanical damage. Small holes in the cell wall allow materials to enter and to leave the cell. The cell wall makes plant cells rigid, preventing free movement of the cell within plant tissue. In contrast, many animal cells can move freely within an organism.

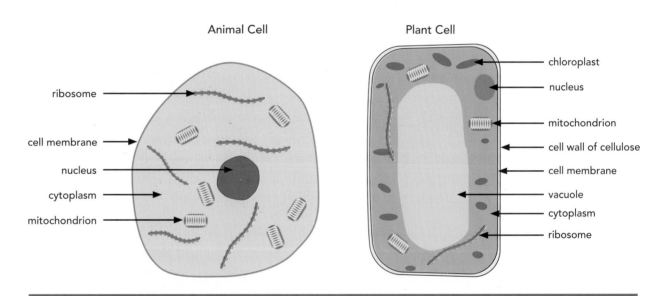

Animal Cell

- ribosome
- cell membrane
- nucleus
- cytoplasm
- mitochondrion

Plant Cell

- chloroplast
- nucleus
- mitochondrion
- cell wall of cellulose
- cell membrane
- vacuole
- cytoplasm
- ribosome

Chloroplasts are found in most plant cells and in some protists but not in animal cells. Chloroplasts allow plants and certain protists to make their own food through photosynthesis. During photosynthesis, chloroplasts use the energy in sunlight to drive a chemical reaction between carbon dioxide and water. This chemical reaction produces oxygen and sugars. The sugars serve as food for the plant.

PLANT CELLS AND ANIMAL CELLS

Although plant cells and animal cells have some organelles in common, they also are quite different. What are some of the structural differences between plant cells and animal cells?

Plant and animal cells differ in the size and function of their vacuoles. Plant cells typically have a single, large vacuole, while some protists and animal cells have smaller, often multiple, vacuoles. In both plant and animal cells, vacuoles store nutrients and waste. Vacuoles in plant cells have the additional function of maintaining pressure against the cell wall. This pressure helps keep the plant upright. The amount of water available to the plant affects the degree to which vacuoles maintain pressure. A shortage of water causes vacuoles to shrink. This, in turn, causes the plant to wilt. When more water becomes available, vacuoles expand and the plant stands upright again.

What Is the Role of Mitochondria in Eukaryotic Cells?

Structure of Mitochondria

Mitochondria are specialized organelles found in eukaryotic cells. The number of mitochondria in cells varies. Most cells contain hundreds of mitochondria. They have an outer and an inner membrane. The smooth outer membrane encloses the organelle and separates it from the surrounding cytoplasm. The inner membrane has a series of deep folds called cristae. This folding increases the surface area of the membrane. The large surface area facilitates the chemical reactions that occur on the inner membrane. Mitochondria are filled with a semifluid matrix that also contains ribosomes and mitochondrial DNA.

INSIDE MITOCHONDRIA

One human liver cell may contain a thousand mitochondria. What is the function of mitochondria, and how would it benefit the liver cells to have so many of them?

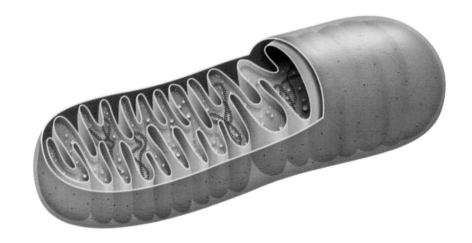

Function of Mitochondria

Mitochondria supply energy to the cell. They do this through a process called cellular respiration. In cellular respiration, oxygen combines with food molecules to release energy in the form of adenosine triphosphate (ATP). Cells use this ATP to provide energy necessary for key cellular processes. These, in turn, drive the activities of tissues, such as muscle contraction and nerve impulses.

What Is the Structure and Function of the Cell Membrane?

The Cell Membrane

All cells are surrounded by a cell membrane, which separates the inside of the cell from its surrounding environment. The cell membrane is composed of a double layer of fat molecules called phospholipids. Proteins embedded within this phospholipid bilayer govern which materials move in and out of the cell.

The phospholipids comprising the cell membrane have a distinct molecular structure. Each phospholipid has a head and two tails. The head is hydrophilic, meaning it is attracted to water. The tails are hydrophobic, meaning they are repelled by water. When the phospholipids are exposed to water, the hydrophobic tails of each layer orient toward the interior of the membrane away from the water layer. The hydrophilic heads of each layer orient away from the interior of the membrane, facing either the inside or outside of the cell, toward the surrounding water environment.

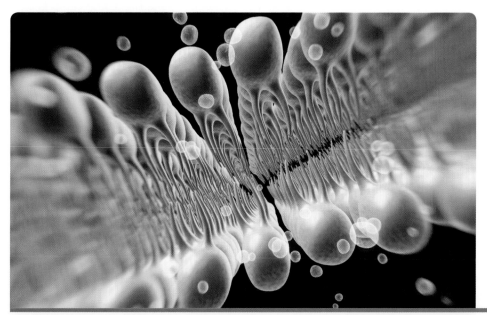

CELL MEMBRANE

Every cell is surrounded by a cell membrane, which is a complex dynamic structure. What is the cell membrane made up of?

Ion Channels and Ion Pumps

Numerous different types of proteins are embedded within the cell membrane. **Ion channels** are proteins that act like pores in the cell membrane. They control the flow of ions into and out of the cell through passive transport. In passive transport, ions move across the membrane and along their concentration gradient, or from a region of higher concentration to a region of lower concentration, without using chemical energy. In contrast, **ion pumps**, which are also proteins, transport ions across the cell membrane against their electrochemical gradient or against their natural direction. This process is called active transport, and it requires chemical energy to move the ions.

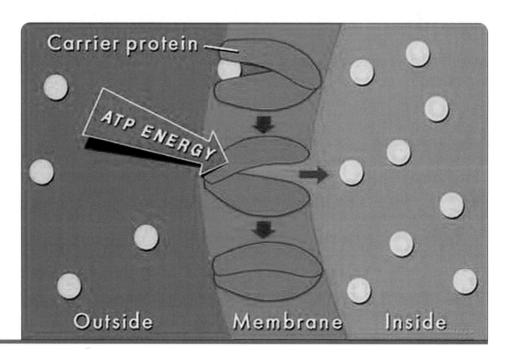

ACTIVE TRANSPORT

Proteins require energy to move through membranes. What is the difference between passive and active transport?

Consider the Explain Question

| **What kind of structures must a cell have that would be analogous to a modern business?**

Go online to complete the scientific explanation.

dlc.com/ca10094s

Check Your Understanding

| **Can you describe the parts (organelles) and function of prokaryotic and eukaryotic cells?**

dlc.com/ca10095s

S T E M in Action

Applying Cell Structure and Function

Bacteria are some of the most common organisms made of prokaryotic cells. People generally think of bacteria as dangerous, but most bacteria are harmless. Some bacteria are actually beneficial to humans and society. For example, a bacterium called *Bifidobacterium animalis* is a rod-shaped bacterium that can be found in the large intestines of most mammals, including humans. Part of the genus *Bifidobacterium*, these rod-shaped bacteria help maintain the body's digestive balance. They attach themselves to the wall of the large intestine, where they compete for food and space. A healthy body with a large colony of *B. animalis* has little room and few nutrients to spare for the harmful bacteria that may try to invade. They are also excellent producers of acids that reduce pH. This helps prevent harmful bacteria that thrive in basic environments from living and reproducing in the intestines.

BACTERIA

How can these bacteria be beneficial to humans?

Some kinds of bacteria are used to remove pollutants from contaminated areas. These bacteria are able to degrade hydrocarbons and use oil as their source of energy. In areas where oil is naturally present, communities of microbes are usually well-established and diverse. After the Deepwater Horizon oil spill in the Gulf of Mexico, naturally occurring bacteria helped break down methane in the oil by converting it into carbon dioxide and water. These bacteria prevented large amounts of methane from being released into the atmosphere and contributing to global warming. Bacteria are also useful in bioremediation for sequestering heavy metals at polluted sites.

STEM and Cell Structure and Function

Even though the structures within cells are extremely small, the processes they carry out are highly complex and essential for the survival of an organism. These processes include protein synthesis and replication of genetic material. Molecular biologists are scientists who study these processes to develop ways to treat diseases, protect the environment, improve agricultural crops, and understand the processes underlying evolution.

MOLECULAR BIOLOGISTS

Molecular biologists study processes of life that occur at the molecular level, including protein synthesis and DNA replication. How could a molecular biologist use his or her knowledge to fight diseases?

Molecular biologists study the chemical compounds and processes that make life possible. What sets them apart from other biologists is that they study life at the molecular level. Their studies take them to the very foundation of living cells. Some molecular biologists study very large molecules, notably nucleic acids and proteins, while others may be concerned with a specific type of cell. In addition, molecular biologists may work on a variety of important problems. A molecular biologist might work on discovering the genetic basis of a disease or creating a new vaccine. Another might work to discover the entire genetic code of an organism or on genetically modifying a crop species. Some molecular biologists study evolutionary paths, while others help law enforcement identify a criminal from DNA evidence.

Even though molecular biologists are interested in the tiniest units of life, they do not spend all day looking through a microscope. In addition to doing research, people in this field often work as teachers and scientific advisors. Molecular biologists frequently collaborate with other experts as part of their research.

Cell Transport

dlc.com/ca10096s

LESSON OVERVIEW

Lesson Question

■ What is the difference between passive and active cell transport?

Lesson Objectives

By the end of the lesson, you should be able to:

■ Distinguish between passive transport (osmosis, diffusion, and facilitated diffusion) and active transport (endocytosis and exocytosis).

■ Interpret cell transport processes in terms of how matter and energy flow through organisms.

■ Relate cell transport processes to biological functions such as digestion and respiration.

Key Vocabulary

Which terms do you already know?

- [ ] active transport
- [ ] adenosine triphosphate (ATP)
- [ ] cell membrane
- [ ] endocytosis
- [ ] exocytosis
- [ ] facilitated diffusion
- [ ] osmosis
- [ ] passive transport
- [ ] selective permeability
- [ ] transport

Exploring Cell Transport

If you have ever caught a flight, you will know that the process of checking in your baggage or getting your carry-on onto the plane is complex. For security reasons, your baggage is tagged, checked, and examined. Then, it is moved via a series of complex machines that work behind the scenes to move your luggage to the plane. How does the way an airport baggage handling system functions relate to a cell?

dlc.com/ca10097s

EXPLAIN QUESTION

How do cells regulate the passage of materials across their membranes in order to maintain homeostasis?

AIRPORT SCREENING

Just as airport screeners control which items are taken onto a plane, cells use membranes to control the passage of materials into a cell. What kinds of materials would a membrane try to block from entering a cell?

What Is the Difference between Passive and Active Cell Transport?

Passive Transport

In solutions such as those found in living organisms, some substances move without added energy. This type of movement is called diffusion. In diffusion, the molecules (or ions) of a substance spread out evenly in the space they occupy. Diffusion is referred to as "passive" because it uses only the existing kinetic energy of the molecules. *Concentration* refers to the number of molecules of a substance in a given volume. And a concentration gradient is an unequal concentration from one region to another. In the absence of other factors, molecules diffuse "down their concentration gradient." This means that molecules move from an area of high concentration to an area of low concentration. Diffusion ends when the molecules have reached equilibrium. This means that the concentration of the substance is equal throughout the space it occupies. There is no longer a concentration gradient, and the molecules in the space are considered to be at dynamic equilibrium.

Passive transport is the diffusion of a substance across a selectively permeable membrane, such as a **cell membrane**. **Selective permeability** means that some substances such as certain small, nonpolar molecules (such as O_2 and CO_2) can move freely across it. But ions and polar molecules such as glucose cannot move freely across the membrane.

OSMOSIS

Water moves across a semipermeable membrane from an area of low solute concentration to an area of high solute concentration by osmosis. How does osmosis allow living organisms to maintain homeostasis?

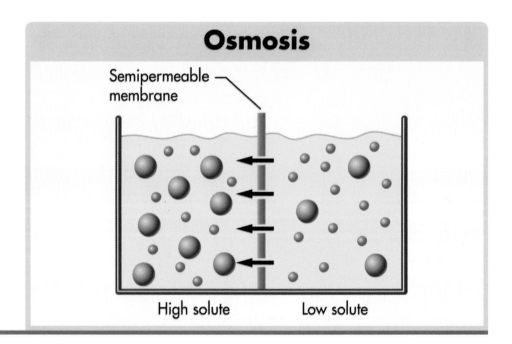

Osmosis

Semipermeable membrane

High solute   Low solute

Osmosis is a type of diffusion in which only water moves. In osmosis, water molecules diffuse across a selectively permeable membrane from an area of high concentration of water molecules to an area of low concentration of water molecules. Think of two liquids separated by a selectively permeable membrane. Pure water exists on one side of the membrane and a glucose/water solution on the other side. In this set-up, water molecules are in lower concentration in the glucose solution. This is because water molecules are "diluted" by glucose molecules. So, if the membrane is permeable to water but not to glucose, water molecules from the pure water side will move into the glucose solution.

Facilitated diffusion is a type of diffusion that allows polar substances like glucose or ions such as sodium and chloride ions to passively move in and out of cells. The cell membrane usually blocks these kinds of substances from traveling through it. Even water molecules, because they are polar, do not diffuse freely through the membrane.

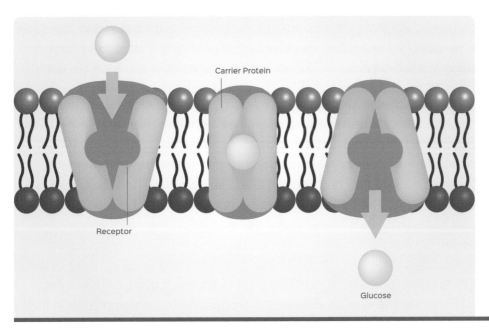

Carrier Protein

Receptor

Glucose

FACILITATED DIFFUSION

In facilitated diffusion, proteins in the cell membrane allow certain materials to move in and out of a cell. What types of molecules pass through the membrane by facilitated diffusion?

In facilitated diffusion, a special protein helps the substances cross the cell membrane. Some proteins form channels through the membrane. Other proteins bind to specific molecules like glucose, allowing them to cross the cell membrane using no energy from ATP. With the help of membrane proteins, facilitated diffusion drives the substances from an area of high concentration to an area of low concentration. Facilitated diffusion is important for many cellular functions. For example, facilitated diffusion of water is used by the kidneys to reabsorb water during production of urine.

Active Transport

Cells work to maintain their internal conditions. This process is called homeostasis. Through cellular **transport**, a cell can maintain an internal equilibrium by adjusting its physiological processes and controlling what enters or leaves through the cell membrane. Homeostasis requires that cells actively transport molecules in and out of the cell to achieve and maintain this balance.

Unlike passive transport, **active transport** requires cellular energy for solutes to move across the cellular membrane. In fact, substances are able to move from an area of low concentration to an area of high concentration during active transport. This is the reverse of the direction of movement that occurs during diffusion.

Adenosine triphosphate (ATP) provides the energy required for active transport to occur. Cells use this energy to push substances in a different direction than they would normally move. It can also help molecules that cannot easily cross the cell membrane enter or exit cells. Active transport is required for many important biological activities. It allows the human body to absorb certain nutrients like fatty acids from the food we eat.

Certain biochemical "pumps" use energy to move molecules and ions through the cell membrane against their concentration gradients. One of the most important pumps in animal cells is the sodium-potassium pump. Animal cells contain much more potassium than the fluid they are bathed in. They contain much less sodium than their fluid surroundings. The cell membrane is impermeable to both sodium and potassium, thus these ions enter and leave the cell through sodium-potassium pumps in the membrane. The sodium-potassium pump uses the energy from ATP to pump three sodium ions out of the cell and two potassium ions into the cell for each cycle of the pump. ATP transfers one of its phosphate groups to the transport protein itself. This transfer changes the shape of the transport protein and moves an ion attached to the protein across the membrane.

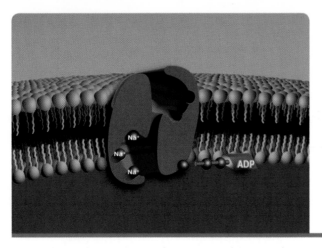 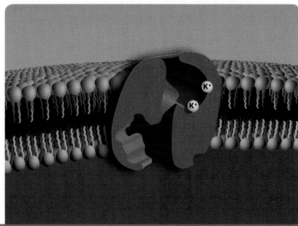

Endocytosis is a form of transport that uses ATP and brings large substances into a cell. The plasma membrane contacts and then folds around a particle outside the cell, forming a pocket. Then the folded membrane pinches off the pocket to form a sac, or vesicle, that encloses the particle inside the cell.

Exocytosis is another form of active transport. However, this process is used to move substances out of a cell. A substance exits the cell through a sac, or vesicle, that engulfs the substance. When the vesicle comes in contact with the cell membrane, the vesicle fuses with the membrane. This opens the vesicle to the outside of the cell, and the substance diffuses away from the cell.

SODIUM-POTASSIUM PUMP

The sodium-potassium pump uses ATP to move sodium ions (Na^+) out of the cell and potassium ions (K^+) into the cell. Why does the sodium-potassium pump require energy to move these ions?

Consider the Explain Question

| **How do cells regulate the passage of materials across their membranes in order to maintain homeostasis?**

Go online to complete the scientific explanation.

dlc.com/ca10098s

Check Your Understanding

| **Can you model active and passive transport?**

dlc.com/ca10099s

STEM in Action

Applying Cell Transport

How does cell transport help doctors and researchers to create new medicines?

An understanding of how substances get into cells is vital to the treatment of many diseases. Scientists investigate how different organelles within a cell respond to particular drugs. They expose the cell to various concentrations of them and observe how they behave. Knowing which parts of the cell are affected by the drug allows scientists to customize the medicine for optimum performance. Scientists are able to calculate the concentrations of the medicine needed to counteract the symptoms. On the other hand, sometimes organelles may absorb the drug in amounts that are undesirable or not effective.

Because finding and designing medicinal drugs is very expensive, pharmaceutical companies need to be certain that the product they are producing does what they intended. Knowing about how cells transport materials through their membranes and how organelles respond to them is essential knowledge to have when working on new treatments.

Another situation in which knowing about cell transport is important is in the understanding of hormones. Hormones are chemical messengers that are sent around an organism's structure (including organisms such as plants) in response to certain stimuli. What happens when you get scared? Your brain signals two small glands on top of your kidneys to release a hormone called epinephrine (adrenaline). This enters your blood and travels to various cells. It then passes through the cell membranes and stimulates the mitochondria to produce more energy. If your cell membranes were not receptive to the epinephrine, you would not receive the signals to escape from the danger.

Knowledge of cell membranes and cell transport has led to the discovery of several antitumor drugs used to treat cancer. What is cancer? It is a disease characterized by tumors that form when the regulatory mechanisms that turn off cell division are damaged. This can happen naturally or as a result of exposure to some environmental factor (such as smoking or radiation). Some of these antitumor drugs work inside the nucleus of the cell. Once inside the nucleus, the drug attaches to the cell's DNA and turns off the proteins that cause cell division. One of these drugs is called carboplatin and contains the element platinum. Platinum is a rare element and is not normally used by or found in cells. Thus, cell membranes do not naturally have a mechanism to transport platinum into the cell.

ARTWORK OF CANCER CELLS DIVIDING

Cancer is characterized by out-of-control cell growth. How does this type of cell growth occur?

How can the drugs that contain platinum be moved across the cell membrane and into the cancer cells? One thing scientists researched was to look at how other metals cross the cell membrane. Researchers discovered that copper is transported across the cell membrane by a particular protein. This transporter protein sits on the cell membrane and works as a carrier molecule to bring the copper from one side to the other. Further investigations led to researchers asking the question of how this behavior can be used to help transport platinum into the cell. They studied the structure of the protein and came up with the idea of making a molecule that would attach to this transporter protein. The molecule they designed holds platinum inside of it. When this molecule arrives at the cell membrane, it attaches to the protein on the membrane and "tricks" the cell into accepting the platinum. The cell behaves as if it is taking in copper and takes in the platinum as well.

STEM and Cell Transport

Scientists are able to apply their knowledge of cell transport when developing lifesaving medical technologies. One example of this is the use of dialysis to help people with kidney disease.

The kidneys are the organs responsible for filtering the blood and removing wastes. They also process all of the water the body uses and create urine. When the kidneys do not function properly, they often have to undergo dialysis. Dialysis is a process that uses a machine to remove waste products from human blood. It is used to treat patients with diabetes and other diseases that affect the kidneys. Quite often, dialysis treatments are ongoing. This means that once a person has been diagnosed with a kidney disease, they must go for treatment regularly, often for the rest of their lives unless a new kidney is implanted.

The blood-filtering machine used in dialysis has a semipermeable membrane similar to the cell membrane of kidney cells. Blood, water, and other fluids move passively through the machine's membrane through diffusion. This process "cleans" the person's blood of waste and other impurities and returns it back into the body.

KIDNEYS

The kidneys are the organs that filter the blood and remove toxins from it. Functioning kidneys are essential to keeping a person alive. What treatments are available if the kidneys stop working?

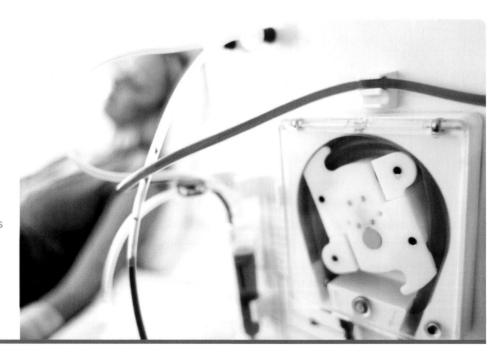

Cell Division

LESSON OVERVIEW

Lesson Questions

- What is the structure of chromosomes?
- What are the processes involved in cellular division?
- What are the differences between cell division among prokaryotes and eukaryotes?
- What is the cell cycle?
- What are the characteristics of cancer cells?

Lesson Objectives

By the end of the lesson, you should be able to:

- Describe the structure of a chromosome.
- Describe the processes involved in cellular division.
- Distinguish among mechanisms of cell division in prokaryotes and single-celled and multicellular eukaryotes.
- Describe the cell cycle.
- Describe the characteristics of cancer cells.

Key Vocabulary

Which terms do you already know?

- [ ] aneuploidy
- [ ] asexual reproduction
- [ ] binary fission
- [ ] cancer cells
- [ ] cell cycle
- [ ] cellular division
- [ ] chromatid
- [ ] chromatin
- [ ] chromosome
- [ ] diploid cell
- [ ] DNA
- [ ] eukaryotic cell
- [ ] fertilization
- [ ] haploid cell
- [ ] meiosis
- [ ] mitosis
- [ ] monosomy
- [ ] nondisjunction
- [ ] nucleus (cell)
- [ ] oogenesis
- [ ] prokaryotic cell
- [ ] sexual reproduction
- [ ] somatic cell nuclear transfer
- [ ] spermatogenesis
- [ ] trisomy

dlc.com/ca10100s

Thinking about Cell Division

dlc.com/ca10101s

There are many things about our daily lives that we often take for granted: the air we breathe, the water we drink, and the many ways that the human body can function and grow. One of these is the processes that enable the body to heal itself when it is damaged. If something happens to one of our organs, how can it be replaced or repaired?

A HEALING BURN INJURY

Any type of burn to your skin can be serious. How can the body heal this type of injury?

EXPLAIN QUESTION

Explain what steps are involved in the cell division of a prokaryote versus a eukaryote.

What Is the Structure of Chromosomes?

Structure of Chromosomes

Individual chromosomes are made up of a long double-stranded **DNA** molecule attached to DNA-binding proteins. In eukaryotes, the chromosomal DNA is tightly wound up around additional proteins. This enables it to fit inside the **nucleus** of the cell. In this state, it is called **chromatin**. The DNA provides the information needed for cells to make the proteins that enable the biochemical processes of an organism. Most eukaryotes have a number of linear chromosomes. These chromosomes are normally present in pairs. For example, normal human cells contain 46 individual, or 23 pairs of, linear chromosomes.

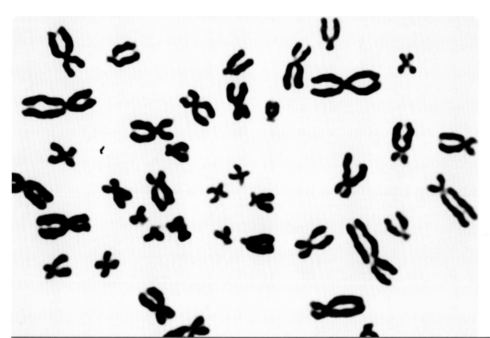

CHROMOSOMES

Chromosomes are found inside every cell of every organism. What is their function?

Prokaryotes generally have one large circular double-stranded DNA molecule. Both prokaryotes and single-celled eukaryotes may also contain several smaller circular DNA molecules called plasmids. Plasmids are not chromosomes because they are not essential to the cell or organism. Plasmids can replicate independently of cell division. Chromosomes are the basic unit for DNA replication and cell division.

What Are the Processes Involved in Cellular Division?

Overview of Cell Division

Cell division describes the process by which one cell duplicates into two daughter cells. In prokaryotes, this is referred to as **binary fission** or prokaryotic fission. Cell division in all eukaryotes involves a process called **mitosis**. In mitosis, the replicated DNA is divided between the two daughter cells.

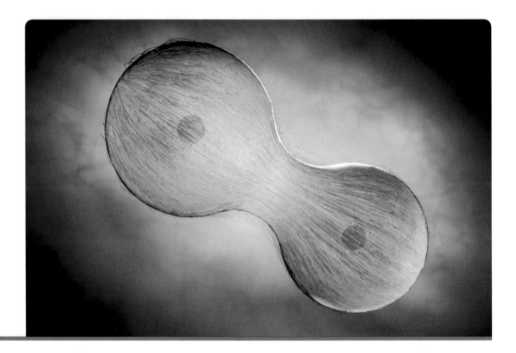

CELL DIVISION

What is happening inside cells as they divide?

What Are the Differences between Cell Division among Prokaryotes and Eukaryotes?

Cell Division

A prokaryote lacks a nucleus and usually contains a single, circular chromosomal DNA molecule. Therefore, **prokaryotic cell** division is much simpler than **eukaryotic cell** division. Binary fission is the process by which prokaryotic cells divide. During binary fission, DNA replicates and each copy attaches to either end of the cell membrane. The DNA copies are then pulled apart during cell division into separate daughter cells. This process ensures that each daughter cell has an entire copy of the genetic information. The smaller circular DNA molecules, or plasmids, often occur in multiple copies and become distributed into daughter cells. Plasmid replication occurs at the same time as genomic DNA replication.

Eukaryotic Cell Division

Cell division in eukaryotes is more complicated. Eukaryotic chromosomes undergo replication, and then the chromosomes separate through a process called mitosis. Mitosis involves several rearrangements of the chromosomes during cell division to ensure that each daughter cell receives an entire set of chromosomes. All of the steps of cell division among eukaryotes are described in what is known as the **cell cycle**.

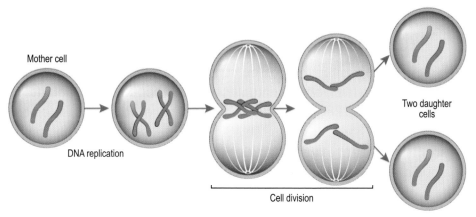

Mother cell

DNA replication

Cell division

Two daughter cells

MITOSIS

Mitosis is a process of cell division that produces two identical daughter cells from one mother cell. What happens to chromosomes during mitosis?

What Is the Cell Cycle?

Cell Cycle

The process of eukaryotic cell division can be separated into four phases called the cell cycle. The cell cycle is the basis for growth in all multicellular eukaryotic organisms. The phases of the cell cycle and their functions are summarized in the table.

Phase	Function
G1 (Gap 1)	Cells grow and prepare for DNA replications.
S (Synthesis)	DNA replication occurs.
G2 (Gap 2)	Cells continue to grow and prepare for the separation of chromosomes.
M (Mitosis)	Cell division occurs.

EUKARYOTIC CELLS

Eukaryotic cell division is a complex process. What happens after cells replicate, and what makes this such an important part of the process?

The first three phases are often collectively referred to as interphase. The M phase is further divided into several stages characterized by the reorganization of chromosomes and cell structures and the division of the cell.

Mitosis

Chromosomes duplicate before mitosis. Each daughter cell needs exactly one copy of each **chromosome**. To achieve this, the chromosomes and the cell undergo several stages during mitosis. The stages of mitosis include prophase, metaphase, anaphase, and telophase.

Within the cell are structures called centrioles. At the start of prophase, the centrioles divide. These centrioles move to opposite ends of the cell. The centrioles begin to produce fine fibers called microtubules or spindle fibers. These fibers stretch across the cell to form the spindle. Meanwhile, inside the nucleus the chromosomes begin to condense. The nucleolus disappears. The nuclear membrane dissolves. The individual chromosomes are now clearly visible. Each chromosome can be seen to consist of two chromatids joined together at a point called the centromere. Proteins begin to build up on each centromere forming a structure called a kinetochore. In the final part of prophase, the spindle fibers attach to the kinetochore.

At the start of metaphase, the spindle fibers pull the chromosomes so that they are lined up across the center of the cell. This ensures that, when the chromosomes are separated, each new cell will receive one copy of each chromosome.

In anaphase, the chromatids of each chromosome are pulled apart. One **chromatid** from each chromosome is pulled to each end or pole of the cell. At this point, each chromatid can be thought of as a new daughter chromosome.

The start of telophase is marked by the daughter chromosomes arriving at the poles of the cell. At each end of the cell, a new nuclear membrane forms around the daughter chromosomes. The chromosomes de-condense and are no longer visible as individual chromosomes. The nucleolus reappears. The spindle fibers disperse and the cell starts to divide.

The final stage of cell division is not strictly part of mitosis. This stage is called cytokinesis. In animal cells, the center of the cell contracts, pinching the cell into two daughter cells. In plant cells, a cell plate is synthesized between the two daughter cells. This eventually forms a new cell wall. Cell division is now complete.

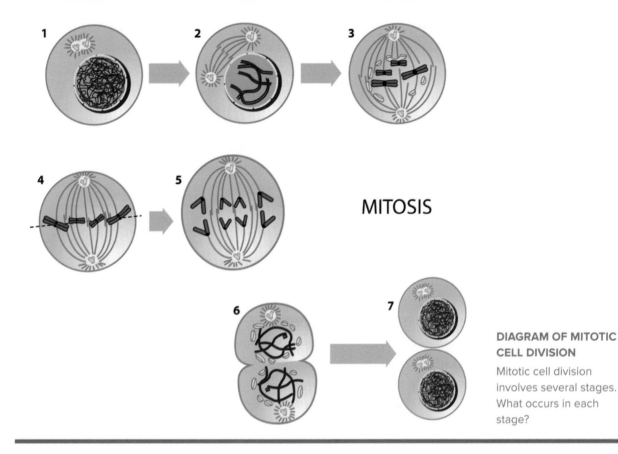

MITOSIS

DIAGRAM OF MITOTIC CELL DIVISION

Mitotic cell division involves several stages. What occurs in each stage?

Producing and Maintaining Complex Organisms

Simple, single cells divide by mitosis. Mitosis allows the formation of complex organisms. Through mitosis, new cells are produced so that an organism can increase in size. By adding more cells, an organism can gain mass. Your growth from infancy to adulthood was the result of millions of cells undergoing mitosis throughout your life. Mitosis is the basis of the formation and growth of almost every structure in a complex organism. For example, the skeletal system is formed through the mitotic division of specialized bone cells.

Mitosis also supports the maintenance of complex organisms. Mitosis replaces new cells to replace those that die. Every day in the adult body, about 2 trillion cells are produced by mitosis to offset the death of old cells. Mitosis also ensures that new cells are the same type as those being replaced when damaged tissues are repaired. For example, if you cut your finger, the wound heals by mitotic division of skin cells that match damaged ones. In some organisms, mitosis can lead to the regrowth or regeneration of body parts. For example, some lizards and amphibians can regrow severed tails or limbs. Scientists are studying the mechanisms by which animals regenerate body parts, hoping to one day allow the same type of regrowth in humans.

What Are the Characteristics of Cancer Cells?

Cancer Cells

In adult plants and animals, normal cell division is tightly regulated and only occurs when there is a need for new cells. For example, human cells divide as a person grows and develops from a fertilized egg to an embryo to an adult. Cell division is also needed to heal a wound or to replace cells that die, like skin cells, in the normal scheme of life.

Cell division is one step, the final step, of the cell cycle. Most adult cells are not rapidly dividing. Instead, they remain functional but not growing, in an early resting checkpoint of the cell cycle called G0. This is because progression through the cell cycle is regulated to prevent uncontrolled growth. Exposure to mutagens can damage cells by altering, or mutating, their DNA. Some DNA mutations can alter normal cell cycle regulation, so the damaged cells lose their ability to divide only when appropriate. In animals, the process of losing the ability to control cell division is known as cell transformation. Thus, a normal, healthy cell transforms into a cancer cell.

Many **cancer cells** do not require external factors like particular nutrients and temperature controls in order to divide. They avoid cell death signals from the body, begin to grow quickly, and form tumors. Cancer cells also produce great amounts of telomerase, an enzyme that maintains the integrity of eukaryotic chromosomes during cell division. These dangerous cells deplete nutrients needed by other parts of the body. In later stages of cancer, tumor cells can move throughout the body. They metastasize, or invade, different tissues, making successful cancer treatment extremely difficult.

Consider the Explain Question

Explain what steps are involved in the cell division of a prokaryote versus a eukaryote.

Go online to complete the scientific explanation.

dlc.com/ca10102s

Check Your Understanding

Why is the cell cycle key to the growth of multicellular organisms?

dlc.com/ca10103s

S T E M in Action

Applying Cell Division

Cancer is a leading cause of death in the United States. It is estimated to cause 550,000 to 600,000 deaths per year, second only to heart disease. Research and development of cancer therapies are major focuses of the pharmaceutical industry. Traditional therapies such as radiation and chemotherapy utilize agents that can prevent cell division, thus halting or slowing the growth of cancer cells. However, one of the major challenges for treating cancer is the fact that tumor cells originate from our own bodies. This makes it difficult to selectively isolate and eradicate them. This is also why traditional treatments include the side effect of destroying healthy cells at the same time.

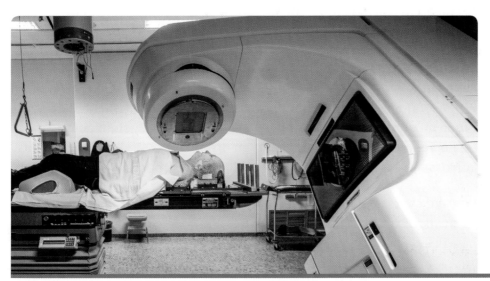

MAN RECEIVING RADIATION THERAPY

When a person is receiving radiation treatment, both cancerous and healthy cells are targeted. How can the therapy selectively recognize cancer cells?

New forms of cancer therapies try to circumvent these challenges by moving beyond inhibiting cell division. Many scientists focus on developing medicines that can selectively recognize cancer cells. Others look at how to boost the immune system so it can destroy the tumor from within. In addition, creative methods such as preventing blood vessel formation around the tumors, thus "starving" them, have been examined.

STEM and Cell Division

Think about how the human body reacts to a small cut versus a large burn. A slight cut on the skin would heal itself, but major burns likely would not. In contrast to the undesired rapid proliferation of cancer cells, the rapid cell division needed to heal a wound is highly desirable for replacing tissues that have suffered major damage. Scientists have discovered that certain cells called stem cells in our bodies have the potential to grow and divide indefinitely and take on the functions of a variety of different tissues, such as skin, blood, or cardiac tissue. These stem cells play a very important role during human growth. However, in normal adults, they can only regenerate limited types of tissues. One major branch of research is focused on trying to understand how stem cells behave so they can be made to form various tissues. This would allow such customized cells to replace dead cells resulting from major traumas. For example, the loss of a group of neurons in a patient's brain causes Parkinson's disease. Efforts are being made to investigate how to use stem cells to create these neurons so the disease can be cured.

A stem cell researcher is a scientist interested in the applications of stem cells. In the future, scientists hope to grow entire organs from stem cells. Right now, a patient requiring an organ transplant must often wait a long time until a donor organ is available. Additionally, the donor organ must be compatible with the patient. However, stem cells can be harvested from individuals, and an organ generated from stem cells could be just like the original one and free of compatibility problems.

Why are stem cells so important? Hundreds of different types of cells make up our bodies, but all have the same genetic code stored in their nuclei. So how does a newly formed cell know what type of cell it is supposed to be?

EXTRACTING STEM CELLS

This image shows the transfer of embryonic stem cells during stem cell research. How are stem cells currently used?

Take your own body, for example. It started off as a single fertilized egg that divided again and again to make the trillions of cells in your body. Some of those embryonic cells had the ability to become any type of cell. These are stem cells. This is why many stem cells used in the lab come from cultures originally derived from embryos. These stem cells differentiated into other types of cells (muscle or nerve cells, for example). How does this happen? It all has to do with which genes are turned on and which are turned off. This is called gene expression.

At what time during development, from a single fertilized egg undergoing cell division to form an embryo all the way to a baby being born, is the fate of each cell decided? Although all of the cells that make up a multicellular organism share the same exact DNA, different cells eventually become specialized and form different types of cells that make up different tissues and organs with unique structures and functions. The process of becoming a specialized cell type is called differentiation and involves the selective expression of genes from DNA to RNA to protein in response to environmental factors, such as the location of a cell within the developing organism.

Cell structure is determined in part by the proteins that are produced by a cell. The expression of a gene that codes for a protein happens in two basic steps; first, the gene is transcribed from DNA into RNA, and then the RNA copy of the gene is translated into protein. Only a part of the cell's DNA genome is expressed at a time. Which parts are expressed determine which proteins are made. Thus, transcription, the process by which the DNA is copied into RNA, is the first step in determining the fate of a cell's development.

Transcription is controlled by molecules that influence which parts of the DNA are "read." These molecules, called regulatory transcription factors, bind to parts of the DNA and determine whether it can be read or not. In effect, they regulate the DNA's code and switch certain genes on and certain genes off. This is called gene regulation. If the cell is to become a muscle cell, then those genes that determine the characteristics of a muscle cell are turned on, and those for, say, a nerve cell are turned off. A number of different environmental factors signal the type of cell that needs to be produced. These include the position within the organism, the cell's immediate and near neighbors, and the concentration of certain chemicals. These signals influence which regulatory transcription factors bind to the DNA and the types of cells and resulting tissues produced.

Plants also have undifferentiated cells that can divide and change into the variety of cell types that make up the organism. These growth areas within the plant are found in a variety of locations called meristems. For example, you can see their division and differentiation near the root tips of plants.

Asexual and Sexual Reproduction

dlc.com/ca10104s

LESSON OVERVIEW

Lesson Questions

- What are the differences between asexual and sexual reproduction?
- What are haploid and diploid cells?
- What is the function of each stage of meiosis?
- What are the differences between mitosis and meiosis?
- What are spermatogenesis and oogenesis?
- What are fertilization and development?
- What is Somatic Cell Nuclear Transfer (SCNT)?
- What are the effects of non-disjunction?
- What are some examples of aneuploidy, monosomy, and trisomy?

Key Vocabulary

Which terms do you already know?

- [ ] aneuploidy
- [ ] asexual reproduction
- [ ] chromatid
- [ ] chromatin
- [ ] diploid cell
- [ ] fertilization
- [ ] haploid cell
- [ ] meiosis
- [ ] mitosis
- [ ] monosomy
- [ ] nondisjunction
- [ ] nucleus (cell)
- [ ] oogenesis
- [ ] sexual reproduction
- [ ] somatic cell nuclear transfer
- [ ] spermatogenesis
- [ ] trisomy

Lesson Objectives

By the end of the lesson, you should be able to:

- Distinguish between asexual and sexual reproduction.
- Compare haploid and diploid cells.
- Describe the purpose and phases of meiosis.
- Distinguish between the processes of mitosis and meiosis.
- Compare the processes of spermatogenesis and oogenesis.
- Describe the processes of fertilization and development.
- Describe the process of Somatic Cell Nuclear Transfer (SCNT).
- Describe the effects of non-disjunction.
- Describe the terms *aneuploidy, monosomy,* and *trisomy* and describe examples.

Exploring Asexual and Sexual Reproduction

dlc.com/ca10105s

New organisms result from a process called reproduction, which means "producing again." Puppies, kittens, ducklings, flowering plants, and many other organisms with which you are familiar are the result of a reproduction strategy called sexual reproduction. Sexual reproduction is when an organism has two parents of different sexes—male and female.

PUPPIES!

These puppies are only a few weeks old. What do you think their parents look like?

EXPLAIN QUESTION

❙ Explain what happens during asexual and sexual reproduction.

What Are the Differences between Asexual and Sexual Reproduction?

Asexual Reproduction

Because **asexual reproduction** and **sexual reproduction** differ in the number of parents needed to produce an offspring, it is no wonder that the methods differ as well.

Asexual reproduction is most common among microorganisms, but other species are able to reproduce this way as well. There are several forms of asexual reproduction. Bacteria usually reproduce through binary fission. A cell replicates its DNA and then divides into two daughter cells, each with identical genetic material.

Certain plants can reproduce through a process called vegetative reproduction. A new plant can be generated by division of the roots, stems, or leaves of a parent plant. Raspberries, for example, can generate offspring using only their stems. As with all asexual reproduction, the offspring have identical DNA to the parent.

Budding and regeneration are two more methods of asexual reproduction in animals. In budding, a new organism grows out of the parent's body. Sometimes the offspring remain attached to the parent's body and sometimes they break off. Hydras are simple aquatic animals that can reproduce by budding.

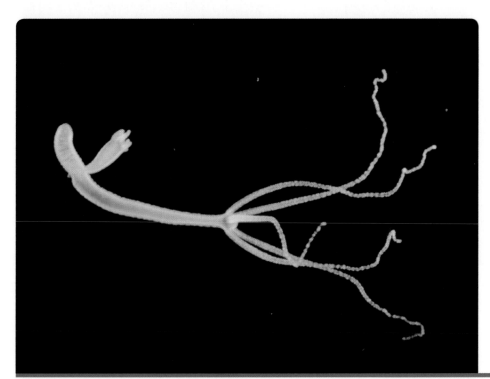

BUDDING

A new offspring buds off the side of this hydra. How does the genotype of the budded offspring compare to the parent?

Regeneration is similar to vegetative reproduction. A piece of the parent's body can develop into a new organism. For example, if one arm of a sea star is cut off, not only will the sea star grow that arm back, but the lost arm also may grow into an entirely new sea star. Regeneration can only occur if the detached piece of the parent contains enough genetic information.

Sexual Reproduction

Sexual reproduction always involves combining genetic material from two organisms to produce offspring. The simplest form of sexual reproduction is conjugation in which two individuals fuse together and exchange genetic material, then separate again. Some algae use conjugation to sexually reproduce.

For most multicellular organisms, sexual reproduction is their primary means of reproduction. In non-conjugation sexual reproduction, sex cells are produced by a process called **meiosis**. These sex cells are called gametes. The male gametes are called the sperm, the female gametes are called ova or eggs. When an egg and sperm fuse together in the process of **fertilization**, a zygote is formed. A zygote is a fertilized egg, and it has the potential to grow into a new organism.

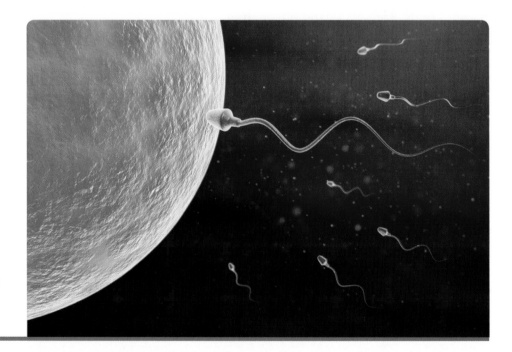

SPERM AND EGG CELLS

For most animals, life begins with sperm and egg. Where do sperm and egg begin?

The process of fertilization differs widely. Organisms have a wide variety of life cycles and structures that have evolved to ensure fertilization.

Flowering plant species go through pollination. The male stamen produces pollen containing the male gamete. Pollen is carried by wind, insect or other mechanisms to a female pistil that contains the ovary. Flowers are an adaption to ensure that pollination occurs.

Animal species have two main methods of fertilization: external and internal. In external fertilization, the male and female release their sperm and eggs into the surrounding environment. Fertilization then takes place. Aquatic species such as amphibians employ this type of sexual reproduction.

Many other animals reproduce internally. The egg remains inside the female's body and the sperm travels to meet it there. Many organisms have evolved into complex organs, and mating displays and rituals have been developed to ensure this happens. Some groups of animals, such as mammals, retain the fertilized egg and developing baby in the body until birth. Others, like birds and some reptiles, lay the fertilized eggs in a nest, protect the eggs, and raise the young when they hatch.

What Are Haploid and Diploid Cells?

Haploid versus Diploid

Not all cells of the human body are alike. There are nerve cells, blood cells, and muscle cells to name a few. Although these cells serve different functions, all are somatic, or body, cells. Somatic cells are **diploid cells**. They contain two complete sets of parental chromosomes. Diploid cells are often labeled as 2N. The 2 represents the fact that for every chromosome, there are two homologous copies—one from the organism's maternal parent and one from the organism's paternal parent.

Other cells, the egg and sperm cells, are haploid cells (N). They contain only a single set of chromosomes, or half the parental number. When the haploid cells of the egg and sperm come together, the resulting cell will be diploid—the combination of two haploid cells.

Diploid and Haploid Cells	
Diploid	**Haploid**
4 pairs of homologous chromosomes	4 nonhomologous chromosomes
Somatic cells	Gametes
2N	1N

DIPLOID AND HAPLOID CELLS

Study the image and refer to the text. What is the purpose of these different cells?

What Is the Function of Each Stage of Meiosis?

Meiosis and Its Function

Egg and sperm cells are called gametes. The haploid cells of the gametes are created in a two-part cell division process called meiosis. Only organisms that reproduce sexually undergo meiosis.

During the two stages of meiosis, the number of chromosomes in the parental diploid cells is reduced by half. In the end, four haploid daughter cells are produced. Before meiosis I begins, DNA replication occurs. Each chromosome is duplicated to form sister **chromatids** connected by a centromere. Then meiosis begins, following the steps outlined below.

Meiosis I

- Prophase I: chromosomes condense and homologous chromosomes pair up. Homologous chromosomes are corresponding chromosomes from each parent. During prophase, chromosomes may cross over. Entire chromosomes or parts of the chromatids cross over one another and switch position. Crossing over (also called recombination) is a major contributor to genetic diversity.
- Prometaphase I: the nuclear envelope disappears and paired homologous chromosomes attach to spindle fibers.
- Metaphase I: paired homologous chromosomes line up in the middle of the cell.

- Anaphase I: paired homologous chromosomes separate and are pulled to opposite ends of the cell.
- Telophase I and cytokinesis: a nuclear envelope forms around each group of chromosomes. The cytoplasm divides, forming two haploid daughter cells.

The chromosomes were reshuffled and separated. Neither haploid daughter cell has the exact same set of chromosomes as the parents.

After meiosis I, the two haploid daughter cells enter a second stage of division.

Meiosis II

- Prophase II: chromosomes condense and the nuclear envelope begins to break down.
- Prometaphase II: the nuclear envelope disappears, spindle fibers form, and the sister chromatids attach to the spindle fibers.
- Metaphase II: the chromosomes line up in the center of the cell.
- Anaphase II: sister chromatids separate at the centromere and are pulled to opposite ends of the cell.
- Telophase II and cytokinesis: a nuclear envelope forms and the cytoplasm divides into separate cells.

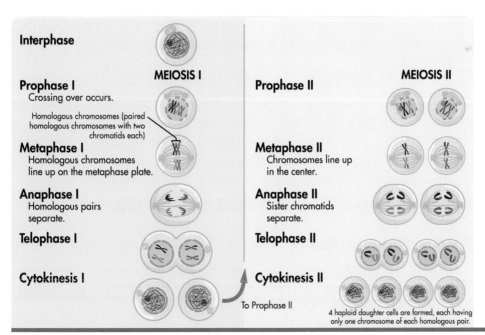

Interphase

MEIOSIS I

Prophase I
Crossing over occurs.

Homologous chromosomes (paired homologous chromosomes with two chromatids each)

Metaphase I
Homologous chromosomes line up on the metaphase plate.

Anaphase I
Homologous pairs separate.

Telophase I

Cytokinesis I

To Prophase II

MEIOSIS II

Prophase II

Metaphase II
Chromosomes line up in the center.

Anaphase II
Sister chromatids separate.

Telophase II

Cytokinesis II

4 haploid daughter cells are formed, each having only one chromosome of each homologous pair.

MEIOSIS

A diploid cell goes through two stages of meiosis to produce four haploid cells. What are sister chromatids and how are they formed?

At the end of meiosis II, there are a total of four haploid cells. Meiosis II is similar to **mitosis**, which is the process of cell division in body cells. However, the chromosomes resulting from meiosis II are no longer identical because they have undergone recombination.

What Are the Differences between Mitosis and Meiosis?

A Comparison of Meiosis and Mitosis

Mitosis and meiosis both involve cell division. However, it is important to remember that these two processes have major distinctions as summarized in the table.

	Mitosis	Meiosis
Types of Cells Involved	somatic cells	gametes
Types of Organisms Involved	all eukaryotes	only those that reproduce sexually
Number of Divisions	1	2
Final Number of Daughter Cells	2	4
Final Chromosome Number	same as parental number (diploid)	half the parental number (haploid)
DNA Replication	always occurs in S- phase before	always occurs before meiosis I
Homologous Chromosomes	no pairing occurs	complete pairing occurs during prophase I
Crossing Over	none; there is no exchange of DNA	during prophase I of meiosis I; DNA of homologous chromosomes can be exchanged
Chromosomes Separate at Centromere	during anaphase	only during anaphase II
Daughter Cell Genotype	identical to parent cell	differ from parent cell because of crossing over

What Are Spermatogenesis and Oogenesis?

The Formation of Sperm

In sexually reproducing organisms, males contribute sperm and females contribute eggs. The process of forming sperm is called **spermatogenesis**. Cells in a male organism called spermatogonia produce sperm. The spermatogonia arise from primary germ cells that undergo cell division. During mitosis, one daughter cell remains a spermatogonium. The other becomes a spermatocyte, which eventually becomes sperm.

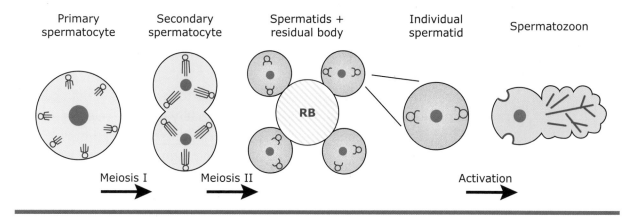

Primary spermatocyte   Secondary spermatocyte   Spermatids + residual body   Individual spermatid   Spermatozoon

Meiosis I   Meiosis II   Activation

Each primary spermatocyte undergoes meiosis I, resulting in two secondary spermatocytes. The secondary spermatocytes undergo meiosis II and cytokinesis. Two spermatids, or young spermatozoa, are produced from each secondary spermatocyte. The spermatozoa develop into mature sperm cells for use in reproduction.

The Formation of Eggs

The process of **oogenesis**, or egg formation, in a sexually reproducing female is somewhat more complex than spermatogenesis. However, like spermatogenesis, the cell that results in the formation of an egg arises from a primary germ cell, called an oocyte, that undergoes cell division to produce a haploid cell. This **haploid cell** is called an ovum, or egg.

SPERMATOCYTOGENESIS

A spermatocyte goes through meiosis to produce spermatids that will mature into sperm. How many primary spermatocytes are there for each spermatid produced?

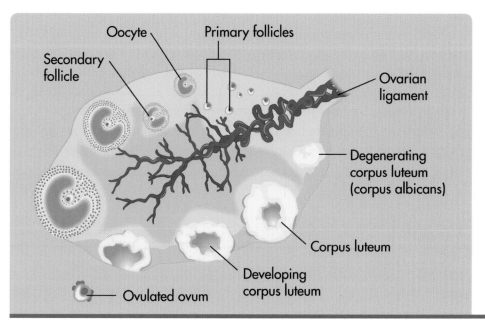

Secondary follicle — Oocyte — Primary follicles — Ovarian ligament — Degenerating corpus luteum (corpus albicans) — Corpus luteum — Developing corpus luteum — Ovulated ovum

OOGENESIS

As the levels of hormones change throughout the month, the ovum matures inside the follicle and is released during ovulation. What structure develops into the corpus luteum?

The ovarian cycle in women carries their bodies through the steps necessary to mature and release an egg cell. A normal cycle follows a series of steps.

Day 1: The hypothalamus in the brain reacts to low levels of estrogen in the blood by stimulating the anterior pituitary gland to release follicle-stimulating hormone (FSH). This hormone causes several primary follicles in the ovary to develop and form secondary follicles.

Around Day 9: Only one healthy secondary follicle remains, with the rest having undergone degeneration. As the follicle grows, it releases large amounts of estrogen. As a result, estrogen levels in the blood dramatically increase. Once reaching a certain level, the hypothalamus reacts to the increased estrogen by triggering a surge of luteinizing hormone (LH).

Around Day 14: The secondary follicle develops a tertiary follicle in response to the burst of LH. Recall that the oocyte undergoes meiosis. The development of this tertiary follicle occurs after the first meiotic division of the primary oocyte. The burst of LH causes the follicle to break open, releasing the egg in a process called ovulation. The empty follicle that is left behind is now called a corpus luteum.

What Are Fertilization and Development?

Fertilization

Ova and sperm serve the single purpose of producing an offspring. The first step to this goal is **fertilization**. Fertilization is the fusion of an ovum with a sperm.

During intercourse, millions of sperm are released into a female's vaginal opening. A protective layer containing binding sites for the sperm surrounds the egg. Enzymes from the sperm head break down the egg's protective layer. This allows a single sperm to enter the egg.

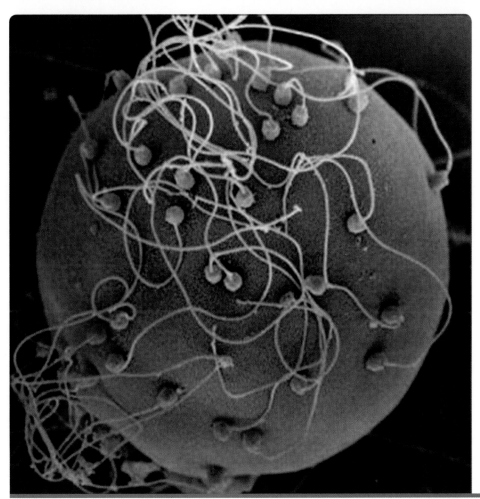

THE MOMENT OF FERTILIZATION

This scanning electron micrograph shows a clam egg being swarmed by sperm. Why are eggs so much larger than sperm?

Following fertilization, the egg is activated and undergoes a series of changes. One such change is the formation of a protective barrier that prevents other sperm from entering. The single sperm that has already entered the egg penetrates the egg cytoplasm. The sperm's nuclear envelope disappears. The sperm **chromatin** unwinds and loosens. This process is called decondensation. Chromatin from both egg and sperm are soon surrounded by a nuclear envelope. The genomes of the two haploid (N) cells fuse to form a **single diploid** cell (2N). The **diploid cell** contains a complete set of chromosomes from each parent. The fertilized cell is called a zygote. It will continue to develop into an embryo.

Development of an Embryo

Almost immediately after its formation, the one-celled zygote begins to undergo mitosis. Cell division allows an organism to grow and develop.

■ As the embryo travels toward the uterus, it undergoes several divisions. It progresses from one cell through 2-cell, 4-cell, 8-cell, 16-cell, and 32-cell stages to form a solid ball of cells called a morula.

■ A morula contains approximately 64 cells.

■ As the cells continue to divide, a cavity develops in the center of the morula. The resulting hollow ball of cells is called a blastula.

■ During implantation, the blastula attaches to the wall of the uterus.

■ As the embryo continues to develop, the single-layered blastula divides into three layers during a process called gastrulation.

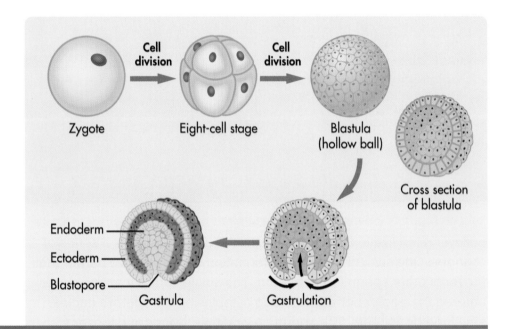

GASTRULATION

Gastrulation is the beginning of cell differentiation. During gastrulation, the single-layered blastula divides into how many layers?

The three layers of cells consist of the ectoderm, mesoderm, and endoderm. They will ultimately form all the tissues and organs of the organism. The ectoderm will develop into the skin and nervous system. Mesoderm cells will become most of the internal structures. These include the bones, muscles, and blood cells. The endoderm will become the cells that line digestive organs, as well as the respiratory and excretory systems.

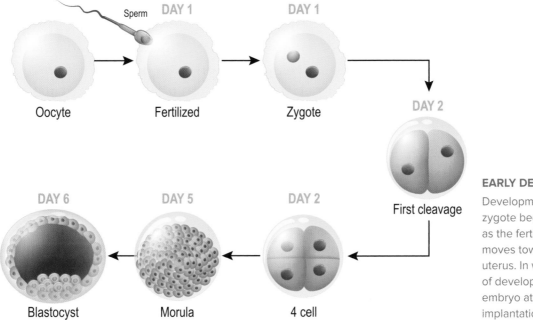

Oocyte · Fertilized · Zygote · DAY 1 · DAY 1 · DAY 2 · First cleavage · DAY 2 · 4 cell · DAY 5 · Morula · DAY 6 · Blastocyst · Sperm

EARLY DEVELOPMENT
Development of the zygote begins even as the fertilized egg moves toward the uterus. In what stage of development is an embryo at the time of implantation?

What Is Somatic Cell Nuclear Transfer (SCNT)?

Reproductive Technology

In a search for better ways to treat diseases and heal injuries, scientists have developed ways to manipulate reproduction. One such method is called **somatic cell nuclear transfer** (SCNT). It allows scientists to implant DNA of a somatic cell (a non-reproductive, body cell) into an egg. The desired organism can then grow and develop with the newly inserted DNA.

The process of SCNT begins by removing the nucleus of a somatic cell. The remainder of the cell is discarded. The nucleus of an egg cell is also removed. However, the nucleus is discarded, leaving all other parts intact. The somatic cell nucleus is inserted into the enucleated egg cell. There, its newly implanted DNA reprograms it as a diploid cell. To begin cell division, the egg is stimulated with an electric shock. After several rounds of mitosis, a blastula forms and the organism grows as a normal zygote. However, the DNA of the zygote is identical to the DNA of the original somatic cell. An organism that might normally only exist from the **sexual reproduction** between an egg and a sperm now exists as a clone. This feat of science is great, but also comes with great controversy.

What Are the Effects of Non-Disjunction?

Non-Disjunction

Given all the complex processes involved in reproduction, it is no wonder that abnormal outcomes sometimes occur. When this happens during meiosis, it is referred to as non-disjunction. When chromosomes fail to separate properly during anaphase I or II, the number of chromosomes in the daughter cells is imbalanced.

Non-disjunction can lead to **aneuploidy**, which is a condition in which an offspring has an abnormal number of chromosomes. **Monosomy** is the condition in which a daughter cell is missing a chromosome or part of a chromosome from one parent. **Trisomy** is a condition in which a daughter cell receives an additional chromosome from one of the parent cells.

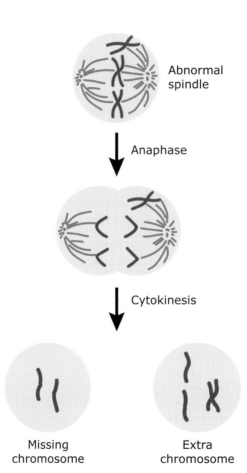

Abnormal spindle

Anaphase

Cytokinesis

Missing chromosome

Extra chromosome

ABNORMAL NUMBERS OF CHROMOSOMES

Non-disjunction results in an abnormal number of chromosomes following cell division. What is an example of a genetic disorder caused by non-disjunction?

Non-disjunction can affect the number of sex chromosomes inherited by an individual. Recall that normal females possess two X chromosomes and normal males possess one X and one Y chromosome. Any discrepancies in these normal pairings result in sex-linked disorders among surviving offspring.

What Are Some Examples of Aneuploidy, Monosomy, and Trisomy?

Aneuploidy and Monosomy

Recall that aneuploidy is a condition in which an individual inherits an abnormal number of chromosomes. Turner syndrome is a sex-linked condition caused by **monosomy**. A female with Turner syndrome has one X chromosome instead of two. The resulting symptoms include incomplete development during puberty, short height, a broad chest, and infertility.

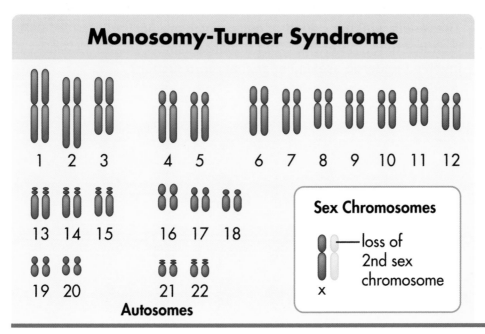

MONOSOMY

This karyotype of a human's chromosomes shows that there is a missing X chromosome, which results in Turner syndrome. What other types of aneuploidy can affect the sex chromosomes?

Aneuploidy and Trisomy

Klinefelter syndrome is a sex-linked disorder found among males. As a result of non-disjunction, males receive an extra X chromosome (XXY). Small testes, enlarged breasts, other feminine body characteristics, and sterility are the typical characteristics of Klinefelter syndrome.

Probably the most common example of **trisomy** is Down syndrome (trisomy 21). This disorder occurs when an offspring receives an extra copy of chromosome 21. Down syndrome affects normal brain and body development in a child.

Another example of trisomy is Patau syndrome (trisomy on chromosome 13). This condition results in serious eye, brain, and circulatory disorders, as well as a cleft palate.

Consider the Explain Question

Explain what happens during asexual and sexual reproduction.

Go online to complete the scientific explanation.

dlc.com/ca10106s

Check Your Understanding

A cell undergoes one round of cell division. The results are four daughter cells, which are not identical to the parent cell. Did the organism involved undergo asexual or sexual reproduction?

dlc.com/ca10107s

STEM in Action

Applying Asexual and Sexual Reproduction

Understanding the processes of **sexual reproduction** has helped scientists develop treatments for fertility. Many couples have difficulty getting pregnant on their own. They often turn to fertility treatments to assist with the natural reproduction processes.

One such treatment is called in vitro **fertilization** (IVF). The couple's own sperm and egg are used in this process. However, they are collected from each parent and joined outside of the woman's body. The fertilization process takes place in a laboratory under ideal conditions. In order to increase the chances of getting pregnant, more than one egg is fertilized. The eggs are monitored to be sure that mitosis begins and an embryo develops.

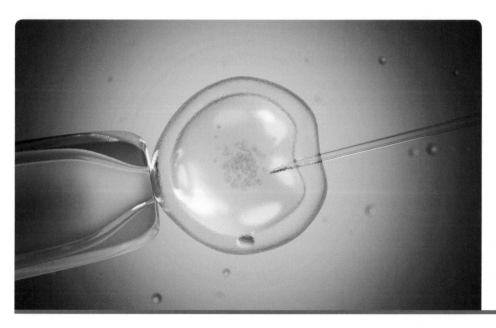

IVF
During one type of IVF, an ovum is fertilized with sperm that are injected through a needle. What will happen to this fertilized egg?

In vitro fertilization is often an effective method for achieving pregnancy. After the embryos divide to about four cells, they are implanted into the woman's uterus. Again, more than one embryo is usually implanted in order to increase the chances for success. This is also the reason that multiple births, such as twins and triplets, are more common among couples who undergo IVF compared to those who achieve pregnancy naturally.

STEM and Asexual and Sexual Reproduction

Advances in technology are changing the face of reproduction. Processes that could previously only be done sexually with an egg and a sperm are becoming asexual. SCNT, commonly known as cloning, is just one such method.

Researchers have developed two distinct uses for cloning: reproductive cloning and therapeutic cloning. In reproductive cloning, scientists remove nuclear genetic material from egg cells and replace it with genetic material from the nucleus of a somatic (non-reproductive) cell. This egg cell is then transferred into the uterus to develop into a baby whose genotype is an exact duplicate of the somatic cell. Reproductive cloning has been tested in animals, including sheep, mice, cats, and dogs, but is considered unethical in humans.

Therapeutic cloning uses a similar method, but the goal is different. The resulting embryonic cells (that is, pluripotent stem cells) are treated to develop not into whole organisms, but into particular tissues or organs. The hope is that the stem cells will replace harmful or damaged cells for people with certain diseases such as Alzheimer's and cancer.

Individual genes can also be cloned. Molecular biologists replicate the process of genetic recombination in the lab, splicing together desirable nucleotide sequences. They then insert the so-called recombinant DNA into bacteria, which replicate the DNA to create many, many copies. The recombinant DNA can be used to create novel proteins; can be inserted into other organisms, which are then known as genetically modified organisms; or can be used to treat disease. The possibilities are endless, but is DNA cloning ethical?

SCNT and molecular cloning technologies raise many concerns and a lot of controversy. Will this lead to human cloning? The debate remains. Many people wonder if this new technology that may be able to treat life-threatening diseases is worth the price of the ethical issues that come with it.

CONCEPT
5.6

Biological Organization and Control

LESSON OVERVIEW

Lesson Questions

- How are organisms organized into cells, tissues and organs?
- How do organs work together to form specific functions?
- Why and how do organisms maintain their internal state?
- How do different parts of the body interact to maintain homeostasis?

Key Vocabulary

Which terms do you already know?

- ☐ artery
- ☐ ATP
- ☐ blood
- ☐ brain stem
- ☐ cellular respiration
- ☐ endocrine system
- ☐ endothermic
- ☐ feedback mechanism
- ☐ glucose
- ☐ heart
- ☐ homeostasis
- ☐ immune system
- ☐ integumentary system
- ☐ lungs
- ☐ mineral nutrients
- ☐ mitochondria
- ☐ muscle
- ☐ musculoskeletal system

dlc.com/ca10108s

Lesson Objectives

By the end of the lesson, you should be able to:

- Identify and classify biological structures according to their level of biological organization.
- Explain the criteria used to classify biological structures into an organizational hierarchy.
- Identify the major roles of different human body systems.
- Construct a flow diagram that explains the function of a negative feedback loop.
- Use examples to explain how the human body maintains homeostasis.

Key Vocabulary continued

- ☐ nerve
- ☐ nervous system
- ☐ neuron
- ☐ phloem
- ☐ respiratory system
- ☐ stem
- ☐ system
- ☐ vein
- ☐ xylem

Working Together

When a person exercises, different organs and systems work together to maintain the body at equilibrium. What systems in the human body are hard at work during exercise?

dlc.com/ca10109s

EXPLAIN QUESTION

How do the different systems of the body work together to maintain appropriate internal conditions?

RUN YOUR WAY TO BETTER FITNESS

Running is one of numerous exercises that assists you in building and maintaining good cardiovascular health. How do you think the cardiovascular system assists the body during running?

How Are Organisms Organized into Cells, Tissues, and Organs?

Most multicellular organisms are complex, containing structures which vary among individuals. This is seen when we observe the difference between a giraffe and a field mouse. All organisms are made of cells, and although cells share many commonalities, they are found in a variety of shapes and sizes. Why is there such variety among cells, and how do the internal organizations of these cells differ from each other?

Cells are specialized to perform very specific functions within an organism. For example, **muscle** cells need to be long fibers in order to provide energy and movement. Muscle cells produce **ATP** (the energy of the cell or adenosine triphosphate) and are able to use the produced ATP for movement of the body. Energy, or ATP production, occurs within the **mitochondria** of cells and muscle cells, due to their function, contain many of these organelles. Muscle cells must also contain microscopic structures, called myofibrils, which enable them to contract because this is how movement occurs. Within the human body, muscles do a variety of jobs—pulling on bones for movement, moving food through the gut during digestion, or forming the **heart** and pumping **blood**. Different muscle types perform different functions within the human body; in order for this to occur, muscle cells must be structured in order for them to function properly. Like muscles, within the body there are many types of cells and almost all have specialized functions.

Muscle cells do not work independently. One cell alone is very small and must work with hundreds of thousands of others to be effective. Muscle cells of the same type are organized into groups called tissues. Below is an illustration of what different muscle tissues look like under the microscope.

THREE DIFFERENT KINDS OF MUSCLE TISSUE

Muscle cells of the same type, organized together, make up muscle tissue. There are three different types of muscle tissue—smooth, skeletal, and cardiac—each with their own shape and function. For example, cardiac muscles are striated in order to perform correctly. What do you think *striated* means, and how does this shape help cardiac muscles?

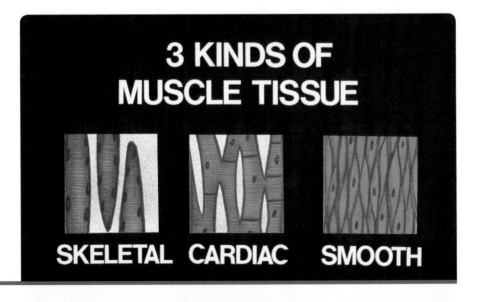

3 KINDS OF MUSCLE TISSUE

SKELETAL   CARDIAC   SMOOTH

In a muscle, such as the biceps muscle on your upper arm, the cells are bundled together and surrounded by connective tissues that hold them in place. Many of these bundles are organized together making the biceps muscle. The biceps muscle is made up of a complex hierarchy of parts, from specialized organelles within specific cells to differing specialized tissues. Each works together to form a muscle that is specialized for moving the forearm. This hierarchy exists throughout the human body. Skeletal muscles can be further organized into pairs, forming the **musculoskeletal system**.

Muscles are just one example of hierarchical organization within organisms. Let's look at another example—nerves. As you might expect, nerves are made of **nerve** cells, called **neurons**, but not all nerve cells are the same. Sensory neurons receive signals from stimuli, such as light, and respond appropriately. For example, the pupils in our eyes respond to light through sensory neurons and then contract accordingly. Motor neurons send signals to aid in making muscles move, and interneurons, or brain cells, connect sensory neurons to motor neurons.

Like muscle cells, neurons are organized into bundles that are themselves organized into specific nerves. These in turn are grouped into subsystems (the peripheral and central nervous systems) that make up the **nervous system**.

Hierarchical Organization in Plants

The organization of muscle and nerve cells into tissues, organs, and **systems** are just two examples of the hierarchical organization in animals. This type of organization also occurs in plants. Plant cells have specialized functions. For example, in the **stems** of taller plants are cells that are organized into vessels for carrying water and **mineral nutrients** throughout the plant. These elongated cells, called **xylem**, are organized in vertically orientated bundles of tissue to form thick-walled, pipe-like structures. Some of the xylem tissues are organized into xylem tracheids, which also carry water and nutrients, and still others, called xylem parenchyma, and fibers that provide support, packing, and storage functions for the plant. These different forms of xylem tissues work together to transport water and **mineral** nutrients, keeping the plant healthy. Xylem is associated with other types of cells, called **phloem**, that move sugars and metabolites around the plant. Together, xylem and phloem form organs called vascular bundles that make up a plant's internal transportation system.

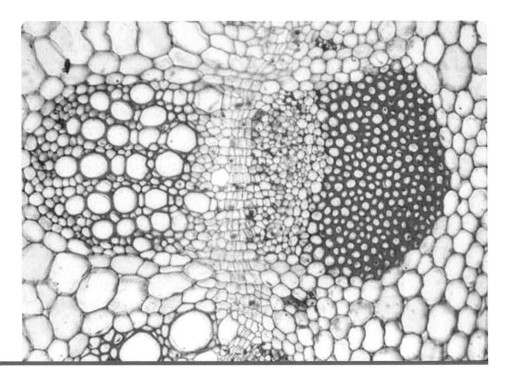

VASCULAR BUNDLE
Xylem (left) and phloem (right) form a vascular bundle, part of a plant's internal transport system.

How Do Organs Work Together to Form Specific Functions?

You are already familiar with many of the organs present in your body. All these organs perform specific functions and all of them work with other organs. Organs that work together to meet a specific need are said to belong to the same system. For example, the heart, arteries, **veins**, capillaries, and blood all work together as part of the circulatory (or cardiovascular) system to move **nutrients**, oxygen, and waste products around the body. Some organs belong to more than one system. For example, the pancreas produces digestive enzymes so it part of the digestive system, but also releases hormones, so it part of the **endocrine system**. Some systems perform unrelated functions—the skin protects the body from pathogens but also regulates temperature and excretes some wastes.

Body systems also interact with one another to perform functions that maintain and support the growth of the organism. The cardiovascular system works with the **respiratory system** to pick up oxygen in the **lungs** and drop off carbon dioxide. The digestive system works with the nervous and endocrine systems to trigger appetite and stimulate eating.

The systems found in the human body, together with some of their interactions, are summarized in the table that follows.

System	Main Function	Major Organs	Some Interactions with Other Systems
Respiratory	Gas exchange	Lungs, trachea, diaphragm, ribs	• Delivers oxygen to, and collects CO_2 from, the circulatory system. • Works with the nervous system to control breathing. • Removes waste CO_2 (excretory system).
Circulatory	Internal transport to and from cells	Heart, arteries, veins, capillaries	• Delivers oxygen from the lungs to cells and takes carbon dioxide from cells to lungs (respiratory and excretory system). • Delivers waste products from the liver to the kidneys (excretory system). • Carries white blood cells for the **immune system**. • Carries nutrients from the gut to cells (digestive system).
Digestive	Ingestion, digestion, absorption, and defecation	Mouth, teeth, tongue, esophagus, stomach, large and small intestines, rectum, and anus	• Delivers digested nutrients to circulatory system. • Muscles in gut move food along (muscular system). • Works with nervous system to control appetite.
Excretory	Removal of waste products of metabolism	Liver, kidneys, ureters, bladder, urethra, lungs, and skin	• Filters waste out of blood (circulatory system). • Circulatory system delivers wastes to the liver to be detoxified. • Lungs remove CO_2 (excretory system). • Works with the **integumentary system** to remove some wastes in sweat.

(Continued)

System	Main Function	Major Organs	Some Interactions with Other Systems
Nervous	Gather and interpret information, control movement and internal conditions	Brain, spinal cord, peripheral nerves, sense organs	• Controls all other body systems.
Endocrine	Regulates some body processes, such as growth	Various glands that produce hormones, including the hypothalamus, pituitary, thyroid, pancreas, testes, and ovaries	• Releases hormones into the circulatory system. • Works with the nervous system to control internal conditions and behavior. • Controls the reproductive system. • Works with many systems to control growth.
Immune	Fights disease	(White blood cells in blood and lymph), skin	• White blood cells are transported by circulatory and lymphatic systems. • White blood cells are made in the bone marrow (musculoskeletal system). • Works with the integumentary system to keep pathogens out of the body.
Musculoskeletal	Moves the body, provides protection, produces blood cells	Bones, different muscles, tendons, ligaments	• Works with the digestive system to push food along the gut. • Arteries, veins, and the heart contain muscles that pump blood (musculoskeletal). • Diaphragm, ribs, and rib muscles enable breathing (respiratory system). • Works with the nervous system to coordinate movement. • Protects vital organs of numerous systems (for example the skull protects the brain—nervous system).

(Continued)

System	Main Function	Major Organs	Some Interactions with Other Systems
Lymphatic	Returns fluid to the blood, protects against disease	Lymph vessels and nodes	• Carries white blood cells for the immune system. • Works with the circulatory system to transport substances to and from cells.
Reproductive	Produces offspring	Testes, ovaries, organs involved in ensuring fertilization	• Works with the endocrine system to control the production and release of sex cells. • Works with the muscular system to control birth process.
Integumentary	Protects body from infection, UV radiation, and toxins; regulates temperature	Skin	• Works with the excretory system to remove waste. • Contains sensory nerves (nervous system). • Works with immune system to prevent pathogen entry.

Why and How Do Organisms Maintain Their Internal State?

From a chilly night to a warm and sunny afternoon, air temperature can vary by 15°C or more in the course of a single day. What happens to your body when it is exposed to such large changes in temperature? The temperature of our bodies normally fluctuates by only one or two degrees from the average human body temperature of 37°C (98.6°F). Humans, along with other **endothermic** animals, maintain an almost constant body temperature despite exposure to often drastic environmental changes. Why does your body work hard to maintain this temperature control? Most of the chemical reactions that occur in the body require enzymes to catalyze them, and many enzymes cease to function above 41°C (106°F). At the other extreme, the heart is likely to stop beating when temperatures fall below 27°C (80°F).

In addition to body temperature regulation, many other properties of our internal environment are kept within specific limits so that our bodies can function properly. This characteristic of organisms is called **homeostasis**. Other properties that are regulated include levels of fluids, salts, gases, and **nutrients**. Multiple systems are involved in homeostasis; for example, the respiratory and urinary systems act together to maintain blood pH at 7.3, the value critical for life. As the external and internal environments change, homeostatic mechanisms act to return the body to optimal operating conditions. There are multiple mechanisms involved in achieving such a balance.

How Homeostasis Works

The most critical mechanism of homeostasis is a control process called a negative feedback loop. A simple example of a negative feedback loop and how it works is the thermostat in a home. The thermostat is set to a desired temperature, and if the air in the room is too cold, the thermostat reacts by turning on the heat. When the room reaches the desired temperature, the heat turns off. This process continues, the heat turning on and off, maintaining the air temperature in a home at the same level all the time. Homeostasis works in a similar fashion in the human body, maintaining everything from body temperature to blood pressure at specific levels.

This type of control system requires three parts:

- A sensor that monitors the set value (in this case, the desired room temperature).
- A processor that determines how far the measured value (air temperature in the room) deviates from the set value (desire room temperature).
- An actuator that can change the measured value.

In the example of a thermostat, the sensor is a thermometer measuring the room temperature. The processor is a machine or computer that compares the measured room temperature with the set value. The actuator is a heater or an air conditioner that heats up or cools down the room.

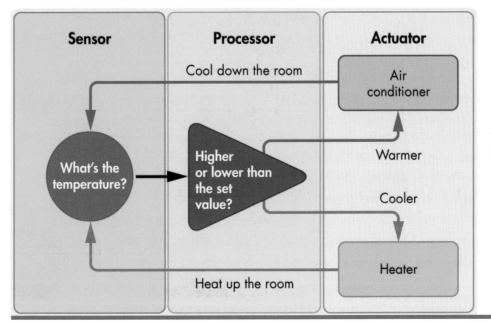

THERMOSTAT

A thermostat is a good model of how a negative feedback loop works to maintain a constant temperature, such as homeostasis in the body. In the example of the thermostat, what happens when the temperature drops below or above a certain level?

Like the thermostat, the human body has sensors, processors, and actuators to maintain the optimum levels of pH, blood **glucose**, body temperature, and more. In addition, these parts must be linked together for the negative **feedback mechanism** to function properly.

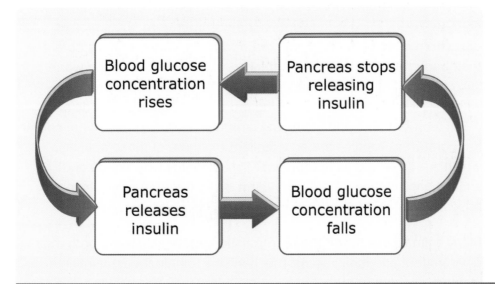

NEGATIVE FEEDBACK LOOP

The pancreas is an organ found in both the digestive and endocrine systems. In the endocrine system, one of its jobs is to help control sugar levels in the blood through the use of insulin. What are the sensors, processors, and actuators in this system?

If the negative feedback system is impaired, homeostasis is not maintained. In the case of blood glucose levels, this can lead to serious diseases like diabetes, chronic high blood pressure, or kidney disease. Homeostatic imbalance eventually will lead to organ failure and death.

How Do Different Parts of the Body Interact to Maintain Homeostasis?

In humans, the nervous and endocrine systems control the other body systems to maintain homeostasis. The hypothalamus in the brain is connected to the pituitary gland by nerves. The hypothalamus (part of the autonomic **nervous system**) is sensitive to many properties of the body's internal environment. It stimulates the pituitary gland to release hormones into the blood. In turn, these pituitary hormones travel around the body and act on different body parts to maintain homeostasis. Together, the hypothalamus and pituitary gland play the role of the main processor for homeostasis. Following are three examples of homeostasis mechanisms.

Example 1: Controlling Body Temperature

The ability of animals to control their body temperature is called thermoregulation. Animals have a range of temperatures in which their biochemical reactions occur most efficiently, but outside this range of temperature, the animal may be unable to function. For some animals, this range is very limited, and significant divergence from the optimum temperature will quickly result in death. These animals are called homeotherms or endotherms and produce heat from their own body tissues to maintain their temperature. Examples of endotherms are humans, mammals, and birds. Other animals obtain their body heat from the environment, such as basking in the warm sun or sitting on a warm rock during the day. Their activity may vary with the air temperature, becoming more active during periods of warm temperatures and hiding in warm places during periods of cooler temperatures. Reptiles are an excellent example of these animals, which are classified as ectotherms. This explains why lizards and snakes bask in the sun or lie on warm rocks during the day, trying to raise or maintain their body temperature.

Many animals use mixed thermoregulation strategies, using both their environment and their internal mechanisms to help them maintain a stable body temperature. For example, birds may use basking as a means of raising their body temperature. Some mammals and birds allow a lower body temperature during cold periods and enter a state of torpor, in which they do not respond to stimulation such as light or heat. This is a means of conserving energy when food, or energy, is not readily available, such as in winter. In general, larger animals rely less on external temperatures than smaller animals because they have a larger heat capacity and, therefore, cool down and warm up more slowly.

Humans maintain a core body temperature of about 37°C (98.6°F). A departure of one or two degrees from this temperature results in an inability to function normally. Raised body temperatures are called hyperthermia. Body temperatures of over 43°C result in brain damage and usually death. Lowered body temperatures are a condition called hypothermia. Body temperatures less than about 25°C usually result in death. The human body has a variety of methods for maintaining an optimum body temperature. Temperature receptors throughout the body monitor internal temperatures, such as the hypothalamus monitoring blood temperature, and transmit these signals to the brain. The brain integrates this information to enable the body to regulate its internal temperature when needed.

If the body is too cold, signals from the hypothalamus will do some or all of the following:

- Stimulate cells to increase **cellular respiration**, which generates more heat in the body.
- Stimulate blood vessels in the skin to constrict, decreasing blood flow to the skin and reducing heat loss from the blood.
- Cause muscles to contract and relax in a spasmodic fashion, which is called shivering. This quick movement of muscles generates heat through friction and warms the outlying tissues.
- Raise hair (goose pimples), to trap a layer of warm air closer to the skin, keeping the organism warm.

If the body gets too hot, signals from the hypothalamus may:

- Stimulate panting to increase heat loss through evaporation from the lungs, cooling the body.
- Stimulate blood vessels in the skin to dilate, increasing blood flow to the surface where more heat is lost to the environment from the skin.
- Stimulate sweat glands to produce sweat, which evaporates off the skin, taking heat with it.

Humans have behavioral adaptations to control the body's heat balance as well. The most obvious are seeking shelter from the cold and shade from the heat of the sun. The loss of body hair in humans is likely to be an adaptation to thermoregulation that adapted humans to the hot climate of the open African savanna. As humans migrated from their original habitat, they adopted new strategies to keep warm or cool. One is the use of clothing.

Some endotherms usually have insulating external coverings, such as feathers, fur, or hair, which are efficient insulators. Blubber, an insulating layer of fat, is widely used by aquatic mammals, such as seals and whales, which would otherwise rapidly lose body heat to the surrounding water. Animal adaptations to hot temperatures include avoidance of high daytime temperatures and anatomical structures that radiate heat such as large ears, thin fur, and naked skin.

Example 2: Control of Water and Electrolytes

Human activities vary greatly throughout the day. One could exercise for half an hour in the morning, then sit in classes for several hours, eat meals, and sleep at night. Different levels and timing of activities require different amounts of energy and produce corresponding wastes. These all contribute to variations in the properties of blood circulating throughout the human body such as acidity, electrolyte, and waste concentrations.

JACKIE JOYNER JUMPING HURDLES

As the athlete jumps hurdles, numerous changes occur throughout the body systems to maintain internal conditions. Can you identify the changes that occur, and what conditions are maintained?

The primary sensors of these blood properties are in the hypothalamus. The hypothalamus is sensitive to the osmolarity—the solute concentration—of the blood and controls the secretions of pituitary hormones from the pituitary gland. These pituitary hormones signal organs such as the kidneys and liver of the excretory system to perform particular functions. For example, if too much water is ingested, the kidneys can remove the excess water from the blood. In contrast, if the water level is low, the hypothalamus will stimulate the pituitary gland. The pituitary gland then sends a signal to the kidneys to conserve water by producing more concentrated, more yellow, urine, and produce the sensation of thirst.

Example 3: Controlling Blood Pressure

A critical role of the circulatory system is to maintain blood pressure. Blood pressure is the pressure of circulating blood on **artery** walls. Blood pressure is influenced by several factors, such as heart rate, the volume of blood that exits the heart per beat (stroke volume), and the amount of resistance to blood flow within the vessels. The resistance to blood flow is further influenced by the diameters of the vessels. Larger vessels have less resistance to flow. These properties of the heart and blood vessels are controlled by the body in order to increase or decrease blood pressure so that it stays within safe limits.

Blood pressure is constantly measured by pressure sensing cells called baroreceptors in the heart and main arteries. These receptors send signals back through nerve fibers to part of the brain called the medulla. The medulla acts as the processor in the negative feedback loop that controls blood pressure. If blood pressure is too low, the brain signals the heart to increase its output of blood. At the same time, the small arteries called arterioles, which supply oxygen to non-critical organs such as the skin and intestines, constrict. This simultaneous increase of blood leaving the heart and constriction of blood to non-vital organs, diverts blood to critical organs such as the brain. If blood pressure is too high, these processes are reversed and cardiac output is reduced and the veins and arterioles dilate.

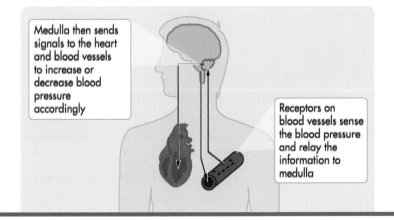

Medulla then sends signals to the heart and blood vessels to increase or decrease blood pressure accordingly

Receptors on blood vessels sense the blood pressure and relay the information to medulla

CONTROL OF BLOOD PRESSURE

The brain regulates the heart and blood vessels to increase or decrease blood output, raising or lowering blood pressure. What are the bodily consequences if blood pressure does not stay within certain parameters?

Consider the Explain Question

How do the different systems of the body work together to maintain internal conditions?

Go online to complete the scientific explanation.

dlc.com/ca10110s

Check Your Understanding

Can you provide examples of positive or negative feedback loops found in the endocrine system?

dlc.com/ca10111s

STEM in Action

Applying Biological Organization and Control

Homeostasis is the process of maintaining the stable internal environment critical to health and function. One of the primary homeostatic mechanisms is maintenance of the acid-base ratio in the blood. Blood pH must remain between 6.8 and 7.8; any deviation is quickly fatal. There are a number of pathways the body uses to control blood pH, but the exhalation of CO_2 is a major pathway. A reduction in the ability to exhale CO_2 can have a significant impact on blood pH levels.

EMPHYSEMA WARNING

Smoking is a major cause of emphysema. What other homeostatic mechanisms might be affected by smoking?

Emphysema is a disease that reduces the body's ability to exhale CO_2. Most often caused by smoking, emphysema is one condition identified as a chronic obstructive pulmonary disease (COPD). In emphysema, the lung tissue is damaged, resulting in a loss of elasticity and trapping of gases. In addition to difficulty breathing and reduced oxygenation of the blood, emphysema can result in respiratory acidosis or increased acidification of the blood.

One of the ways that emphysema is diagnosed is through computerized tomography, or CT scan. Computerized tomography is an x-ray procedure that uses powerful software to combine multiple x-ray images into cross-sectional images, and even three-dimensional images, of the internal organs and structures of the body. In patients with emphysema, CT scans will show pockets of damaged lung tissue where gases are trapped. Emphysema diagnosis is only one way that CT scans are used to help physicians diagnose problems with homeostatic control. CT scans can also be used to examine calcium and **glucose homeostasis**, brain homeostasis, and a variety of other conditions.

STEM and Biological Control and Organization

Long-term disruption in homeostasis can lead to chronic diseases, such as diabetes. Under normal conditions, blood glucose is taken up by the cells to fuel their metabolism. However, this process is inhibited in diabetes patients because of a breakdown in the hormonal response that normally maintains blood glucose levels. Specialized cells in the pancreas, called beta cells, release the hormone insulin. Insulin is secreted when blood glucose levels are elevated. The insulin will then induce cells to take up glucose, lowering the level circulating in the blood. However, diabetes patients either produce too little insulin (a disorder called type I diabetes) or their cells somehow fail to respond to insulin (type II diabetes).

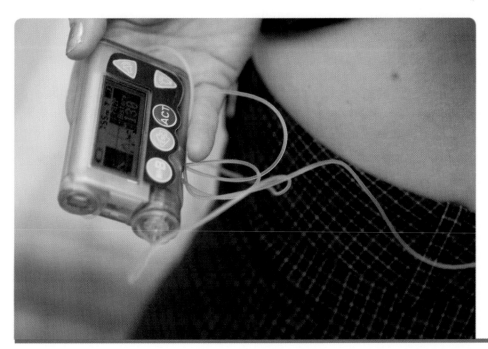

INSULIN PUMP FOR DIABETES

In what ways might this technology improve the quality of life of a person with diabetes?

People with diabetes must monitor their blood glucose levels regularly and adjust their diet, activity, and treatment to keep glucose levels within the safe range. Many people with diabetes must inject insulin daily in order to maintain appropriate blood glucose levels. You might imagine how much constant monitoring and injections would impact your life. For many people, the development of the insulin pump has made a significant impact in both their ability to manage their blood glucose levels and their quality of life with diabetes. The insulin pump is a computerized insulin delivery system that provides a low level of continuous insulin, much like how the pancreas functions. In addition, extra insulin can be delivered to account for individual, and varied, diet and activity levels.

Currently, more than 300 million people worldwide and 18 million Americans suffer from diabetes. It is one of the most prevalent chronic diseases in the world. The number of new cases is growing each year, and the populations suffering from the disease are also increasing; children and adolescents are a growing population of diabetic sufferers. Furthermore, it is estimated that in the United States alone approximately one quarter of all cases are undiagnosed.

Efforts to increase early detection of the disease are important, as early intervention can greatly improve prognosis and increase quality of life. Technology is providing new methods for disease diagnosis. One such method under development is the use of a breathalyzer that could detect a variety of chemicals in the breath that are indicative of chronic or infectious disease, including diabetes. Such a device could make screening easier, cheaper, and more palatable.

The insulin pump and the breathalyzer are just two examples of contributions engineers have made in the fields of disease diagnosis and treatment.

Natural Resources

LESSON OVERVIEW

Lesson Question

■ What are natural resources, and how do we use them?

Lesson Objectives

By the end of the lesson, you should be able to:

■ Identify natural resources and understand how humans use them.

■ Describe where natural resources come from.

■ Explain the difference between renewable and nonrenewable natural resources.

■ Describe some environmental effects of using natural resources.

■ Describe and explain ways that we can conserve natural resources.

Key Vocabulary

Which terms do you already know?

☐ bio-fuel
☐ biomass
☐ coal
☐ conservation
☐ geothermal energy
☐ global warming
☐ greenhouse gas
☐ groundwater
☐ heat energy
☐ hydroelectric energy
☐ natural gas
☐ natural resource
☐ nonrenewable resource
☐ oil
☐ petroleum
☐ renewable resource
☐ solar energy
☐ sustainable
☐ tidal energy
☐ wind energy

dlc.com/ca10112s

Thinking about Natural Resources

dlc.com/ca10113s

Consider for a moment all the things you need in order to live: air, food, water, shelter, clothing, and medicine. What about things that make life easier or better, but that you do not need in order to survive? Electricity, transportation, and entertainment might spring to mind. Where do these things come from, and how do humans use them to make life better?

A CAFÉ AT NIGHT

How many natural resources can you spot in this scene?

EXPLAIN QUESTION

How do we use natural resources, and why is conservation of natural resources important?

What Are Natural Resources, and How Do We Use Them?

Nonrenewable Resources

Nonrenewable resources are materials or energy sources that cannot be replenished once used. These resources typically form very slowly by natural processes. When we use up nonrenewable resources, they will not form again in the course of human lifetimes. Important nonrenewable resources include fossil fuels, metals, and other mineral ores. Soil is sometimes considered a nonrenewable resource because it can take hundreds of years to form significant amounts.

Fossil Fuels

Coal, **petroleum** (commonly called **oil**), and **natural gas** are all fossil fuels. We depend heavily on fossil fuels for all our energy needs, including transportation, electricity, and heating. In addition to being energy resources, fossil fuels provide materials for making human-made resources. For example, we make plastics from petroleum.

What exactly are fossil fuels? They are fuels formed from the bodies of once-living things that were buried beneath sediment and transformed by geologic processes. Hundreds of millions of years ago, Earth's climate was warmer, and swampland was more abundant. As vegetation and other organisms died, their remains accumulated into layers, and low oxygen levels prevented the complete decomposition of the organic matter. As millions of years passed, this layer of organic matter was gradually buried by thousands of feet of sediment, subjecting it to intense heat and pressure. Coal formed in those regions of ancient swampland and peat bogs. The intense pressure removed much of the water and other compounds, leaving a carbon-rich layer of soft rock. The peat goes through several transformations as more and more pressure is added. Eventually, the peat turns into coal. The coal can be burned to release energy.

Unlike coal, which formed from ancient peat bogs, oil and natural gas formed from organic matter largely composed of once-living aquatic organisms, such as algae, that accumulated at the bottom of shallow seas and lakes. As the sediment accumulated over millions of years, pressure and heat converted the organic remains into shale and petroleum. In areas where the sediment was deepest, higher pressures and temperatures resulted in the formation of natural gas. In each case, once-living organic material was transformed into fuel. At first, all this oil and natural gas was trapped in tiny pores in the shale itself. As pressure increased over time, the oil and natural gas were squeezed out of these pores and travelled laterally to a much more porous rock, such as sandstone or limestone. If the porous rock was capped by a rock that was not porous, the oil and natural gas became trapped. By drilling through the cap rock, oil companies can release the oil and gas below.

The energy from fossil fuels came originally from the sun. Plants and microorganisms on Earth changed sunlight into chemical energy by photosynthesis. This chemical energy is released when fossil fuels are burned. But burning fossil fuels releases carbon from the fuels into the atmosphere as carbon dioxide, a **greenhouse gas** that causes the atmosphere to warm as concentration increases. Burning fossil fuels also releases other pollutants into the atmosphere that lead to smog.

Air pollution and climate change are two major environmental problems confronting us today. But these are not the only environmental problems related to the burning of fossil fuels. Mining, drilling, and transporting fossil fuels all pose risks to ecosystems and human health. Coal mining damages natural habitats and can pollute land and water. Oil spills caused by accidents during drilling and transporting oil have caused serious harm to many ecosystems. Fracking, a process that is used to extract natural gas from shale, has the potential to pollute water supplies. As fossil fuel supplies run low, we are mining and drilling in harder-to-reach places to find new supplies, increasing the risk of accidents that can further harm people and the environment. Decreasing our dependence on fossil fuels is an important priority. Simple steps to conserve energy, such as turning off lights and walking instead of driving, can help decrease fossil fuel use.

**KEEPING PACE
WITH NEED**

Can coal keep up with
energy demand? What
will we do if we run out?

Rocks and Minerals

The rocks of Earth's crust contain hundreds of different minerals,
including metal ores, which provide the material resources that we use
to make things. Some minerals are common, whereas others are rare.
Because rocks and minerals take millions of years to form, they are
considered nonrenewable resources.

Crushed rock and minerals are important ingredients in building
materials such as concrete and asphalt that are used in major
structures of modern cities and towns. Computer technologies require
certain metals, many of which are relatively rare. Earth's rock layers
also provide the minerals we use to make glass and the fossil fuels
we use to make plastic. Nearly everything we use in our daily lives
contains plastic, metals, rock materials, or glass. However, using these
resources comes at a cost. Rock and mineral resources must be mined
from beneath the ground. Some forms of mining remove large amounts
of soil and natural habitat, whereas other forms require us to dig
deep tunnels. Mining is a dangerous job that can pollute air and water
supplies of surrounding communities. In addition, competition for rare
minerals can lead to disputes between nations.

LAYERED MINERALS

This rock contains many layers of minerals of different colors. What are some uses for rocks and minerals?

Conserving material resources helps to lessen some of these problems. Recycling is an important practice that helps conserve rock and mineral resources. We can also use fewer resources by reusing objects instead of using disposable items. Choosing items with less packaging also cuts down on resource waste.

Soil

Soil is a critical resource for meeting some of our most basic needs for food and clothing. We depend on soil for growing crops that we eat and feed to farm animals. We also use crops grown in soil to make fabrics such as cotton, and we use trees for lumber and paper. Soil contains both organic matter—the broken-down remains of once-living things—and sediment formed by the weathering and of rock. These processes can take a long time: depending on the climate, from one hundred to one thousand years per inch of soil.

Soil can be lost by erosion and degraded by intensive farming and forestry practices. For example, clear-cut logging removes all of the trees in an area. Without tree roots to hold the soil in place, large amounts of soil can quickly wash away. Removing all of the crops from a field at the same time can cause similar problems.

CLEAR-CUT LOGGING

Soil quickly erodes from a clear-cut hillside. Why does clear cutting cause soil erosion?

It is very important to conserve soil by stopping erosion and degradation. Soil **conservation** strategies include contour plowing, strip-cropping, and terracing. Farmers who follow these practices shape their fields to follow the natural slope of the land, which slows water as it flows downhill. Because water carries more soil when it moves faster, slowing the water lessens soil erosion. Flattened areas on the slope can actually catch some of the soil that the water carries as the water slows. Planting cover crops on open fields also helps conserve soils. Different types of plants deplete different nutrients from the soil, and some types of plants add nutrients to the soil. Rotating crops so that different crops are planted each season helps stop soil degradation.

Renewable Resources

What types of resources are renewable? Trees and other plants are usually considered renewable, as are freshwater resources such as streams and **groundwater**. The water cycle naturally "recycles" water as it moves between the land and the atmosphere. When water evaporates, the water molecules are separated from pollutants and other impurities. When the water falls back to Earth as precipitation, we can use it once again. However, pollution or overuse can destroy local water supplies.

The biosphere provides many of the materials and services that are used by humans. For example, agricultural land provides us with food. Forests provide wood used in construction, furniture manufacture, and paper making. Forests also provide many other services. They are a major source of modern medicines, prevent soil erosion, and remove carbon dioxide from the atmosphere. They are also a reservoir for biodiversity. Careful management of the world's forests is a vital part of sustaining life on Earth.

In addition, many types of energy resource are renewable. These include **biomass**, **solar energy**, **wind energy**, **hydroelectric energy**, **geothermal energy**, and **tidal energy**. People around the world are working hard to develop these renewable energy resources to help end our dependence on fossil fuels.

Replacing nonrenewable resources with **renewable resources** will help our economies and societies become more stable. Because renewable resources do not run out, we can use them at certain **sustainable** levels for long periods of time. When we use renewable resources sustainably, they are conserved for future use. The resulting certainty in supply contributes to economic and social stability. Prices tend to remain even instead of increasing wildly with demand. Nations can depend on their own steady supplies of resources. This helps reduce conflict around the world.

Let's take a closer look at some of the ways that people are trying to substitute renewable resources for nonrenewable ones.

Examining Renewable Energy Resources

Biomass fuel, or **biofuel**, is fuel that comes from plants or other living things. Wood is a very common form of biofuel. Lots of people around the world still produce heat and cook by burning wood. Ethanol fuel from corn is another example of biofuel. Increasingly, companies are using algae to make biofuels. Compared to corn, algae grow more quickly and require less space and fewer resources to grow. Using algae also frees more corn for people to eat, thereby keeping down the cost of this crucial food crop.

Solar energy is the radiant energy received on Earth from the sun in the form of heat and light. Most people think of solar panels when they think of solar energy. Solar panels convert light energy to electric energy. However, there are other ways to harvest solar energy—for example, solar water heaters heat water naturally by focusing sunlight on water in containers. Even drying clothes on a clothesline is a use of solar energy.

Wind energy is harvested by wind turbines that convert the kinetic energy of wind to mechanical energy, which is then converted to electrical energy by generators. Hydroelectric energy harnesses the gravitational potential energy of water stored in a reservoir. The potential energy is converted into kinetic energy as water from the reservoir flows down through penstocks (pipes) in the dam. The flowing water spins turbines inside the dam. The mechanical energy of the turbine is then used to turn a generator that converts the mechanical energy into electrical energy. Though hydroelectric energy does not produce pollution, the dams can damage river ecosystems.

RENEWABLE ENERGY

Solar energy and other renewable energy resources can replace nonrenewable resources. Why are renewable energy resources considered sustainable?

Geothermal energy is **heat energy** from Earth's interior. This energy can be used to heat water. Rising steam from the water spins turbines, which turn generators that produce electrical energy. Geothermal energy is also used to heat some homes.

Tidal energy is the energy derived from the periodic rise and fall of sea level near shores. Tidal power plants convert the gravitational potential energy stored behind large estuarial dams (called barrages) into kinetic energy as water flows through pipes in the dam. Unlike a hydroelectric dam, the direction of the water flow through a tidal dam changes depending on the direction of the tide. In either case, the flowing water is converted into usable mechanical energy as it spins turbines within the dam. Similar to wind and hydroelectric power, the turbines turn generators, converting the mechanical energy into electrical energy.

Consider the Explain Question

| How do we use natural resources, and why is conservation of natural resources important?

Go online to complete the scientific explanation.

dlc.com/ca10114s

Check Your Understanding

| Go online to check your understanding of this concept's key ideas.

dlc.com/ca10115s

STEM in Action

Applying Natural Resources

Biofuel can be made from nearly any once-living matter. Common sources include grass clippings, farm waste, and compost. However, biofuels usually do not have as much concentrated energy as fossil fuels like gasoline. The intense pressure from the geologic processes that form fossil fuels squeezes the energy-containing carbon molecules into smaller volumes. In contrast, recently deceased organisms are less dense. Most vehicles could be made to run on today's biofuels, but they would likely sacrifice power. Tomorrow's biofuels may be more concentrated, however.

GROWING ENERGY CROPS

Some farmers grow crops to be used for fuel. How do you think this might affect agriculture?

Biologists are applying cutting-edge biotechnologies to the development of biofuels. Biologists can genetically engineer organisms like bacteria and fungi. These organisms can quickly break down organic matter and convert it into a concentrated fuel. These "super decomposers" could allow us to turn wasted parts of crop plants and food scraps into fuel. Biologists can also genetically engineer algae to create a fast-growing, energy-rich source of organic matter for fuel. Tomorrow's cars, buses, trains, and planes may be running on fuel made from waste instead of fossil fuels.

STEM and Natural Resources

Scientists and engineers around the world are hard at work developing technologies that use **natural resources** more effectively. Whether exploring for oil or creating better solar panels, people who develop natural resources have likely studied science and engineering. Engineers working with natural resources may have knowledge of chemistry, biology, and geology. Furthermore, understanding energy requires a solid foundation in physical science.

Professionals in other fields also use knowledge of natural resources. For example, as part of their designs, architects typically consider how best to conserve natural resources. Architects can use their understanding of solar energy to design homes and other buildings that do not depend on fossil fuels. Adding solar cells to a building provides electricity needed to run lights and appliances. Many other design elements incorporate light and heat from the sun directly into the building. These passive solar elements include skylights, south-facing windows, and dampers to control air flow. Planting shade trees around the building can also help to regulate temperatures.

Relationships between Human Activity and Earth's Systems

dlc.com/ca10116s

LESSON OVERVIEW

Lesson Questions

- How has an abundance of natural resources altered human activity?
- How have Earth's systems affected human activity?
- How have human technological designs affected the environment?
- What relationships exist between Earth's systems and human activities?

Lesson Objectives

By the end of the lesson, you should be able to:

- Explain how the availability of natural resources has affected human activity.
- Explain how natural hazards and climate influence human activity.
- Understand that human activity can affect the global environment and Earth systems.
- Recognize that the success of technological designs is dependent on economic, environmental, ethical, and societal demands.

Key Vocabulary

Which terms do you already know?

- ☐ biogeochemistry
- ☐ biomagnification
- ☐ discharge (stream)
- ☐ extinction rate
- ☐ Industrial Revolution
- ☐ invertebrate
- ☐ non-point source
- ☐ nonrenewable resource
- ☐ per capita
- ☐ point source
- ☐ population demographics
- ☐ renewable resource
- ☐ sustainable
- ☐ technology
- ☐ water cycle
- ☐ wind energy

Image: Getty Images

Exploring Relationships between Human Activity and Earth's Systems

Did you use any plastic today? Did you ride in a car or other gasoline-powered vehicle? If so, you have used nonrenewable resources.

dlc.com/ca10113s

EXPLAIN QUESTION

What effects have increases in population and advancements in technology had on the way humans use Earth's natural resources?

HUMAN POPULATION SIZE

Earth's human population is projected to be near 10 billion in the coming years. What impact does the increase in human population have on the availability of natural resources?

How Has an Abundance of Natural Resources Altered Human Activity?

Resources and Technology

With each new technological development, human populations have been able to ensure their successful survival. Safe and steady water supplies, dependable sources of food, and effective shelters to keep out the elements have resulted in more offspring reaching adulthood. In addition, spending less time searching for the basic necessities for survival also has meant there was extra time for some of the population to spend on other pursuits. This luxury of extra time has allowed people to devise ways to improve their circumstances by improving their **technology**. It also has provided time to invent new ways to combine and exploit natural resources. Early technologies relied on stone, wood, and clay. With these resources, humans have been able to build strong fortresses and walled cities to protect themselves and cisterns and aqueducts to supply them with water. Over a period of a few thousand years, societies have developed techniques to smelt metals—first copper and tin and then iron—from ores. Metal tools and weapons, particularly those forged from iron, were a major leap forward in technology.

Most work still was human powered, but animals also were used, and some civilizations harnessed flowing water and wind to lift water or grind grain. Simple machines, such as the wheel and the sailboat, improved transport and trade and enabled these early civilizations to spread their influence further. This led to the rise of empires such as those of China, Greece, and Rome. Sailing enabled access to valuable, new resources, such as fish in the deep oceans and spices and gold from far-off lands. More important, meeting other groups of humans with unique experiences created an explosion of new ideas.

Some scholars began to study the world systematically. This process eventually evolved into the scientific method and a better understanding of how the world works. This improved understanding produced rapid improvements in technology. Beginning about 250 years ago, the **Industrial Revolution** introduced a technological explosion that altered the way humans make things and how they exploit their environment. The Industrial Revolution produced the steam engine, railways, modern medicine, and eventually the global economy of the late twentieth century. While it spurred huge increases in human population, the Industrial Revolution vastly increased the environmental impact of humankind.

How Have Earth's Systems Affected Human Activity?

Earth's Impact on Human Settlement

The environment on Earth can provide ideal conditions for human settlement, and just as quickly, take them away. Despite the technology humans have employed in an attempt to ensure their security in the face of nature, history is littered with the remains of civilizations. Many of these civilizations lasted for hundreds, sometimes thousands, of years, but disappeared over a few decades. Many of them collapsed as a result of natural changes in the environment. Others were destroyed by their own folly, often by the way in which they exploited the environment. Slow changes over time can alter growing conditions, water supplies, and climate. Once the availability of resources is impaired, large populations of humans no longer may be able to inhabit an area, no matter how sophisticated their society. Researchers speculate that huge empires, such as the Mayas, ancient Pakistani civilizations, and the Canaanites, collapsed after a series of climatic changes brought drought and dried up water resources.

Environmental catastrophes can occur almost instantaneously. Earthquakes, tsunamis, volcanic eruptions, and storms can change life on Earth instantly. Despite sophisticated technology, these changes still can decimate populations. Some regions on the globe have never recovered enough to support large populations after these sudden changes altered the environment.

How Have Human Technological Designs Affected the Environment?

Human Impacts on Earth

Earth's environment certainly can impact human populations. However, humans can have a major impact on Earth's biosphere, hydrosphere, atmosphere, and geosphere. The seven billion people on Earth all need food, water, clothing, and shelter. Most consume far more than they require. The impact upon Earth differs from one society to the next.

In industrialized societies such as those found in Europe and the United States, people have a much greater **per capita** impact on their environments than do those living in the simple rural communities of Africa and Asia.

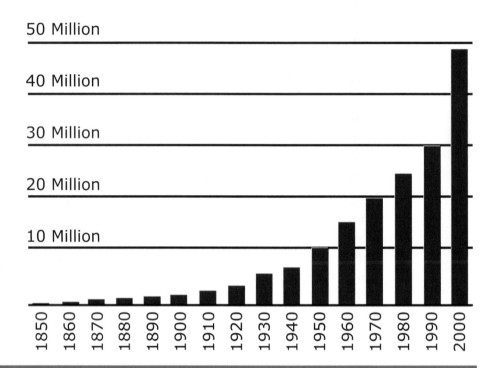

California Population

POPULATION OF CALIFORNIA FROM 1850 TO 2000

California has experienced a significant increase in population since 1850. How has this increase strained the natural resources in the state?

Human Impacts on the Biosphere

Over the planet as a whole, humankind has a major impact on the numbers and diversity of other living things. Clearing the land for agriculture, forestry, mining, or building removes natural vegetation and destroys natural ecosystems. These ecosystems are replaced with ones that are less diverse in terms of the variety of animal and plant species they contain. This loss of diversity also takes place in aquatic ecosystems as a result of over-fishing the rivers and oceans and through pollution. The **extinction rate** of animals and plants is currently at its highest in human history. The extinction rate has been compared to that of the five other mass extinctions that have occurred in Earth's geological history. Some of this destruction comes from the effort to meet the basic needs of the expanding population, but much of it results from the manufacture and consumption of luxuries and careless use of resources.

Human Impacts on the Geosphere

The geosphere makes up most of the mass of Earth. Currently, all human activities are restricted to the top few kilometers of the geosphere. Most of this impact is visible on the surface. The biggest of these is the movement of soil. Humans have altered the physical and chemical nature of large areas of soil, mainly for the purpose of growing food. Some of these activities have decreased soil productivity by removing nutrients, but many agricultural societies also work hard to improve soil productivity. In both these cases, the soil chemistry is altered by human activity. Of greater concern is the erosion of soil by human activities. Over large swathes of land, soil is being lost faster than it is being formed.

A more obvious impact on the geosphere comes from mining. The extraction of materials from Earth includes the removal of stone for building, the extraction of fossil fuels, and the extraction of ores and minerals used in manufacturing. The impacts of mining are most extreme in the case of mountain top removal in which major geological features are permanently altered. This method of coal mining blasts away mountain tops. Big holes from surface mining create new landscape features, such as lakes, when they fill with water. Underground mining brings minerals and waste to the surface. The extraction of oil and gas has a variety of impacts. In the process commonly known as fracking, water is injected into oil- or gas-bearing rocks. This process may destabilize some faults, causing earth tremors. The injected water contains chemicals that may alter the **biogeochemistry** of the geosphere. Many of the elements extracted during mining and drilling are not commonly found in large quantities near the surface. They may cause problems when they enter the biosphere. Heavy metals, released from mining activities and the use of its products, are particularly hazardous to living things.

COAL STRIP MINING

Strip mining is a process by which large quantities of dirt and soil are removed in order to excavate resources such as coal. How might this process negatively impact the environment?

Engineering activities move large quantities of the geosphere. Building levels existing scenery, brings rocks to the surface, and often buries valuable soil. Large structures, such as dams, have major impacts on the landscape. The lakes they create drown valleys and sometimes cause earthquakes. The storage of toxic waste deep underground, such as that produced by the nuclear industry, may contaminate the geosphere.

Human Impacts on the Hydrosphere

Water is common on the surface of Earth. It is vital to the existence of all life. Terrestrial life, including humankind, relies on freshwater, which only accounts for about 4 percent of all the water on the planet. This small percentage must supply all the water needed for continental ecosystems, agriculture, and human consumption. It also is used to remove waste, both human and industrial. There is an obvious conflict between these two uses. Waste pollutes water and may make it unfit for further consumption by humans and other organisms. Great efforts are made to prevent water pollution by treating water and removing toxins. Sadly, water pollution is still a major problem, particularly from **non-point sources**. These are sources that do not enter a river or lake by a pipe, but enter them when they are washed off the land or dissolved from the air. Examples of non-point source pollution are fertilizer runoff and acid rain. Humans divert freshwater from natural watercourses, drying up some rivers and creating new ones. Groundwater is used extensively to provide water supplies in arid areas. Some groundwater is ancient water that has remained hidden underground for millennia. In many places, groundwater is being used faster than it is being replenished by precipitation. Humans store water in reservoirs and cisterns, artificially interrupting the **water cycle**.

The oceans contain most of the living things and about 96 percent of the water on the planet. Many of the pollutants that enter freshwater eventually flow into the sea. These alter the chemistry of the seawater and become concentrated in aquatic food webs that in turn deposit these products during the process of decomposition. Airborne pollutants are also a problem. Excessive levels of atmospheric carbon dioxide result in the acidification of ocean water. Carbon dioxide produced by human activities is one cause of global warming. Global warming causes an increase in water temperatures and expansion of water molecules, which contributes to rising sea levels. Global warming alters the distribution of warm and cold water and has the potential to change the pattern of ocean currents.

Human Impacts on the Atmosphere

Human modifications to the atmosphere were minimal until the mid-19th century when the impacts of the Industrial Revolution began to make themselves apparent. Air pollution was first noticed at a local level, particularly in cities, where the burning of wood and coal caused choking smog. As well as smoke particles, this pollution released ozone and sulfur compounds, the latter of which forms acid when mixed with water droplets in the air. This mixture caused breathing problems and some premature deaths.

AIR POLLUTION

Smog and ozone are serious problems. How do they impact humans?

The effect of burning fossil fuels is now recognized as a global problem, mainly because of the production of the greenhouse gas carbon dioxide. This and the extensive removal of forests (that absorb the gas) have almost tripled concentration of carbon dioxide in Earth's atmosphere. This is recognized as the primary cause of global warming. At a global level, human activities (agriculture, landfills, and gas and oil drilling) have released large amounts of methane, another more potent greenhouse gas, into the atmosphere. Gases used in refrigerators and air conditioners, particularly a group called the chlorofluorocarbons (CFCs), have escaped into the atmosphere, adding to greenhouse emissions and also damaging the ozone layer—a layer of ozone high in the atmosphere that protects life from deadly ultraviolet radiation.

What Relationships Exist between Earth's Systems and Human Activities?

The Impacts of Energy Use on the Environment

All human activities require energy in one form or another. Whether it is the energy from food or from fuels, most of this energy is derived from the sun. Energy for human activities comes from:

Conventional Sources	Alternative Sources
Fossil Fuels	Biomass
Nuclear Energy	Solar
	Wind
	Hydroelectricty
	Geothermal Energy

Fossil Fuels

Fossil fuels are stored chemical energy from living things that lived millions of years ago. Fossil fuels include coal, oil, and natural gas. These are very useful fuels because they provide concentrated source of chemical potential energy. This concentrated energy is used to power vehicles—cars, trains, and planes—or to generate electricity. Fossil fuels were formed by the process of photosynthesis, which removed carbon dioxide from Earth's ancient atmosphere. When we burn those fuels, we release this carbon dioxide back into the atmosphere and change its composition. We now know that this release is causing global temperatures to rise gradually. This is because carbon dioxide acts like a blanket or greenhouse, preventing some of the sun's heat energy from escaping Earth's atmosphere.

Another greenhouse gas, methane, escapes from oil wells, pipelines, and urban gas systems. As we release more of these gases, the global temperature rises. Warmer climates create changes in weather patterns. The increased temperature levels cause polar ice caps to melt. Sea levels rise as ocean water expands and water from melting ice is added. Burning fossil fuels also release other pollutants into the atmosphere. Sulfur-rich fuels produce sulfur dioxide, the main cause of acid rain. Coal releases toxic heavy metals, such as mercury. Some fossil fuels burn more cleanly than others. Coal combustion is particularly dirty, whereas natural gas produces the fewest pollutants.

Fossil fuels impact the environment in other ways, since most plastics are made from them. Plastics are some of the most widely used and diverse materials available. They are used in all aspects of our lives from electronics to medical devices. Every aspect of life is made easier and safer because of plastic. However, there is a dark side to plastic. Some forms of plastic take thousands of years to degrade. Since we use plastics so widely, we are left with huge amounts of plastic waste all over the world. From the depths of the ocean to uninhabited tropical islands, plastic is invading the environment.

Nuclear Energy

Nuclear energy uses radioactive substances such as uranium to produce steam in a nuclear reactor. This steam then is used to generate electricity. Nuclear power plants are an important source of electricity. Nuclear power plants do not produce greenhouse gases, but the mining and refining of uranium uses lots of energy. Nuclear power plants are very expensive to build, and they produce highly toxic radioactive waste. This waste can last for thousands of years and is very difficult to dispose of. Nuclear power plants are susceptible to earthquakes, tsunamis, and terrorism, which can cause catastrophic releases of radioactive materials into the environment.

Biomass

Biomass is energy that comes from animals and plants. Some forms of biomass can be burned to provide energy—wood is the best-known example. Other examples include ethanol derived from corn or sugar cane and vegetable oil used in special diesel engines. The use of these resources impacts the environment because they require land, fertilizers, and often machinery for their production. The products of their combustion, mainly smoke and carbon dioxide, contribute to air pollution. Biomass has the advantage that plants can be regrown after harvesting. However, the use of land for growing biomass for fuel removes it from crop production for food and reduces the land area available for recreation and wildlife conservation.

Solar Energy

Solar energy covers all energy—light and heat—directly obtained from the sun. This energy can be harnessed through the use of:

- Solar thermal technology, where the sun's heat is concentrated to heat water or make steam to generate electricity.
- Passive solar heating—using carefully placed windows and other architectural features to make the maximum use of the sun to warm buildings.
- Photovoltaic cells, which convert solar energy to electricity.

SOLAR PANELS

Solar panels gather energy from the sun that can be converted to electricity. What are some other renewable energy resources?

Solar energy is expensive to implement, but once in place, solar devices use free energy. Solar technologies have a low impact because they use only the energy from the sun and produce no pollution.

Wind Energy

Wind energy indirectly uses the energy of the sun. As the sun heats Earth, it causes winds. These winds can be harnessed using turbines, usually very large structures. They cost a lot to build and have high maintenance costs. Their rotating blades are noisy and kill millions of birds every year. They usually are placed along scenic coasts or mountain ranges where there is plenty of wind. On the positive side, they use a free, **renewable resource** and once constructed, produce no pollution.

Hydroelectricity

Hydroelectric plants convert the kinetic energy of falling water into electricity. Normally this involves building a dam across a river. This has negative impacts on the ecology of the river and the land flooded by the reservoir formed behind the dam. Tidal currents also can be harnessed to produce electricity. Once in place, hydroelectric plants produce no pollutants.

Geothermal Energy

The interior of Earth is hot. This heat is called geothermal energy. This energy can be captured by pumping water underground into hot rocks and using the steam produced to generate electricity. Hot water from hot springs can be used to directly heat buildings. Geothermal heat pumps extract heat close to Earth's surface. This heat can be used to heat buildings. Geothermal energy is a non-polluting energy source.

GEOTHERMAL ENERGY
Geothermal plants use thermal energy from within Earth's interior to create electricity. What advantage does geothermal energy have over other sources of power, such as fossil fuels?

The Impacts of Food Production on the Environment

Earth's human population is growing rapidly. With this growth in population comes the need to produce more food. Increasingly, in the developed world, agriculture is becoming a process that is managed on a large scale, while in less-developed countries most agriculture is conducted by farmers on small holdings. Other forms of food production, such as the harvesting of wildlife, accounts for only a small proportion of food production but can have a big impact on wild populations. These include fishing, which is rapidly depleting fish stocks and damaging marine ecosystems.

Industrial Food and Livestock Production

Much of the food we eat is the product of industrial-style crop and livestock production. Modern methods of production have economies of scale that, when combined with efficient transport, packaging, and marketing, make food cheap, readily available, and consistently high quality.

All forms of agriculture have negative impacts on the natural environment. Planting crops requires the replacement of diverse natural ecosystems with simplified agricultural ecosystems. These agricultural ecosystems are designed to support the crop at the expense of most other species. All aspects of their cultivation are geared to increasing food production. The use of mechanized cultivation, artificial fertilizers, pesticides, and irrigation are common components of this type of agriculture. These inputs require the use of fossil fuels for their manufacture and transport. Some negative environmental impacts of industrialized farming include:

- Reduction in biodiversity
- Loss of soil through erosion
- Changes in soil composition, structure, and fertility
- Runoff of excess nutrients from artificial fertilizers
- Contamination of the food and water supply by pesticides
- Generation of greenhouse gases

Industrial livestock production involves raising animals under controlled conditions, often inside sheds or on confined lots. This type of livestock production enables the farmer to control the growth and monitor the health of large numbers of animals to bring them rapidly to market. On the downside, these large concentrations of animals can:

- Create large quantities of solid and liquid waste
- Produce polluting gases and unpleasant smells
- Lead to the contamination of the food supply with antibiotics and other treatments
- Cause stress to animals when many animals are kept in a small space

Many of the negative effects of industrial agriculture extend far from their point of origin on farms. For example, excess nutrients from some farms in the Midwest are carried in the waters of the Mississippi River to the Gulf of Mexico. Here they contribute to the formation of a large "dead zone" in the Gulf of Mexico where marine life cannot survive. Many scientists believe that industrial agriculture is not **sustainable** in the long term.

Sustainable Agriculture

It is impossible to prevent all the negative impacts of growing food. Some people think that we can reduce the impact of agriculture by using techniques based on our understanding of ecology. This type of farming is called sustainable agriculture. Sustainable agriculture uses plant and animal production techniques that are tailored carefully to fit the ecology of the local area. These techniques are designed not to deplete natural resources. This approach has many positive impacts. It:

- Reduces or eliminates fossil fuel inputs
- Reduces or eliminates the use of artificial fertilizers
- Removes pesticides from the environment
- Recycles plant and animal waste on the farm
- Grows crops adapted to local conditions
- Provides more humane conditions for livestock
- Produces food for sale in local markets, thereby reducing transport costs

Sustainable agriculture is often more labor intensive than its industrial counterpart. It is possible that food produced by this approach will be more expensive.

Fishing Industries

Aquatic organisms are important sources of food. Some aquatic algae and plants, such as seaweeds, are eaten. Most types of food obtained from aquatic biomes are animals, including fish and **invertebrates**, such as shrimp, lobsters, oysters, and sea cucumbers, also are consumed.

Fish make up around one-fifth of the protein eaten by humans. About 120 million metric tons of fish are consumed per year. Some of this fish comes from aquaculture, the growing of fish under artificial conditions. In some areas of the world, freshwater fishing resources are important for local economies, and freshwater aquaculture, using fish ponds, is common. However, internationally, most fishing takes place in the ocean. Over the past 50 years, fishing has become more industrialized.

Modern large fishing vessels use efficient fishing techniques, which rapidly leads to overfishing. If nets with a fine mesh are used, young fish are caught, impacting the future breeding population. Year-round fishing may catch fish during important spawning seasons; combined with fishing in breeding areas, this may diminish future fish stocks. Many fisheries in the open ocean where fish are caught are over-exploited and have declined. In the Atlantic, catches of cod, haddock, and red hake have all declined. Fisheries all around the world are showing signs of overfishing.

All countries with a coastline have areas over which they control fishing. Most countries have regulations determining the methods of fishing allowed and the seasons in which it can be conducted. Some countries, such as Canada and the United States, carefully monitor fishing in their waters. By regulating fishing zones, net mesh size, fishing season, and catch quotas, governments have helped depleted fishing stocks recover. In international waters outside these limits, there are no such regulations.

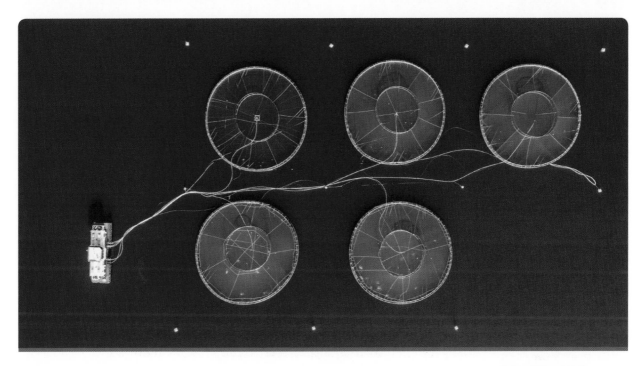

Aquaculture is becoming an increasingly important source of marine food. This involves farming fish and other aquatic organisms under controlled conditions. These organisms may be farmed in ponds or in cages in lakes or the sea. Some of these organisms are genetically engineered. There are concerns that when genetically engineered fish escape into the environment, they will breed with and alter the genetic make-up of wild fish.

AQUACULTURE

This fish farm in Norway raises salmon for food. What are some benefits of using aquaculture to raise fish?

Human Impacts on Wetlands and Water Resources

Available water resources are under continuous threat from changes in the landscape, changes in the climate, and human activities. The main threats to water resources come from human actions. Human activities damage wetland ecosystems that help purify water by:

- Increasing the amount of sediment in rivers and lakes
- Polluting important water sources
- Changing the landscape and distribution of water through engineering activities such as dam construction and the removal of excessive amounts of water for human use
- Altering the climate and changing patterns of precipitation and evaporation

Suspended sediments are found naturally in water as a result of the erosion of rock and soil. However, human activities alter or remove the natural vegetation cover. Once vegetation is removed from soil, the rate of runoff, and the soil it carries, increases. This runoff is carried to rivers and increases their sediment loads—the amount of sediment they carry. Rivers may carry sediments into lakes where they are deposited, altering the structure of the ecosystem and eventually turning them into marsh. Where rivers flow into the sea, the increased sediment load can threaten coastal habitats such as coral reefs and other important nurseries for fish.

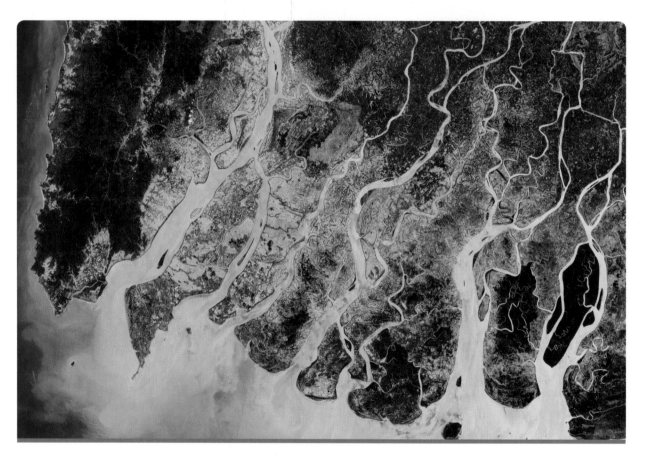

SEDIMENTS FROM RUNOFF

Sediments carried by rivers can threaten coastal habitats. What kinds of coastal animals could be impacted by high sediment levels?

Humans have long used water as a means of disposing of waste. This pollution takes a variety of forms and comes from numerous different sources. These include:

- Acid rain that lowers the pH of surface and ground water
- Deposition of other airborne pollutants, such as mercury from the burning of coal
- Nutrient and pesticide pollution from non-point sources, such as fields and gardens
- Pollution from **point sources**, such as pipes from factories and sewage outlets

The main method for reducing wetland pollution is effective enforcement of legislation. For example, the Clean Water Act in the United States has greatly reduced water pollution from unacceptable levels in the past. Treatment of sewage and industrial water is vital. Simple measures, such as retaining natural vegetation, the correct application of fertilizers and pesticides, planting cover crops to protect fallow land, and using soil fences and sedimentation ponds, can be very effective. Control of air pollution, particularly from cars and industry, can reduce water pollution greatly.

Human activities change the landscape and its drainage patterns. The most obvious example is the construction of dams across rivers. Although dams may be great for storing water and generating electricity, they also adversely impact water resources by:

- Altering water ecosystems, such as transforming moving rivers into non-flowing reservoirs
- Drowning land ecosystems
- Preventing fish migration

Undesirable effects of dam construction can be avoided by anticipating outcomes and designing solutions throughout the engineering process. Water collected behind dams often is redistributed to other areas through pipes and canals. This redistribution can impact other ecosystems, particularly when it is used for irrigation. Building dams reduces water flow and may deprive downstream users of water resources. The flows of some river systems and lakes have been disrupted to the point that, at certain times of the year, they contain no water. Some lakes have become saline as a result of the diversion of water.

Climate change, whether natural or human induced, changes patterns of precipitation and evaporation. Changing temperatures can cause increased evaporation over the ocean, creating more and more severe tropical storms and hurricanes. This may increase precipitation in some areas. Increased temperature over land may reduce available water resources through evaporation. It also can dry out soils reducing crop yields. Attempts to fix this problem include irrigation from water obtained from wells. This depletes groundwater resources that have accumulated over thousands of years. Increased temperature also can influence the seasonal flow of water. For example, rising temperatures reduce snowfall in mountains. Accumulated snow and ice act as a slow-release reservoir that keeps many rivers flowing at high volumes throughout the year. When snow and ice no longer form in large volumes, this flow pattern is altered. Preventing human-induced climate change through better education and international treaties may help reduce these impacts.

Consider the Explain Question

What effects have increases in population and advancements in technology had on the way humans use Earth's natural resources?

Go online to complete the scientific explanation.

dlc.com/ca10118s

Check Your Understanding

How are density-dependent factors different from density-independent factors?

dlc.com/ca10119s

STEM in Action

Applying Relationships between Human Activity and Earth's Systems

Is an increasing reliance on technology good for humans and Earth?

Historically, civilizations succeeded or failed on the basis of small changes in the environment. Today, civilizations rely more on technological systems than on Earth's systems for their ultimate success. Our technological systems are taking us beyond the boundaries of our needs and our own environment. For example, we have technology that allows us to explore the ocean and outer space. The technological systems we have embraced may seem to separate us from reliance on Earth's systems, but this is only an illusion. We have invented, designed, and created with the grand plan of improving the human condition, but in the end we are still an intricately connected part of Earth's systems.

HUMAN IMPACTS

Technology can help humans but harm the environment. How has technology damaged natural areas shown in this photo?

As humans, we still need the same basic resources as our ancestors: food, water, and shelter. With the help of technology, we are better able to collect these resources and transport them in the quantities and to the locations that we desire. We also use technology to repair small changes that in the past would have affected us. For example, if water becomes polluted, we clean it. If we notice that our supply of fossil fuels is dwindling, we build another pipeline or come up with ways to get energy from renewable resources. Through technology, we have the ability to gather more resources to support an increasing population and to develop tools and resources to improve conditions not only for our own future as humans, but also for the future of all living things.

STEM and Relationships between Human Activity and Earth's Systems

As the population and the demand for Earth's natural resources continue to increase, some scientists are working to develop new technologies designed to reduce the effects on Earth's systems. These scientists are called conservation scientists, or environmental and conservation biologists. Many conservation scientists focus on helping government and private landowners improve their use of land. This includes advising farmers about sustainable agricultural practices and advising engineers and urban planners on ways to build communities that reduce soil erosion and keep other natural resources intact.

Conservation scientists are natural problem solvers. They develop new technologies and practices to improve the ways people interact with natural resources. The majority of their work focuses on soil and water. Conservation scientists regularly leave their offices and visit farms and forests, where they study firsthand the effects that traditional practices have on the natural resources. For example, they may study how the use of pesticides on a farm affects the groundwater supply. In a city, they may look at how a proposed development will cause erosion. In a forest, a conservation scientist may measure the height and width of trees to detect subtle changes in their growth. On farms or in local communities, they may look for evidence of erosion or take soil and groundwater samples to determine the risk of contamination. After collecting their data, they analyze it and provide ways to improve farming, business, and building practices that do not negatively impact natural resources.

Understanding Climate and Climate Change

LESSON OVERVIEW

Lesson Questions

- What factors determine climate?
- What processes are involved in climate change?

Key Vocabulary

Which terms do you already know?

- [ ] adiabatic cooling
- [ ] anthropogenic
- [ ] anthropogenic
- [ ] atmosphere
- [ ] carbon reservoir
- [ ] climate
- [ ] elevation
- [ ] El Niño
- [ ] eustatic (change)
- [ ] fossil
- [ ] fossil fuel
- [ ] glacial varve
- [ ] glacier
- [ ] global warming
- [ ] greenhouse gas
- [ ] ice cap
- [ ] ice core
- [ ] latitude
- [ ] methane

dlc.com/ca10120s

Lesson Objectives

By the end of the lesson, you should be able to:

- Differentiate the factors that determine climate.
- Investigate the processes involved in climate change.

Key Vocabulary continued

- [ ] Milankovitch cycle
- [ ] orogeny
- [ ] ozone
- [ ] plankton
- [ ] precipitation (crystallization)
- [ ] sediment
- [ ] solar energy
- [ ] sunspot
- [ ] temperature
- [ ] thermal energy
- [ ] topography
- [ ] tree ring

Thinking about Climate and Climate Change

Think about the last time you looked up a weather forecast, checked a weather app on your phone, or watched the weather report on television. The impact weather has on our daily lives is significant; we plan our days around it. But what about the impact of climate on our daily lives—is it as significant?

dlc.com/ca10121s

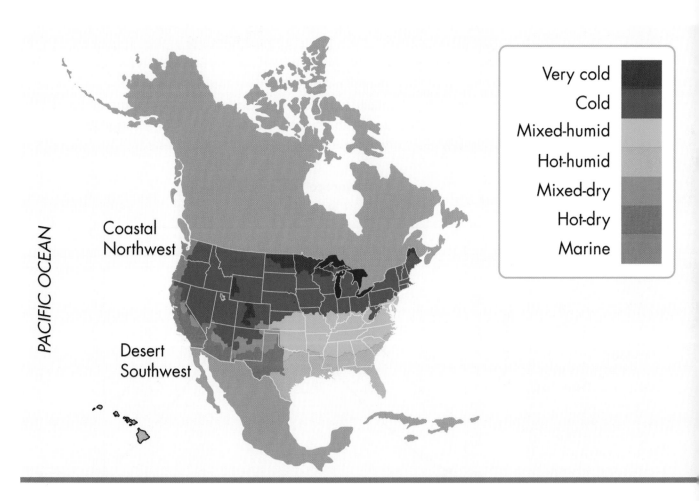

Coastal Northwest

Desert Southwest

PACIFIC OCEAN

Legend:
- Very cold
- Cold
- Mixed-humid
- Hot-humid
- Mixed-dry
- Hot-dry
- Marine

EXPLAIN QUESTION

▎ How do human activities change the world's climate?

U.S. CLIMATE REGIONS

What does this map show you about climate in the United States and what factors affect the climate regions found within the United States?

What Factors Determine Climate?

Climate Conditions and Regions

Scientists commonly describe **climate** in terms of **temperature**, precipitation, humidity, and wind. These are the same factors used to describe weather. However, climate involves longer-term measurements. Climate conditions are typically reported as daily, monthly, seasonal, or yearly averages calculated from decades of weather data. In fact, the National Weather Service uses 30-year averages, updated at the end of each decade, to describe the climate at a specific location.

For example, the data in these graphs show that Memphis, Tennessee, experiences a different average precipitation each month. In general, however, average monthly precipitation ranges between 5 cm (in October) and 14 or 15 cm (in April). Similarly, temperatures in the Memphis region typically fall to about 0°C during the winter months and rise to about 25°C during the summer. The overall picture suggests a moderately wet, temperate climate.

AVERAGE TEMPERATURES IN MEMPHIS, TENNESSEE

Climate data are reported as average conditions over time. What months have the coldest and warmest temperatures in Memphis, Tennessee?

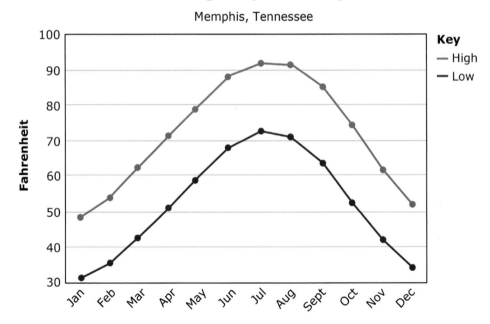

Average Temperature Range

Memphis, Tennessee

Key
— High
— Low

Average Monthly Precipitation

Memphis, Tennessee

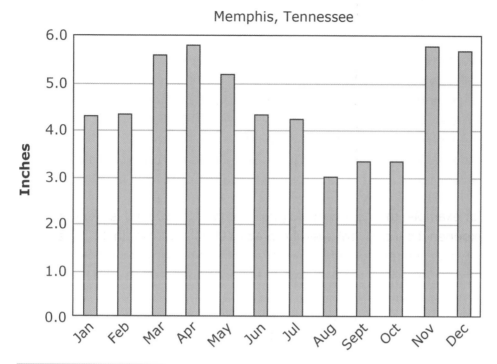

AVERAGE PRECIPITATION IN MEMPHIS, TENNESSEE

Climate data are reported as average conditions over time. On average, which season has the least amount of rain in Memphis, Tennessee—spring or fall?

Are all climate regions the size of a city such as Memphis, Tennessee? There is not an official size of a climate region; rather, the discussions and analyses of climate can apply to many different scales. For example, climate regions can be large, consisting of geographically similar areas like the deserts of the southwestern United States. A desert, as well as a grassland or a tropical rainforest, is a biome, and many biomes have similar climate characteristics; though, they may occur in different regions around the world. There are low-**latitude** deserts in Africa and the Middle East, as well as the United States, but they all have hot, dry climates.

Climate can also be analyzed on a small scale. For instance, local conditions, like the presence of a creek, affect climate in the creek's immediate vicinity. A microclimate is the climate in a small area that may differ from that of the climate found in a general region. Microclimates can vary in size from a few square meters to several square kilometers. At the other end of the spectrum, scientists study Earth's climate as a whole, averaging information about conditions like temperature and precipitation from all over the world. These analyses are useful for studying global climate change.

Factors That Affect Climate

Weather, and therefore climate, patterns result from the transfer of energy into and out of the **atmosphere**. **Solar energy** is the primary source of energy that drives weather patterns. As solar energy in the form of radiation enters the atmosphere, some is absorbed by gases, some is reflected by clouds, and the remainder strikes Earth's surface and is reflected or absorbed. When solar energy is absorbed, most of it changes directly to **thermal energy**. This warms the air, the ground, and the ocean surfaces. This thermal energy is redistributed and cycled between and within various Earth systems before being reradiated out into space.

On Earth, the energy received equals the energy radiated back into space. It is this equilibrium that maintains Earth's temperature at a level suitable for life. Modifications in the amount of sunlight reflected or absorbed will alter this equilibrium and change the temperature of the planet.

The energy cycling through a region ultimately determines its climate. However, various geographical factors influence the transfer of energy into and out of a region. They include the following:

- **Latitude**. The sun's energy is the primary factor that drives weather, and a region's latitude determines the amount of solar radiation it receives. Because Earth's surface is curved, sunlight strikes different latitudes at different angles, resulting in certain regions receiving more intense energy per unit area than others. Because the position of the sun is almost directly overhead, the equatorial regions receive the most solar energy throughout the year and therefore, tend to be warmer throughout the year. Conversely, polar regions receive the least solar energy and tend to be colder throughout the year.

- **Albedo**. Albedo is a measure of how reflective Earth's surface is and albedo determines how much of the sun's energy is reflected back into space. Reflection of solar radiation can happen when it reaches clouds and when it reaches Earth's surface, reflecting off lakes, rivers, the ocean, and snow.

About 30 percent of total solar radiation reaching the top of Earth's atmosphere is reflected directly back into space and does not contribute to heating the atmosphere. The other 70 percent is either absorbed by atmospheric gases or is reflected back into space from Earth's surface. Some of the radiation reflected from Earth's surface is also absorbed by the atmosphere, contributing to the greenhouse effect. When Earth's energy gains and losses are balanced, all radiation entering the atmosphere is ultimately reflected or retransmitted back into space.

At Earth's surface, albedo is greatest for light colored, highly reflective material. Snow cover, water, and clouds are the biggest contributors to Earth's surface albedo. Water bodies, such as oceans and lakes, reflect as much as 80 percent of the radiation reaching their surfaces. Clouds have an albedo measurement ranging from 30 to 90 percent, depending on their thicknesses. Surface albedo increases in winter because of increased snow cover, giving it an albedo as high as 90 percent. Particulates from pollution and dust also influence albedo when they become suspended in the atmosphere. Volcanic eruptions can significantly increase albedo by adding sulfur dioxide to the atmosphere, a gas that reflects solar energy. Several large volcanic eruptions in Earth's history have caused periods of global cooling.

■ **Topography and Elevation**. The shape of the land, or **topography**, influences both regional and local climates. In the region of the atmosphere where weather occurs, temperature decreases with altitude. Therefore, areas of higher **elevation**, like mountains, tend to have cooler climates. Mountain ranges also affect precipitation patterns. As an air mass rises on one side of a mountain, it expands and cools. This process is called **adiabatic cooling**. Because cooler air temperatures cannot hold as much moisture as warm air temperatures, the cloud's moisture then falls as precipitation. The air mass is therefore much drier when it descends on the other side of the mountain. As a result, mountain ranges tend to have one wet side and one dry side, exhibiting the rain shadow effect.

Rain Shadow

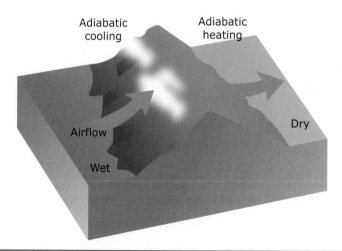

RAIN SHADOW

As an air mass rises over one side of a mountain, it releases its moisture as precipitation; the air mass is then dry as it travels over the other side of the mountain, producing a rain shadow. How do rain shadows impact a region's climate?

■ **Proximity to Oceans**. Oceans have a significant effect on both regional and global climate patterns. The regional effects result from differences in how quickly water and air change temperature as they absorb heat. For instance, water takes much longer than air to heat up and cool down. The ocean's surface carries a vast amount of stored heat from absorbed solar radiation. Surface ocean currents transport this heat around the globe, influencing global and regional climate patterns. Compared to inland areas, coastal regions tend to have more stable temperatures due to ocean currents. Cold ocean currents cool some regions while warm ocean currents raise the average temperature and influence local precipitation. For example, where warm air meets a cold ocean current, fog can form. In some areas, such as along the western coast of South America, these fog banks might be the main source of precipitation.

■ **Atmospheric Circulation**. General atmospheric circulation patterns—known as prevailing winds—also affect climate both globally and regionally. Heat transfer in the atmosphere sets up huge convection cells—called Hadley cells—which impact global climate patterns. Warm air rises around the equator, losing moisture as it cools and producing clouds and precipitation. The resulting cooler, drier air moves northward and southward away from the Equator, then sinks back to the surface around 30° North and South latitude. This band of Earth's surface experiences dry conditions and contains many of the world's large deserts, including the Sahara in Northern Africa.

Atmosphere Circulation
Prevailing Winds

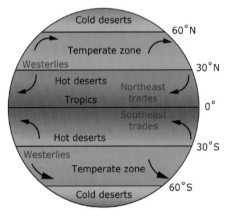

ATMOSPHERIC CIRCULATION

The prevailing winds that result from atmospheric convection affect climate. How do these prevailing winds influence climate at various latitudes?

Convection cells between 60° and 90° North and South latitude are known as Polar Cells. They produce moist conditions around 60° latitude North and South, where moist air rises, producing drizzly, rainy conditions. The resulting dry air moves toward the poles and produces dry polar deserts.

Prevailing winds also affect climates regionally. For example, great currents of wind—called jet streams—circle the globe. Jet streams typically separate warmer, wetter air masses from colder, drier air masses. The exact location of a jet stream changes seasonally. These shifts can result in dramatic seasonal changes, such as the beginning and end of monsoon season.

A monsoon, or seasonal shift in prevailing winds, drastically impacts the climates of many regions of the world, including India, Western Africa, Australia, and the Southwestern United States. Though monsoon is commonly misused as a synonym for heavy rainfall, the term merely refers to the seasonal shift in prevailing winds. These shifts often result in both a wet season and a dry season, depending on the time of year.

Seasonal Changes

Seasonal changes are part of the climate of all regions on Earth. Seasonal changes are related to latitude, and because Earth's axis is tilted, when it is summer in the northern hemisphere, that part of Earth is tilted towards the sun. Additionally, when it is winter in the northern hemisphere, that part of the Earth receives less direct solar radiation than the southern hemisphere. How does the tilt of Earth create seasons? Surprisingly, it has nothing to do with the distance from the sun. When a part of Earth is tilted toward the sun, it receives more incoming solar radiation for each square kilometer of its surface than compared to other parts of Earth. This increase in the solar radiation per unit area causes a rise in temperature and creates the warmer seasons. Near the equator, seasonal affects are minimized because the intensity of solar radiation received is similar throughout the year, resulting in the tropics not having a true winter or summer.

Climate Zones

Various geographic factors affecting climate combine to form global climate zones. Similar zones may appear in different parts of the world due to a variety of factors. Example of these zones are the great Sonoran Desert in the American southwest and northwest Mexico. The climate in these areas are the result of dry prevailing winds blowing at 30°N latitude, while smaller deserts, like those in eastern Oregon and California, exist because of the rain shadows from the Cascade and Sierra Nevada Mountains.

SANDY DESERT

Deserts are dry areas that are often hot. Where on Earth can you find deserts?

Scientists divide climate zones into systems of climate types and subtypes. The Köppen climate classification system recognizes five major climate types. These are:

- Tropical (hot, moist)
- Arid (dry)
- Temperate (warm summers, cool winters)
- Continental (hot summers, cold winters)
- Polar (cold)

Each of these types can be further subdivided. For example, arid climates can be further divided into deserts, semi-arid regions, and grasslands.

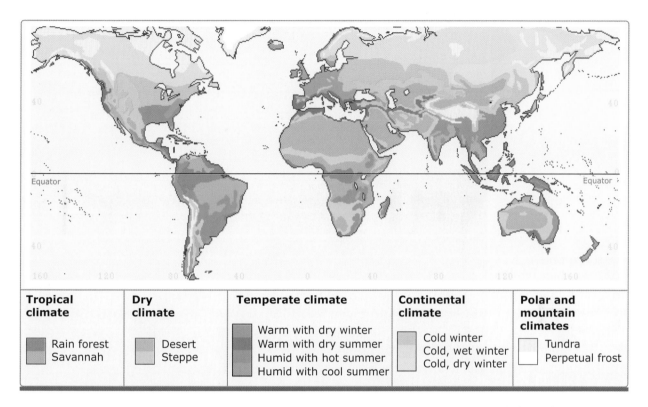

Tropical climate	Dry climate	Temperate climate	Continental climate	Polar and mountain climates
Rain forest Savannah	Desert Steppe	Warm with dry winter Warm with dry summer Humid with hot summer Humid with cool summer	Cold winter Cold, wet winter Cold, dry winter	Tundra Perpetual frost

GLOBAL CLIMATE ZONE MAP

Scientists divide climate zones into systems, one of which is Köppen's system, shown here. What climate zone do you live in?

What Processes Are Involved in Climate Change?

Evidence of Past Climate Change

How do scientists know about **climate** change? Scientists find evidence of past climate conditions in many places, including tree rings, glacial varves, seafloor sediments, fossils, and ice cores. Each source of evidence provides information about climate conditions in certain locations and specific time frames, and the combining evidence from these different sources improves the validity of conclusions about past global climate changes.

Tree rings are not only useful for studying climate conditions in the recent past, but also result from annual growth patterns. Wide rings represent years of fast growth and, therefore, warm years, while narrower rings represent colder years. The chemistry of the wood in the rings also provides information about climate conditions.

RINGS IN A TREE

Narrow tree rings represent years when the tree grew a little; wider rings represent years when the tree grew more. What does increased growth, or wider rings, indicate about the region's climate?

Glacial varves are annual deposits that result from seasonal cycles of glacial melting and freezing. Glaciers trap **sediment** as they advance over land when the **temperature** falls, and when temperatures rise, the glaciers melt and retreat. When glacial melting occurs, they release some sediment. Warmer years result in greater melting and thicker deposits, while cooler years result in less melting and thinner deposits. **Glacial varve** deposits exist in the rock record long after glaciers have disappeared. Scientists can use glacial varve deposits to learn about climate changes going back tens of thousands of years.

Scientists take deep core samples of seafloor sediments to study climate conditions dating back to 250 million years ago. Seafloor sediments contain tiny shells of the **plankton** that populated the ocean's surface waters. These shells sank to the ocean floor when these tiny organisms died. The shells preserved a chemical record of ocean conditions which existed when the shell formed, such as water temperature and sea levels. Significant changes in Earth's climate cause changes in sea levels, called eustatic changes. When the cycle of high and low tides is considered, the average global sea level is changed.

Sedimentary rocks record these changes as transgressive and regressive sequences. Transgression and regression describe the changing depths of ocean water in which sediments are deposited. Transgression is recognized by the vertical upward change in rock from conglomerate to sandstone to shale to limestone. This specific sequence of changes indicates that the depositional environment changed from shallow water to deep water conditions. This is an example of positive **eustatic change**. Likewise, with regression, you will see the vertical upward change from limestone to shale to sandstone to conglomerate, showing sediments in progressively shallower water. Melting polar ice raises sea levels, resulting in transgressive sedimentary sequences. The formation and growth of polar ice caps lowers sea level, resulting in regressive sedimentary sequences.

Preserved remains of organisms also provide evidence of past climate conditions. Scientists can infer climate conditions at the time a fossilized organism lived by analyzing the organism's climate requirements. For example, scientists know that ferns require warm, humid conditions, so when scientists find fossils of ferns in a polar region, they infer the climate of that region has changed dramatically over time.

Ice sheets provide another line of evidence for past climate conditions, dating back to the origin of ice sheets. The formation of ice sheets generally occurred tens or, in some cases, hundreds of thousands of years ago. Scientists take deep core samples and study the chemical properties of the ice. These analyses provide evidence of atmospheric conditions at the time the ice was formed.

Some Natural Causes of Climate Change

Climatologists have learned that Earth's climate changes in different ways over the course of geologic history. Some of these changes are cyclical or repetitive in nature while others are rapid and often catastrophic. Usually a number of factors combine to cause major climatic change. These factors include:

■ **Milankovitch Cycles**. Milankovitch cycles are caused by changes in the shape of Earth's orbit, the tilt of its axis, and the direction of its axis. Milankovitch cycles have long periods—tens of thousands to hundreds of thousands of years—and during these cycles, Earth receives varying amounts of **solar energy**. Scientists think that Milankovitch cycles are partially responsible for many of the major changes in our planet's climate, for example, they have contributed to the periodic ice ages that have come and gone over the past several million years.

- **Solar Variation**. Solar variation is the change in the amount of radiation emitted by the sun. This change may occur over periods of a few years to millennia, and the variations have cyclic components that is best known as the approximately 11-year solar cycle, or as it is also called, the sunspot cycle. Sunspots are magnetic storms on the surface of the sun and when they are present, Earth receives slightly less solar radiation. Interestingly, evidence of other longer cycles of solar output has also been detected.

- **Changes in Ocean Currents**. Ocean currents influence climate, and when currents change position, climates also change. Perhaps best known are the patterns of surface ocean currents known as **El Niño** and La Niña in the equatorial Pacific Ocean. These cause alternate warming and cooling trends every few years. During **El Niño**, surface currents are unusually warm, while La Niña is characterized by unusually cool surface currents. Ocean currents are influenced by climate.

- **Volcanic Eruptions**. Volcanoes are agents of rapid climate change. Eruptions produce clouds of dust and gases that can circle the globe and change its albedo. The gas that has the biggest climate impact is sulfur dioxide, and large eruptions thrust the sulfur dioxide high into the **atmosphere**. Contact with water droplets in clouds forms sulfuric acid droplets called *aerosols*, and each droplet absorbs some of the radiation from the sun, reducing the amount that reaches Earth's surface. During the 1900s, there were three volcanic eruptions that cooled the planet by as much as 1°C. There is evidence that huge volcanic eruptions had major impacts on Earth's climate that lasted for millennia.

- **Meteorite Impact**. About 65 million years ago, a meteorite about 10 km wide slammed into Earth, and its impact blasted billions of tons of dust and gas into the atmosphere. It is thought that this impact caused a drop in Earth's temperature of around 5°C that lasted for a decade.

- **Tectonic Plate Movement and Orogeny**. The movements of Earth's tectonic plates have cause major changes in climate. As continents move, they move to different latitudes and experience changes in insolation, and the movement of these plates also alters ocean currents, albedo, and the distribution of heat around the globe. Orogenic processes create areas of high **elevation** with low temperatures, in addition to these mountains altering the distribution of precipitation.

Anthropogenic Climate Change

Anthropogenic refers to influences that humans have on the environment. Over the past 100 years, anthropogenic emissions of carbon dioxide (CO_2), largely due to **fossil fuel** burning, have caused the average global temperature to increase. Scientists have measured this temperature increase in both the atmosphere and the oceans. This increase is called **global warming**, which is thought to be largely the result of increased concentration of carbon dioxide and other greenhouse gases in the atmosphere.

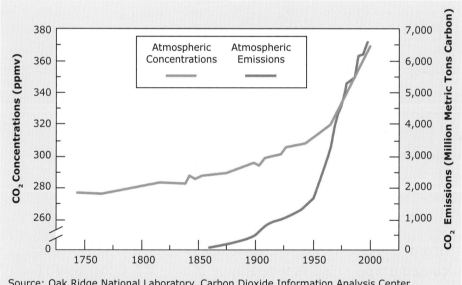

Source: Oak Ridge National Laboratory, Carbon Dioxide Information Analysis Center, http://cdac.esd.oml.gov/.

CARBON DIOXIDE CONCENTRATION IN THE ATMOSPHERE

Anthropogenic carbon dioxide emissions have increased the concentration of atmospheric carbon dioxide to levels significantly above normal. What impact has this increase had on global climate?

Greenhouse gases in the atmosphere absorb radiant energy from Earth's surface; without greenhouse gases, most of this energy would be lost to space. The greenhouse effect causes the atmosphere to warm. The major greenhouse gases include water vapor, **methane**, carbon dioxide, nitrous oxide, and **ozone**. The ozone from human activity functions differently from the ozone in Earth's stratosphere. Stratospheric ozone forms naturally and helps protect Earth's surface by filtering out harmful ultraviolet radiation. In contrast, tropospheric ozone is a pollutant that results from chemical interactions between nitrous oxides and volatile organic compounds in the presence of sunlight.

ANTHROPOGENIC GREENHOUSE GAS EMISSIONS

Human activities result in the emissions of several types of greenhouse gases in addition to carbon dioxide. Are human activities more influential on the climate than natural activities?

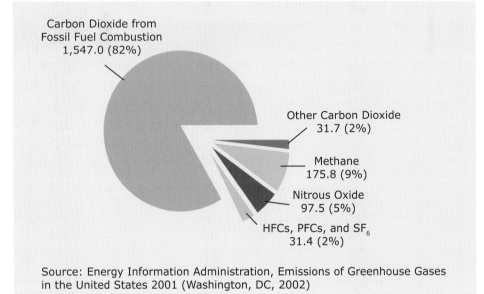

Carbon Dioxide from Fossil Fuel Combustion 1,547.0 (82%)

Other Carbon Dioxide 31.7 (2%)

Methane 175.8 (9%)

Nitrous Oxide 97.5 (5%)

HFCs, PFCs, and SF$_6$ 31.4 (2%)

Source: Energy Information Administration, Emissions of Greenhouse Gases in the United States 2001 (Washington, DC, 2002)

Certain amounts of greenhouse gases occur naturally in the atmosphere, keeping Earth's temperature at a level that allows life to flourish. But the concentration of greenhouse gases is increasing, due to human activity, which could result in enhanced global warming, causing temperatures to rise to potentially catastrophic levels. Life on Earth is adapted to very specific climate conditions, and if these conditions change too much, the ability of Earth to support life could diminish. The nearby planets, Mars and Venus, have different levels of greenhouse gases when compared to Earth and their climates are unsuitable for life (as we know it).

People around the world are currently working on the problem of global warming. Scientists use computer models, based on factors such as increasing emission of greenhouse gases, to predict climate change. Governments are trying to pass laws and agreements to limit the emissions of greenhouse gases. Scientists and engineers are developing alternative sources of energy that do not cause **greenhouse gas** emissions. People around the world are making efforts to replace **fossil** fuels with alternative energy resources.

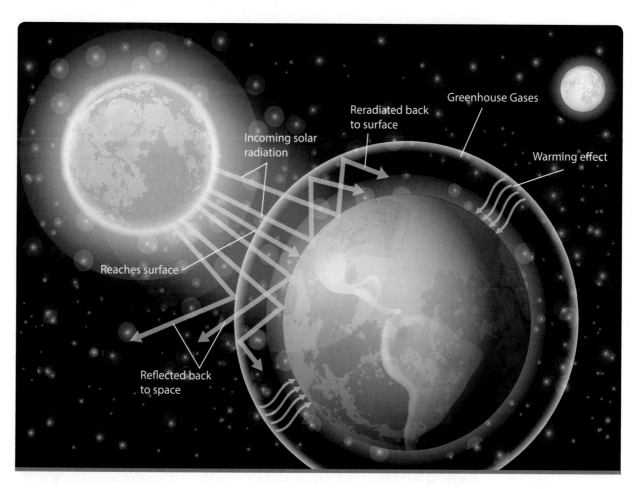

THE GREENHOUSE EFFECT

Earth retains warmth from the sun because greenhouse gases trap solar radiation. How are humans contributing to the amounts and types of greenhouse gases?

Glaciers and Climate Change

Glaciers are made of ice that has been compressed from layers of snow over many centuries. Most glaciers are found primarily near the North or South Pole, while some glaciers are found in mountainous regions of Earth.

Much discussion of climate change focuses on how increasing global temperatures might cause glaciers to melt, leading to increasing sea levels along with other impacts on Earth. Because glaciers are usually very light in color, they tend to reflect sunlight rather than absorb it. Some of this reflected energy is absorbed by the atmosphere, perhaps tending to slightly increase atmospheric temperature. However, most of this reflected radiation is not within the frequency range for absorption by atmospheric gases and much of this energy will return to space, cooling the atmosphere. In this way, reflection contributes to a state of dynamic equilibrium which serves to regulate temperatures.

Reflection of solar radiation is not the only way glaciers influence climate. Moisture evaporates relatively easily to form clouds, but the water in glaciers does not evaporate easily. As a result, a glaciated area may actually generate few clouds. Consequently, more sunlight reaches Earth's surface when glaciers are plentiful. This tends to mitigate cooling in a minor way, but the dominant effect of glaciation is to lower temperatures. For this reason, evidence of glaciation in the geological record serves as a geothermometer, indicating trends of atmospheric cooling.

GLACIER CALVING

When glaciers reach the sea, they often melt and break apart, forming icebergs in a process called calving. How has global climate change increased the calving process?

Climate Feedback Loops

Earth's climate is a balanced system, yet there are many factors that cause or prevent climate change. For example, a volcanic eruption may temporarily cool Earth's surface due to an increase in reflected solar radiation. Volcanic debris in our atmosphere reflects more sunlight than normal. Other factors can directly influence each other. For example, increased solar radiation can increase surface temperatures. Surface temperatures, in turn, can increase evaporation, which can increase cloud formation. These clouds reflect more solar radiation, reducing surface temperatures. Such a series of events is called a negative feedback loop, or feedback which reverses change and tends to return a condition to its original state. Many of Earth's systems exhibit negative feedback loops. These loops, like the thermostat that controls the temperature of a house, helps keep systems stable. However, Earth's climate is a very complex system, which considers many factors. For example, water vapor is a greenhouse gas. During times of increased evaporation, the atmosphere will become warmer. However, when it comes to climate change, many of the feedback loops are positive and can accelerate the process.

The cryosphere is involved in a number of positive feedback loops. In a time of global warming, the ice cover of Earth decreases, and with less ice, Earth's albedo decreases. This raises the temperature further, more ice melts, and the loop continues. The reverse can also occur; if Earth experiences a period of global cooling, more ice forms and as Earth reflects more solar energy and cools faster, even more ice will form.

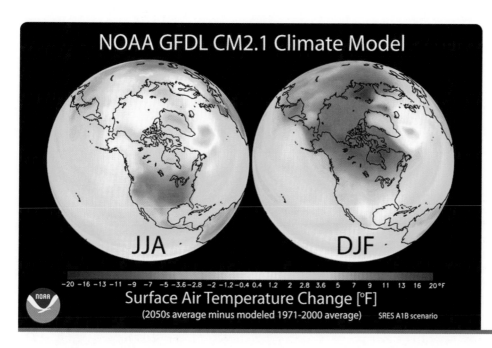

CLIMATE MODEL

This climate change model shows changes in surface air temperature averages for North America and regions around the North Pole. Changes in summer (left) are compared to changes in winter (right). Where were the changes in temperature greatest in summer?

Air Temperature Predictions

Scientists are very concerned that positive feedback loops could exacerbate the process of global climate change, causing runaway warming. They have information about twenty such loops that could speed up the process. One is the increase in methane that is normally trapped in tundra permafrost and ice beneath the ocean. Methane is a powerful greenhouse gas. As more is added to the atmosphere, the hotter the planet gets and the more that is released from the melting ice.

Consider the Explain Question

▌ **How do human activities change the world's climate?**

Go online to complete the scientific explanation.

dlc.com/ca10122s

Check Your Understanding

▌ **Go online to check your understanding of this concept's key ideas.**

dlc.com/ca10123s

STEM in Action

Applying Understanding Climate and Climate Change

Global warming is already causing problems for people and the environment. Ecosystems are being disrupted by the loss of species that can no longer tolerate the deteriorating climatic conditions. In aquatic ecosystems, higher temperatures reduce the solubility of oxygen in water. This means less oxygen is available for aquatic life. As streams become warmer, those species that need high oxygen levels, such as trout, disappear. Higher temperatures can also increase algal growth in some ecosystems. This can create red tides of toxic algae that poison other aquatic animals. Large concentrations of algae can also reduce the penetration of sunlight into the water, which, in turn, reduces the light available for underwater plants. Coral lives in warm water but is intolerant of higher temperatures. A 1° or 2° C increase in water **temperature** can kill coral by destroying the algae that live inside their bodies. This leads to a phenomenon called coral bleaching. In hotter waters, living coral dies and leaves a reef consisting of only white coral skeletons.

Terrestrial ecosystems are also impacted by increases in temperature, which increases transpiration, the movement of water from plants to the **atmosphere**. When transpiration is excessive, plants wilt and die. Drought-tolerant species replace those that previously occupied the area. Some crop species will no longer grow in their old locations. Animal species have a range of temperature to which they are best suited and will migrate in response to temperature change. When temperatures in their summer ranges increase substantially, flocks and herds will move farther north (in the northern hemisphere) and arrive at their summer ranges earlier and depart later. Some species will move into areas they did not previously occupy.

Disease-carrying organisms, such as mosquitoes, that were once limited or killed off by freezing winters, now survive and spread. They can also reproduce for longer periods throughout the year, increasing the size of their populations and potentially spreading more disease. People and wildlife alike are being affected by the increased spread of diseases in the warming world.

Physical changes such as melting glaciers and rising sea levels are consequences of higher temperature which are altering ecosystems. Rising sea levels inundate coastal areas, displacing people and collapsing existing land ecosystems. Freshwater supplies are contaminated by seawater, killing plants and animals that are not adapted to salty waters—often dooming entire food webs. Seasonal glacial melt provides a source of freshwater for plants in many areas. When the glaciers abate and melt away, the regional **climate** can become arid and no longer support forests and agriculture.

THE IMPACT OF GLACIERS

This is a blue glacial iceberg floating in summer along the northwest coast of Spitsbergen, Norway. What effect can melting of glaciers such as this one have on environments around the world?

Rising temperatures in the atmosphere and oceans also cause more extreme weather. Storms such as hurricanes and cyclones gather more strength in warmer conditions as increased evaporation from warmer ocean water transfers energy into the atmosphere. Large-scale circulation patterns in the oceans and the atmosphere change as global temperatures rise. These changes affect weather patterns around the globe. Some areas become prone to flooding and storms. Others experience drought. When agricultural zones change, food supplies diminish.

STEM and Understanding Climate and Climate Change

Climatologists, oceanographers, marine biologists, and meteorologists perform a wide array of climate research all over the world to understand the causes and implications of climate change. They must have knowledge in such fields as chemistry, atmospheric science, geology, physics, ecology, and mathematics. It is also useful to have a hunger for adventure! Important research is conducted in remote areas such as polar ice caps and the bottom of the ocean.

UNIVERSITY OF CALIFORNIA MARINE BIOLOGISTS GATHERING KRILL SAMPLES, MONTEREY BAY, CALIFORNIA
What kinds of information about climate can marine biologists apply to marine life?

Technology plays important roles in climate research. Computers analyze huge amounts of data, and computer models allow scientists to predict possible rates and outcomes of climate change. Heavy equipment is used to obtain cores of ice and seafloor **sediment** for research.

Other professionals in non-science fields also make use of the growing understanding of climate. Because many of the world's largest cities lie on coastlines, urban planners use climate models to predict how rising sea levels will impact areas of the city. Governments use these predictions to plan evacuation routes in case of extreme weather events. Humanitarian organizations study climate change to assess how extreme weather and rising sea levels may affect a community's demands for food, water, and safe shelter.

CONCEPT
6.4

Impacts on Biodiversity

dlc.com/ca10124s

LESSON OVERVIEW

Lesson Questions

■ Why Does Biodiversity Matter?

■ What is the Relationship Between Human Population Size and Rates of Extinction?

■ What Are the Main Causes of Biodiversity Loss?

■ What Steps Can Humans Take to Prevent the Loss of Biodiversity?

Lesson Objectives

By the end of the lesson, you should be able to:

■ Explain the nature of biodiversity.

■ Explain how increasing human population poses a threat to biodiversity.

■ Identify and describe the main causes of biodiversity loss.

■ Identify and explain steps that can be taken to prevent the loss of biodiversity.

Key Vocabulary

Which terms do you already know?

☐ ecosystem
☐ extinction
☐ species

© Discovery Education | www.discoveryeducation.com • Dennis W Donohue / Shutterstock

The Last Male

Occasionally extinction is in the news, such as in 2018 when it was announced that a species of rhino, the Northern White Rhino, was now almost considered extinct. It was hunted nearly to extinction for its horn, and only two females remained in captivity. However, for every species extinction that makes the news, hundreds, and possibly thousands, go unnoticed. What is causing this mass extinction event?

dlc.com/ca10125s

EXPLAIN QUESTION

▌ What can humans do to reduce the extinction rate?

PARK RANGER HOLDING ALLIGATOR SKIN

The American Alligator was hunted nearly to the point of extinction for its beautiful skin. How was the alligator saved from extinction?

Why Does Biodiversity Matter?

Scientists don't know how many **species** exist on Earth. Current estimates are around 8.9 million species, but some scientists think it is much higher, perhaps ten times that number. Whatever the precise number of species, one thing is for sure: there is a lot of diversity of life out there, and the closer scientists look, the more species they find. This diversity is referred to as biological diversity or biodiversity, and the term *biodiversity* is actually more inclusive than just the number of species. It can be applied at a number of biological levels and includes the variety of different genes within a species, the variety of species, and the variety of different communities and ecosystems. Scientists also talk about global biodiversity, referring to the Earth at large; though, it is also referred to on the local or regional level.

Biodiversity is the result of genetic changes produced by evolution over billions of years. It includes the genetic information in all organisms. This diversity becomes even more mind-boggling when one considers that a teaspoon of soil commonly contains more than 20,000 species of bacteria. Many of these bacteria contain over 2000 genes, some of them unique to their species. Imagine how many different species or genes there are in a rain forest, a coral reef, or inside the human gut. Of the few species that scientists have discovered and named, little is known about their roles or interactions within ecosystems. In many cases, human activities are wiping out species before their importance in an **ecosystem** is understood, often before the species is even made known to science.

So why is all this biodiversity important? The air you breathe, the water you drink, and the food you eat are all products of biodiversity. Without plants such as trees or grasses, or phytoplankton that live in the ocean, there would be no oxygen for us to breathe. Without the organisms that live in wetlands or sewage treatment plants, water quality would decline. No insects or other bugs would be available to pollinate crop plants, and without the organisms that populate the soil, many plants would not grow, and nutrient recycling would come to a halt. Then there are all the other benefits we get from living things, from the materials that make up our clothes, to the wood we use to build our homes, to antibiotics we use to treat disease. In economic terms, the services provided by ecosystems are worth trillions of dollars annually. Can you list any other direct benefits of biodiversity?

Then there are the moral, cultural, and recreational reasons for preserving biodiversity. Humans are the only organism on Earth that has the power and ability to conserve or destroy many of the species that have evolved. By conserving species, they support the ecosystems that will sustain future generations of humans and other organisms and provide future human generations with the opportunities to experience biodiversity. Biodiversity has always been a source of cultural inspiration for humans. Many of our religions, stories, and much of our art have their origins in the biodiversity that surrounds us.

MANGROVE SWAMPS

Mangrove swamps are very diverse ecosystems that support thousands of species and act as a nursery for many fish. They also protect coastal regions from erosion and hurricanes. What are some other reasons to protect mangrove swamps?

Many humans enjoy their encounters with biodiverse ecosystems and seek them out for relaxation and recreation. Biodiversity also has a huge scientific value. When scientists study biodiversity, they learn more about the mechanisms behind evolution, the economic value of organisms and ecosystems, and gain insights into animal behavior, including our own.

What Is the Relationship between Human Population Size and Rates of Extinction?

Most of the organisms that have evolved are now extinct. **Extinction** is an essential part of life's history, as **species** become extinct they are replaced by new ones that fill the same or newly formed niches. Extinction does not occur at a constant rate. However, scientists have calculated a rate for extinction that occurs between mass extinction events. This extinction rate can be interpreted in a variety of ways. For example, out of a million species, about one species becomes extinct every year. To put it another way, species are usually around from between 5 hundred thousand to a million years before they become extinct. The figure differs between groups of animals, but these figures are useful comparisons to use when comparing them with modern extinction rates which are around one thousand to ten thousand times higher! This is higher than the extinction rate in some earlier mass extinction events. To understand why this new, sixth extinction event is happening, we need to look at how human activities are causing environmental change that is impacting the biosphere.

Modern humans (*Homo sapiens*) migrated out of Africa about 100,000 years ago and over the next 90,000 years spread across most of the Earth, making it to the most remote islands around 2,000 years ago. During most of this time, global human populations remained small, a few million. Even at these levels human activities have a negative impact on biodiversity, particularly the diversity of species that were important sources of food. For example, human migration into North America (around 16,000 years ago) coincides with the disappearance of most of the continent's large mammals. This mega fauna included now extinct species of giant mammals—giant sloths, mastodons and giant beavers. Most of these mammals became extinct within just 4 thousand years of the arrival of humans. Most likely they were hunted to extinction.

With the invention of agriculture around 10 thousand years ago, human populations began expanding rapidly. Agriculture, with the cultivation of crops, grazing of domestic livestock, and the diversion and damming of water courses, also reduces biodiversity—agricultural systems are much simpler than natural ecosystems. This impact increased further with the development of more modern farming practices in the 18th and 19th centuries and the accompanying Industrial Revolution. Human population and its devastating impact on biodiversity have continued to grow. The current human population stands at around 7 billion.

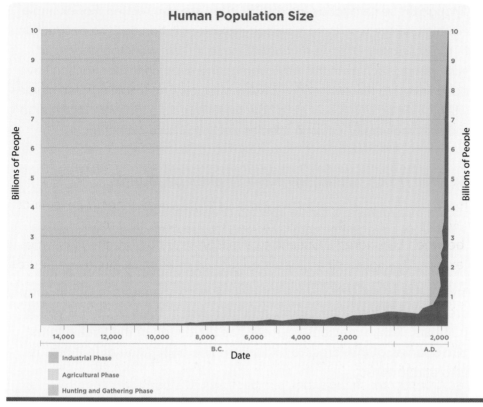

Human Population Size

Billions of People

14,000   12,000   10,000   8,000   6,000   4,000   2,000

B.C.   Date   A.D.

■ Industrial Phase
■ Agricultural Phase
■ Hunting and Gathering Phase

HUMAN POPULATION GROWTH OVER THE LAST 15,000 YEARS

Earth's human population is projected to be near 10 billion by 2050. What impact does the rapid increase in human population have on biodiversity?

As human populations rise, so does the amount of resources consumed per person. This per capita increase exacerbates **ecosystem** destruction.

Currently about 50 percent of Earth's land surface is used by humans, most of this for human food production. Human activities consume half the world's freshwater and move more rock and soil than natural erosion. At this point in Earth's history our planet is dominated by human activity.

What Are the Main Causes of Biodiversity Loss?

The loss of biodiversity is mainly the result of human activities that can be classified under five threat categories:

■ Habitat destruction
■ Global climate change
■ Introduction of invasive **species**
■ Overharvesting of resources such as overhunting and overfishing
■ Pollution

Though these categories are distinct, they are also related. For example, climate change results from carbon-dioxide pollution and the destruction of forest habitat. Often, a number of these threats work together in an **ecosystem**, such as in the way overhunting and habitat destruction have been linked to the **extinction** of many species. The following case studies will provide an illustration as to how these threats often work together to reduce biodiversity, causing species decline and/or extinction.

Snakes on an Island: Invasive Snakes on Guam

Brown tree snakes, a native species of Australia and some Pacific Islands, are thought to have arrived on the Pacific Island of Guam by ship sometime in the 1950s. Guam, an American Territory, is an island of about 500 km^2 that now has a population of over 2 million of this invasive species. Brown tree snakes have no predators in Guam, they are nocturnal forest predators, and their diet is small birds and young fruit bats. Their voracious appetite has driven ten of the twelve forest bird species of the forest to extinction. The population of fruit bats is also endangered.

The native trees of Guam are species that produce fruit with small seeds. When birds and fruit bats eat the fruit, they defecate the fruit seeds onto the forest floor. To effectively germinate, the seeds need to first pass through an animal's gut. With the loss of most of the birds and bats, fewer seeds are germinating. The numbers of new seedlings of some species have dropped 90%. Fewer individuals of these species result in a loss of other organisms that inhabit or rely on them in some other way. The loss of some trees, once common, is altering the entire structure of the island's forest ecosystem.

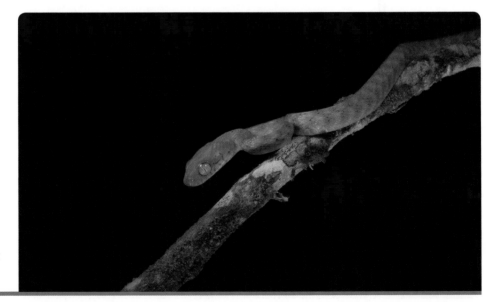

THE BROWN TREE SNAKE

The brown tree snake is an invasive species on the island of Guam. Where did it originate? Why are its numbers out of control?

With declining bird and bat populations, brown tree snakes are turning their appetites to organisms they wouldn't usually eat. Now species of geckos and small mammals are becoming rare. Insects, once eaten by these organisms are becoming more common, some reaching pest status. Sometimes the snakes attack young children who, because the snakes are mildly poisonous, can get sick when bitten. They also crawl onto power lines and cause power outages that cost the island millions of dollars each year. Many methods—using traps, poisons, and parasites—have been tried to control the snakes, but none have proven effective.

Hawaiian Birds: Habitat Loss, Disease and Climate Change

Birds arrived on the Hawaiian Islands long before humans. For millions of years, they evolved into a wide variety of species, like Hawaiian owls, geese, honeycreepers, and crows. Some flew, others stalked the ground, filling niches normally occupied by mammals. Today most of these birds are extinct, and the wave of extinction started with the arrival of humans. The ground-dwelling birds were the first to go, finding their way via trapping and hunting, to the cooking pot. Others were killed to make decorative feather cloaks. As new islanders cultivated the land, lowland habitats were destroyed. Introduced animals also became new predators to many of the birds. With the arrival of Europeans, this process accelerated as newly introduced predators arrived and more land was converted to plantations, golf courses, and neighborhoods.

ONE OF THE RAREST BIRDS IN THE UNITED STATES

This is one of 18 species of honeycreeper that are threatened by human activities on the Hawaiian Islands. What are these threats?

A disease spread by mosquitos, avian malaria, was accidentally introduced. Hawaii's forest birds had little resistance to the disease, causing more species to become extinct or creep further towards extinction. Some birds managed to move out of range of the mosquitos by moving to cooler habitats higher up in Hawaii's mountains. Now as human-induced climate change warms the planet, disease-carrying mosquitos are moving into these once cool areas.

Dying Forests: Logging, Climate Change, Pollution, Invasive Species, and Disease

Most of the eastern (and many western) forests of the United States were cut down following the colonization of North America. Some have since grown back, but these forests are not the same as the ones that preceded them. The pre-colonial forests contained trees larger than most we see today, many were hundreds of years old, and the soils they sheltered were rich and deep. Removal of the trees for timber and farm steading led to soil erosion. When many of the farms were deserted in the early and mid-20th century, the trees began to take over again.

EARLY LOGGERS AND VERY STRONG HORSES

The climax forest of the United States was almost eliminated by logging, but many of these forests have returned. In what ways are they different from the original forest?

These new eastern forests lacked one dominant tree, the North American Chestnut. Billions of these trees were killed by a fungus that was accidentally introduced from Asia. It is called chestnut blight, and it spread out from its first points of infection in New York state. The fungus spread rapidly, expanding its range by tens of miles each year. This was a major blow to the re-establishment of the old forest ecosystem. Other tree species took the chestnuts' place, but soon many of them were experiencing their own problems.

The oaks that replaced the chestnuts in many forests are being attacked by insects introduced from Europe, like gypsy moths, and by diseases such as oak wilt and sudden oak death. The American Elm, a magnificent tree particularly common in damper parts of the forest near streams and rivers, began to die off in the 1930s because of newly introduced Dutch Elm disease. Within 40 years, it had killed most American elms, and the story is ongoing—white walnut (butternut) is being obliterated by butternut canker and American beech trees by beech bark disease. A beetle, the emerald ash borer (a native of China) is devastating ash tree populations, having killed about 100 million trees so far. The Asian long-horned beetle, which attacks maples, birches, and willows, is beginning to spread. The list goes on and includes other broad-leafed trees and many species of conifers, such as pines, firs, and hemlocks. Introduced diseases and invasive species are only half the story. Climate change, particularly drought, stresses trees and makes them more vulnerable to both introduced and native diseases. More dead trees provide timber for forest fires that burn large areas. In the eastern United States, sulfur pollution from obsolete coal-fired plants also damages forests.

DYING TREES

Trees in some parts of the United States are stressed by the changing climate, particularly by longer periods of drought. They may die because of lack of water or because the stress of water shortage makes them more vulnerable to disease. How could this affect the incidence of forest fires?

When trees die, so do many of the organisms that rely on them. Most tree species in temperate forests support between 50-100 species of insects, numerous other species of invertebrates, and woodland vertebrates such as birds and mammals. Indirectly the leaf litter they produce, and the soil that forms from it, support hundreds of more invertebrates. So, loss of tree diversity alters the entire forest ecosystem, including the loss of timber, oxygen, water, soil conservation, and recreation, all invaluable services for humans.

Soup and the Fate of Sharks: Increased Consumption and Overharvesting

Sharks were one of the top predators in oceanic food webs. There are around 400 species, and although none have yet gone extinct, most are on the decline and many species are at risk. What is happening? They have been displaced from their top predator status by a more dangerous organism—humans. As human populations have expanded so has their consumption of seafood. When it comes to sharks, it is estimated that humans kill around 100 million each year. This toll has caused a 90% decline in shark numbers across the world's oceans and is altering the composition structures of shark populations. Many sharks take over a decade to mature, so fishing has reduced the age and size of sharks in the population, as well as their ability to renew themselves. To make matters worse, many sharks are killed just for their fins. The rest of the live shark is returned to the ocean to die, and their fins are used to make shark-fin soup. Others are said to be caught by mistake and are returned, injured or dead, to the sea.

TIGER SHARK

Sharks are top predators in the ocean. How and why are humans impacting their populations?

The loss of top predators in an ecosystem reverberates down the food chain. Declines in predatory sharks in the north Atlantic have allowed populations of the sharks' prey to explode. Sharks eat rays that feed on scallops, so fewer sharks mean more rays and fewer scallops. Scallop fisheries have closed because there are too few of the bivalves to support a sustainable fishery. Studies are revealing many more repercussions of removing these top predators.

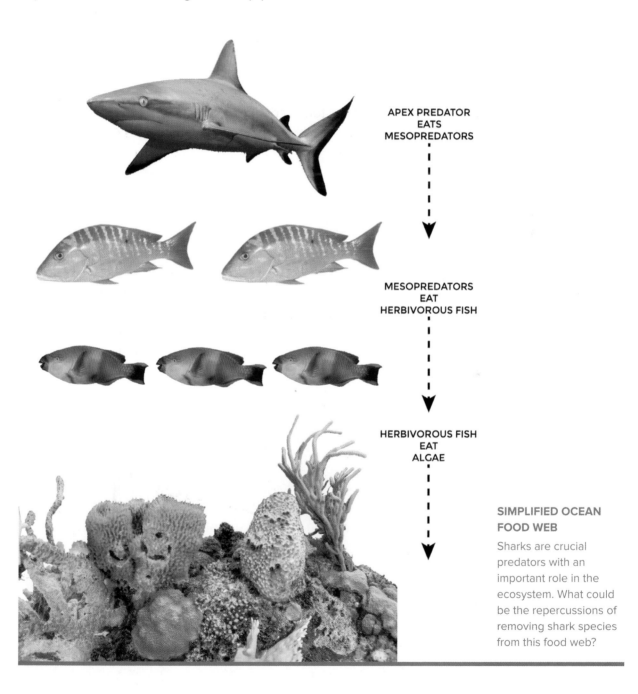

APEX PREDATOR
EATS
MESOPREDATORS

MESOPREDATORS
EAT
HERBIVOROUS FISH

HERBIVOROUS FISH
EAT
ALGAE

SIMPLIFIED OCEAN FOOD WEB

Sharks are crucial predators with an important role in the ecosystem. What could be the repercussions of removing shark species from this food web?

Sharks not only affect populations by consuming prey, but they also influence the distribution of prey. Fear of shark predation causes some species to switch their feeding areas or alter their activity level. This prevents the prey species from overusing a food resource in a specific area, ensuring an abundance of organisms at lower trophic levels in the food web and maintaining species diversity. It may seem counter-intuitive that more predators lead to greater biodiversity, but comparisons of areas with and without top predators show that apex predators, like sharks, create greater biodiversity, while areas without top predators have fewer species. Predatory sharks also ensure the health of prey populations by removing sick or weak individuals.

What Steps Can Humans Take to Prevent the Loss of Biodiversity?

The loss of biodiversity is occurring over most of the world. Therefore, stopping or reversing biodiversity loss should be a priority for all the planet's citizens. We can look at biodiversity conservation from two overlapping perspectives—the global and the personal. Globally, first steps could include:

- Identifying threatened areas with high biodiversity and establishing them as a priority for conservation. These areas, known as "biological hotspots," require indefinite, irreversible protection and should include both terrestrial and aquatic ecosystems.

- Identifying and protecting areas which provide the greatest benefits in terms **ecosystem** services. For example, wetlands that purify water and protect communities from flooding.

- Stabilizing and then reducing overall human consumption and adopting more sustainable approaches to natural resource use. This entails stabilizing human populations and reducing poverty in many countries, while reining in over-consumption in others.

- Better integrating human communities with natural systems. This includes the greening of cities and suburbs, so they better use resources to produce what they need.

- Effectively regulating the spread of invasive **species** and diseases that threaten biodiversity.

- Reducing pollution, including carbon dioxide and methane pollution, the prime causes of global climate change, and gases that damage the ozone on the upper atmosphere.

DEFORESTATION

Deforestation removes trees from an area. How could deforestation affect biodiversity?

Individuals can act to support the conservation of biodiversity. Such actions could include the more efficient use of resources (for example by increasing recycling), reducing consumption (for example by conserving energy), eating less meat, and purchasing local organic foods that have not been grown using pesticides. Individuals can volunteer for conservation initiatives that help in the protection of nature reserves and national parks, perhaps by helping in the removal of trash and invasive species. Writing letters to politicians and newspapers in support of policies that are sustainable and biodiversity-friendly can also be very effective.

Consider the Explain Question

▎ **What can humans do to reduce the extinction rate?**

Go online to complete the scientific explanation.

dlc.com/ca10126s

Check Your Understanding

▎ **Go online to check your understanding of this concept's key ideas.**

dlc.com/ca10127s

STEM in Action

Applying Impacts on Biodiversity

Biodiversity, or the variety of life on Earth, is in crisis. According to scientists, the rate of extinctions today is estimated to be at least one thousand times the natural background rate. Coral reefs and tropical rainforests are undergoing the greatest losses. These biomes have the highest species richness, hence impacts are proportionally greater compared to less biodiverse regions. However, all Earth's biomes have species that are at risk of extinction due to human activities. Since 1900, around five hundred species have gone extinct as a result of human impacts on natural habitats. That might not sound like many, but according to the fossil record, no more than ten species should have gone extinct in that time.

SPECIES RICHNESS

Areas with high biodiversity have high species richness. What kinds of actions can threaten the biodiversity of an area like this meadow?

The unprecedented rate of extinction today compared to that in the fossil record has led scientists to believe that life on Earth is undergoing a mass extinction. The fossil record indicates that Earth has undergone five mass extinctions in its four-billion-year history. It is remarkable to think that humans are having an impact that is significant over geological time scales. We are having a great enough impact that some geologists propose that we are initiating a new geological epoch, dubbed the Anthropocene.

Scientists identify six main drivers of extinction. These include loss and degradation of ecosystems, invasive species, effects of climate change, exploitation (hunting, fishing, etc.), pollution, and disease.

Of these, the main threat is the destruction and degradation of natural habitats. Such destruction occurs due to logging, mining, and urban development. For example, research by Australian scientists found that habitat loss is responsible for four-fifths of threatened species in that country.

The second greatest impact on biodiversity is due to invasive species. Only a few invasive species have caused numerous extinctions. For example, rats and cats on the Hawaiian Islands are the culprits behind extinctions of many endemic birds there. Of 142 bird species found nowhere else, 95 are now extinct. Around the world, island populations are particularly vulnerable to extinction. Perhaps the most famous modern extinction is that of the dodo bird. It lived only on the island of Mauritius, going extinct around 1700, barely a century after its discovery.

Disease is another serious threat. The chytrid fungus has been linked to major declines in frog populations worldwide. The Tasmanian devil, the world's biggest marsupial predator, has undergone a decline of more than 60% due to an infectious oral cancer.

Whatever the causes of extinction, there is little doubt that loss of biodiversity will severely impact human quality of life. Some scientists predict that ultimately the human species will be a victim of the current mass extinction. The challenge facing scientists is how to manage biodiversity loss. First, measures must be taken to reduce the rate of extinction. Such measures range from breeding and re-introduction programs to conservation and restoration of threatened habitats.

WATER POLLUTION
Plastics can clog waterways and damage aquatic ecosystems. How could we avoid this kind of plastic pollution?

STEM and Impacts on Biodiversity

In order to limit human impacts on biodiversity, conservationists are using science-based approaches. One approach is to use remote sensing technology to map biodiversity hotspots. For example, scientists in Panama analyzed images from airborne imaging spectroscopy. The images enable the researchers to identify the number of tree species in areas of tropical rainforest. This method allows comparison of areas for tree species diversity, and hence prioritization of conservation efforts. The precision of the method allows scientists to map a single species, if needed, across broad areas of forest.

Another application of technology in conservation is to use genetics to measure gene diversity in populations. Species with low genetic diversity are at greater risk of extinction. The data can be used to ensure captive breeding programs do not suffer from the effects of inbreeding. Genetic studies can also indicate the health of wild populations. Since an organic sample (such as fur or scat) can be used for genetic analysis, such studies can be carried out at lower cost and with no need to capture individual animals.

One of the most pronounced impacts of human activity on tropical rainforests is fragmentation. Forest is fragmented because some areas are easier to convert to farmland, or more easily logged. For example, lowlying area are more suited to growing crops than mountainous areas. The effect of fragmentation is to isolate and reduce populations. In turn, smaller populations are more likely to go extinct. Over time, entire species will go extinct.

To address the problem of fragmentation, one conservation strategy is to connect fragments. The connections create corridors allowing animals to move between fragments. In this way, populations can inter-breed, increasing genetic diversity and overall population size. Most corridors are areas of forest that are purchased or set aside for conservation. Former farmland purchased by conservation organizations can be restored. Such restoration may occur by natural regeneration or replanting programs. Scientists use satellite images to monitor regrowth of restored areas. In Brazil, scientists have worked with the government in a unique engineering project to build a physical bridge over a major highway. The bridge is designed to provide a natural corridor along which animals can move from one forest fragment to another.

Given the current loss of species worldwide, scientists want to quantify the rate of loss. A simple measure is the number of species that go extinct over time. For example, one bird species will go extinct every 400 years. However, due to the uncertainty of the total number of species, this measurement cannot be used to quantify mass extinction. One way around this is to measure the number of extinctions relative to species-years (extinctions per million species-years, E/MSY). For example, if the extinction rate is 1 E/MSY, out of a million species, one will go extinct every year. Alternatively, one species will go extinct in a million years. The predicted rate by 2100 is 1500 E/MSY. That means 15,000 times more species will be going extinct compared to the background rate.

English ———————— A ———————— Español

English	Español
abiotic non-living, physical components of the environment	**abiótico** componentes físicos no vivos del medio ambiente
abrasion a type of mechanical weathering caused by the scraping and scratching of rocks by loose particles that are transported over the rocks by wind, water, glaciers, etc.	**abrasión** tipo de desgaste mecánico originado por el rozamiento o fricción de partículas sueltas arrastradas por el viento, el agua, los glaciares, etc. sobre las rocas
activation energy the minimum amount of energy required to initiate a chemical reaction; written as Ea and measured in kilojoules	**energía de activación** cantidad mínima de energía necesaria para iniciar una reacción química; se representa como Ea y se mide en kilojulios
active transport movement of ions or molecules across a membrane, often against a concentration gradient; requires energy input; endocytosis is a type of active transport	**transporte activo** movimiento de iones o moléculas a través de una membrana, con frecuencia contra un gradiente de concentración; requiere un aporte de energía; la endocitosis es un tipo de transporte activo
adaptation a change in the function or structure of an organism that makes it better suited to its environment	**adaptación** cambio en la función o estructura de un organismo que lo hace más apto para su medio ambiente
adenine one of the four nitrogenous bases contained in a DNA molecule; adenine is complementary to guanine	**adenina** una de las cuatro bases nitrogenadas que forman parte de una molécula de ADN; la adenina es complementaria a la guanina
adenosine triphosphate (ATP) a chemical compound that is able to store and transport chemical energy within cells; also known as ATP	**trifosfato de adenosina** compuesto químico capaz de almacenar y transportar energía química en las células; también se conoce como ATP
adiabatic cooling occurs when the temperature of an air mass decreases as a result of the expansion of the air mass as it rises	**enfriamiento adiabático** se produce cuando la temperatura de una masa de aire disminuye como resultado de la expansión de dicha masa a medida que asciende
ADP ADP, adenosine diphosphate is a nucleotide that is involved in the transfers of energy in biological systems.	**ADP** adenosín difosfato es un nucleótido que interviene en la transferencia de energía en los sistemas biológicos.
aerobic respiration the form of in cell respiration that requires free oxygen	**respiración aeróbica** forma de respiración celular que requiere oxígeno
age pyramid a graphic depiction of the age and sex distribution of a population	**pirámide de edad** representación gráfica de la distribución por edad y sexo de una población

allele   any of several possible forms of a gene

alelo   cualesquiera de las varias formas posibles de un gen

---

allopatric speciation   the evolution of a population into a new species when the population is separated from other members of the original species by a geographic barrier

especiación alopátrica   evolución de una población dando lugar a especies nuevas cuando la población se separa de otros miembros de la especie original mediante una barrera geográfica

---

amino acid   one of the 20 types of molecules that combine to form proteins

aminoácido   uno de los 20 tipos de moléculas que se combinan para formar proteínas

---

anaerobic respiration   the form of cell respiration that can take place in the absence of free oxygen

respiración anaeróbica   tipo de respiración celular que puede tener lugar en ausencia de oxígeno

---

aneuploidy   a condition in which one or more chromosomes are present in extra copies or are absent

aneuploidía   condición en la cual existen copias adicionales de uno o más cromosomas o cromosomas ausentes

---

angular unconformity   an unconformity in which younger sediments have been deposited on top of the eroded surface of tilted or folded older rock layers

discordancia angular   discordancia en la cual los sedimentos más jóvenes se encuentran depositados sobre la superficie erosionada de capas de roca más antiguas dobladas o inclinadas

---

animal cell   a form of a eukaryotic cell that is distinct from plant cells in that it does not have a rigid cell wall

célula animal   tipo de célula eucariota que es diferente de la células vegetales; la célula animal no tiene una pared celular rígida

---

anthropogenic   caused or originating from human beings

antropogénico   causado por los seres humanos u originado en ellos

---

antibiotic   a chemical that kills or inhibits growth of bacteria

antibiótico   sustancia química que mata o inhibe el crecimiento de bacterias

---

anticodon   a sequence of 3 nucleotides on a tRNA molecule that is complementary to a codon on mRNA

anticodón   secuencia de 3 nucleótidos en una molécula de ARNt que es complementario de un codón en una molécula de ARNm

---

Archaea   one of three domains of living organisms; single-celled prokaryotic micro-organisms that lack a nucleus; similar in size and shape to bacteria; often found in harsh environments

Archaea   uno de los tres dominios de los seres vivos; microorganismos procariotas unicelulares que carecen de núcleo; semejantes en tamaño y forma a las bacterias; con frecuencia se encuentran en ambientes extremos

artery   a blood vessel that carries blood away from the heart

arteria   vaso sanguíneo que lleva sangre desde el corazón

---

artificial selection   selective breeding of plants and animals by humans

selección artificial   cría selectiva de plantas y animales llevada a cabo por los seres humanos

---

asexual reproduction   the generation of offspring from a single parent that occurs without the fusion of gametes

reproducción asexual   generación de descendencia a partir de un solo progenitor que se produce sin que haya fusión de gametos

---

asthenosphere   the layer of soft but solid mobile rock found below the lithosphere. The asthenosphere begins about 100 km below Earth's surface and extends to a depth of about 350 km; the lower part of the upper mantle.

astenosfera   capa de roca capaz de moverse, blanda pero sólida, que se encuentra bajo la litosfera. La astenosfera comienza aproximadamente a 100 km bajo la superficie de la Tierra y se extiende hasta una profundidad de unos 350 km; parte inferior del manto superior.

---

atmosphere   the layers of gases that surround a planet

atmósfera   capas de gases que rodean un planeta

---

autosomal dominant disorder   a disorder in which a person needs only to inherit an abnormal gene from one parent in order to develop the disease

trastorno autosómico dominante   trastorno en el cual una persona necesita solo heredar un gen anormal de uno de los progenitores para desarrollar la enfermedad

---

autosomal recessive disorder   a disorder in which a person must inherit two copies of an abnormal gene—one from each parent—in order for the disease or trait to develop

trastorno autosómico recesivo   trastorno en el cual una persona debe heredar dos copias de un gen anormal (uno de cada progenitor) para desarrollar la enfermedad o el rasgo

---

autotroph   organism that can create its own food from simple molecules

autótrofo   organismo que puede producir su propio alimento a partir de moléculas simples

B

bacteria   one of three domains of living organisms; single-celled prokaryotic organisms that lack an organized nucleus; similar in size and shape to Archaea; can be found in nearly every habitat on Earth

bacteria   uno de los tres dominios de los seres vivos; procariotas unicelulares que carecen de núcleo organizado; semejantes en tamaño y forma a las Archaea; se pueden encontrar en casi cualquier hábitat en la Tierra

---

bilateral symmetry   a characteristic of organisms that can be divided in half along a midline yielding similar left and right halves

simetría bilateral   característica de los organismos según la cual estos pueden dividirse a la mitad a lo largo de una línea central, dando lugar a dos mitades similares, una derecha y otra izquierda

binary fission   a method of asexual reproduction in which single-celled organisms like bacteria reproduce by replicating their DNA and splitting in half

biodiversity   the variety of species that exist in an environment

bio-fuel   a type of renewable energy source created from organisms

biogeochemistry   a combination of disciplines that studies the biochemistry of flora and fauna in a geographical context

biogeography   the study of the environmental distribution of organisms

biomagnification   the increase in or process of increasing the concentration of a substance (usually a toxin) in living tissue at each level of the food chain

biomass   the mass of dried living matter in a given area or volume of habitat

biome   a major ecological community such as grassland, tropical rain forest, or desert

biosphere   the part of Earth in which living organisms are known to exist

biotic   living, physical components of the environment

blood   tissue that brings oxygen and nutrients to the cells of the body and removes wastes from the cells of the body

bottleneck effect   a limited variety of alleles in a population due to a dramatic decrease in population size

brain stem   the part of the brain that connects to the spinal cord

fisión binaria   método de reproducción asexual en el cual organismos unicelulares como las bacterias se reproducen replicando su ADN y dividiéndose en dos mitades

biodiversidad   variedad de especies que existen en un medio ambiente

biocombustible   tipo de energía renovable producida a partir de organismos

biogeoquímica   combinación de disciplinas que estudia la bioquímica de la flora y la fauna en un contexto geográfico

biogeografía   estudio de la distribución de los organismos en los medioambientes

biomagnificación   aumento o proceso de aumento de la concentración de una sustancia (por lo general, una toxina) en tejidos vivos en cada nivel de la cadena alimentaria

biomasa   masa de materia orgánica seca que se encuentra en un área dada o en un volumen de hábitat

bioma   gran comunidad ecológica, como una pradera, una selva tropical o un desierto

biósfera   parte de la Tierra en la que existen los organismos vivos

biótico   vivo, componentes físicos del medio ambiente

sangre   tejido que lleva oxígeno y nutrientes a las células del cuerpo y remueve los desechos de las células del cuerpo

efecto cuello de botella   limitada variedad de alelos en una población debida a una disminución drástica del tamaño de la población

tronco encefálico   parte del cerebro que está conectada con la médula espinal

C

Calvin cycle   the carbon-fixing reaction in photosynthesis, also known as the dark or light-independent reactions; the Calvin cycle uses ATP and NADPH produced in the light reactions to incorporate the carbon from carbon dioxide into carbohydrates

ciclo de Calvin   reacción de fijación del carbono en la fotosíntesis, también conocida como reacciones independientes clara y oscura; en el ciclo de Calvin se usa ATP y NADPH producidos en las reacciones claras para incorporar el carbono procedente del dióxido de carbono y producir hidratos de carbono

Cambrian explosion   a period of rapid growth in life's diversity from 540 to 485 million years ago

explosión cámbrica   período de crecimiento rápido en la biodiversidad hace 540 a 485 millones de años

cancer cells   cells that grow and divide continuously at an unregulated pace

células cancerosas   células que crecen y se dividen continuamente a un ritmo descontrolado

carbohydrate   one of four major classes of organic compounds in living cells and an important source of nutritional energy; includes simple sugars, and more complex sugars such as starch sugars or many sugars; can also serve as a structural molecule

hidrato de carbono   una de las cuatro clases principales de compuestos orgánicos presentes en las células vivas e importante fuente de energía nutricional; este tipo de compuesto incluye azúcares simples, azúcares más complejos como el almidón y muchos azúcares; también puede funcionar como molécula estructural

carbon cycle   a natural cycle in which carbon compounds, mainly carbon dioxide, are incorporated into living tissue through photosynthesis and returned to the atmosphere by respiration, decay of dead organisms, and the burning of fossil fuels

ciclo del carbono   ciclo natural en el cual los compuestos de carbono, principalmente el dióxido de carbono, se incorporan en los tejidos vivos a través de la fotosíntesis y regresan a la atmósfera por medio de la respiración, la desintegración de organismos muertos y la quema de combustibles fósiles

carbon reservoir   a component in the carbon cycle in which carbon is stored, such as the atmosphere, oceans, biosphere, or lithosphere. Reservoirs can serve as carbon sinks or carbon sources.

depósito de carbono   componente en el ciclo del carbono en el cual se almacena el carbono, como la atmósfera, los océanos, la biosfera o la litosfera. Los depósitos pueden servir como sumideros de carbono o fuentes de carbono.

carbon   the chemical element with the atomic number 6

carbono   elemento químico con número atómico 6

carbonate   an ion composed of carbon and oxygen in a 1:3 ratio with a positive 2 charge (CO_3^{+2}); a general term for minerals and other substances that contain carbonate ions as part of their chemical structure, such as calcite, aragonite, and dolomite

carbonato   ión compuesto por carbono y oxígeno en una proporción 1:3 con 2 cargas positivas (CO_3^{+2}); término general para minerales y otras sustancias que contienen iones de carbonato como parte de su estructura química, como la calcita, el aragonito y la dolomita

---

carnivore   an animal that eats only other animals

carnívoro   animal que se alimenta solo de otros animales

---

carrying capacity   indicates the greatest number of any species that can indefinitely exist within a specific habitat without threatening the existence of other species also living in the habitat

capacidad de carga   indica el mayor número de individuos de cualquier especie que puede existir indefinidamente en un hábitat específico sin poner en riesgo la existencia de otras especies que también viven en ese hábitat

---

catalyst   substance that increases the rate of a chemical reaction by lowering the amount of energy needed for the reaction to occur, but is not changed by the reaction

catalizador   sustancia que aumenta la velocidad de una reacción química al disminuir la cantidad de energía necesaria para que la reacción se produzca, pero no es modificada por la reacción

---

cell cycle   the sequence of phases that a eukaryotic cell progresses through beginning with its origin in the division of a parent cell and ending with its own division

ciclo celular   secuencia de fases por las que atraviesa una célula eucariota, desde el principio con su origen en la división de una célula progenitora hasta terminar con su propia división

---

cell membrane   a biological membrane, also called the plasma membrane, that surrounds a cell and selectively controls which substances can enter or leave the cell

membrana celular   membrana biológica, también llamada membrana plasmática, que rodea a la célula y controla, de manera selectiva, qué sustancias pueden entrar en la célula o salir de ella

---

cell theory   the theory that (1) all organisms are made out of one or more cells; (2) cells are the smallest units of life; (3) cells come from pre-existing cells via cell division

teoría celular   teoría de que (1) todos los organismos están compuestos por una o más células; (2) las células son las unidades de vida más pequeñas; (3) las células provienen de células preexistentes mediante división celular

---

cellular division   the process in which a cell splits in two; part of the larger cell cycle. In eukaryotes, there are two kinds of cell division: mitosis and meiosis. Prokaryotes divide by the process of binary fission.

división celular   proceso en el cual una célula se divide en dos; parte del ciclo celular más largo. En las eucariotas hay dos tipos de división celular: mitosis y meiosis. Las procariotas se dividen mediante el proceso de fisión binaria.

cellular respiration the process that occurs when the chemical energy of "food" molecules, carbohydrates, fats, and proteins, is released and partially captured in the form of adenosine triphosphate (ATP)

respiración celular proceso que ocurre cuando la energía química de las moléculas de "comida," hidratos de carbono, grasas y proteínas, se libera y es capturado parcialmente en forma de trifosfato de adenosina (ATP)

cellulose an insoluble polymer that is the main substance in plant cell walls.

celulosa polímero insoluble que es la sustancia principal de las paredes de las células vegetales

chaparral biome an ecological community characterized by a hot, dry summer and mild, wet winters, scrub vegetation, flat plains, rocky hills, and mountain slopes

bioma de chaparral comunidad ecológica caracterizada por veranos secos y cálidos e inviernos húmedos, vegetación de arbustos, llanuras, colinas rocosas y montañas de pendientes suaves

Charles Darwin (1809–1882) British scientist, laid the foundation of modern with his concept that all species have developed from a common ancestor through the process of natural selection.

Charles Darwin (1809–1882) Científico británico, sentó la base de la biología moderna con su concepto de que todas las especies se han desarrollado a partir de un ancestro común a través del proceso de selección natural.

chemical energy the energy that is stored in the bonds between atoms

energía química energía que se encuentra almacenada en los enlaces entre átomos

chemical weathering changes to rocks and minerals on Earth's surface that are caused by chemical reactions

meteorización química cambios en las rocas y minerales de la superficie de la Tierra causados por reacciones químicas

chlorophyll a green pigment found in photosynthetic organisms

clorofila pigmento verde que se encuentra en los organismos fotosintéticos

chloroplast an organelle in plant and algae cells that converts energy from sunlight into chemical energy that the plant can use

cloroplasto orgánulo en las células de las plantas y las algas que convierte la energía de la luz solar en energía química que la planta puede usar

chromatid a replicated chromosome, joined by the centromere to a copy of the chromosome

cromátido cromosoma replicado, unido por el centrómero a una copia del cromosoma

chromatin a macromolecular complex enabling efficient packaging of DNA

cromatina complejo macromolecular que permite la envoltura eficiente del ADN

chromosomal abnormalities errors in the structure or number of chromosomes

anormalidades cromosomáticas errores en la estructura o en el número de cromosomas

chromosome   Chromosomes are the intracellular structures made of the cell's double-stranded DNA genome packaged bound to DNA-binding proteins.

cromosoma   Los cromosomas son estructuras intracelulares hechas de paquetes de genoma de dobles hebras de ADN de la célula unido a proteínas de enlace de ADN.

climate   the current or past long-term weather conditions characteristic of a region or the entire Earth

clima   condiciones atmosféricas, actuales o pasadas, durante un largo periodo de tiempo, características de una región o de toda la Tierra

coal   a solid fossil fuel composed primarily of carbon that forms from decomposed plant materials

carbón   combustible fósil compuesto principalmente por carbón que se forma a partir de materia vegetal descompuesta

codominant allele   a version of a gene that is co-expressed with another allele in the heterozygote

alelo codominante   versión de un gen que está co-expresada con otro alelo en el heterocigoto

codon   the portion of a DNA or mRNA molecule that encodes for a specific amino acid or marks the starting or stopping of protein production

codon   parte de la molécula del ADN o del ARNm que codifica para un aminoácido específico o que marca el comienzo o el cese de la producción de proteína

coenzyme   an organic molecule that binds to an enzyme's active site to enable catalysis

coenzima   molécula orgánica que se une al sitio activo de una enzima para permitir la catálisis

commensalism   a relationship between two species of a plant, animal, or fungus in which one lives with, on, or in the other without damage to either

comensalismo   relación entre dos especies de una planta, animal u hongos en la cual uno vive en el otro sin dañarlo

community   a group of different populations that live together and interact in an environment

comunidad   grupo de poblaciones diferentes que viven juntas e interactúan en un medio ambiente

comparative morphology   comparing the structures and features of organisms to determine evolutionary relationships

morfología comparativa   comparación de estructuras y características de organismos para determinar relaciones evolutivas

competition   the interaction between organisms or species that use the same resources in which the health of one is negatively affected by the presence of the other

competencia   interacción entre organismos o especies que usan los mismos recursos en la cual la salud de uno se ve afectada de manera negativa por la presencia del otro

condensation   the process by which a gas changes into a liquid

condensación   proceso mediante el cual un gas cambia a estado líquido

conservation   the act of preserving natural resources, the environment, or other valuable commodities

conservación   acto de preservar los recursos naturales, el medio ambiente u otras cosas valiosas

continental crust   the rocks of Earth's crust that make up the base of the continents, ranging in thickness from about 35 km to 60 km under mountain ranges. Continental crust is generally less dense than oceanic crust.

corteza continental   rocas de la corteza terrestre que constituyen la base de los continentes, su espesor va desde alrededor de 35 km hasta 60 km bajo cadenas montañosas. Por lo general la corteza continental es menos densa que la corteza oceánica.

continental drift   the movement of Earth's continents relative to each other

deriva continental   movimiento de los continentes de la Tierra respecto los unos de los otros

convection   the transfer of heat from one place to another caused by movement of molecules

convección   transferencia de calor de un lugar a otro producido por el movimiento de moléculas

convergent boundary   a tectonic plate boundary at which two tectonic plates move toward each other, causing collisions and subduction zones

límite convergente   límite de una placa tectónica en el cual dos placas se mueven una hacia otra y producen colisiones y zonas de subducción

convergent evolution   a process by which two unrelated organisms will share similar features due to the similar pressures of natural selection

evolución congervente   proceso por el que dos organismos no relacionados comparten características similares debido a las presiones similares de la selección natural

core   the innermost layer of Earth, comprised of the liquid outer core and solid inner core; consists mainly of iron and nickel

núcleo   capa más interna de la Tierra, consta del núcleo externo líquido y el núcleo interno sólido; constituido principalmente por hierro y níquel

crust   the outermost rocky layer of a rocky planet or moon, which is chemically distinct from an underlying mantle

corteza   capa rocosa más externa de un planeta o luna rocoso que se distingue químicamente del manto subyacente

cryosphere   all of the solid water on Earth, including snow and ice

criósfera   toda el agua sólida de la Tierra, incluyendo nieve y hielo

cyanobacteria   phylum of photosynthetic bacteria, also called "blue-green algae"

cianobacterias   filo de bacterias fotosintéticas, también llamadas "algas azules verdosas"

cytosine   one of the four nitrogenous bases contained in a DNA molecule. Cytosine is complementary to guanine.

citosina   una de las cuatro bases nitrogenadas que forman parte de una molécula de ADN. La citosina es complementaria a la guanina.

cytoskeleton   a network of protein fibers found in eukaryotic cells

citoesqueleto   red de fibras de proteínas que se halla en las células eucariotas

cytosol   the fluid part of a cell

citosol   parte líquida de una célula

D

decomposer   organisms which carry out the process of decomposition by breaking down dead or decaying organisms

descomponedor   organismo que lleva a cabo el proceso de descomposición mediante la desintegración de los organismos muertos

density-dependent factors   environmental factors that are affected by the population density, or the number of organisms in a specific area

factores dependientes de la densidad   factores medioambientales que se ven afectados por la densidad de población o número de organismos en un área específica

density-independent factors   environmental factors that are not affected by the population size or density

factores independientes de la densidad   factores medioambientales que no se ven afectados por el tamaño de la población ni por su densidad

deposition (sedimentary)   occurs when eroded sediments are dropped in another location, ending the process of erosion

deposición (sedimentaria)   ocurre cuando los sedimentos erosionados se trasladan a otra ubicación y se quedan ahí, poniendo así fin al proceso de erosión

desert biome   a major ecological community defined by hot, arid conditions and extremely low rainfall

bioma de desierto   gran comunidad ecológica con condiciones cálidas, áridas y cantidades de lluvia extremadamente bajas

detritivore   an organism that gains nutrition by consuming decomposing plant and animal material as well as organic fecal matter

detritívoro   organismo que se nutre de materia animal y vegetal en descomposición y materias fecales orgánicas

detritus   material resulting from erosion, waste or debris resulting from biological decomposition

detritus   material producto de la erosión, desecho o residuo producto de la descomposición biológica

differential weathering   the chemical or physical weathering of rocks that occurs at different rates, producing an uneven surface in the rock layers

meteorización diferencial   meteorización química o física de las rocas que ocurre a diferentes velocidades, produciendo una superficie irregular en las capas rocosas

dihybrid cross   a cross between two organisms that are each heterozygous for two traits of interest

cruce dihíbrido   cruce entre dos organismos heterocigóticos para dos rasgos en los que se tiene interés

diploid cell   a cell that has two complete sets of chromosomes and is designated as 2n

célula diploide   célula que tiene dos grupos completos de cromosomas y se designa como 2n

directional selection   a type of natural selection where selective pressures on a species favors one phenotype to be selected

selección direccional   tipo de selección natural en la que las presiones selectivas sobre una especie favorece la selección de un fenotipo

discharge (stream)   flow of water (as from a stream, river or pipe)

descarga (corriente)   flujo de agua (de un arroyo, río o tubería)

disconformity   an unconformity in which the rock layers are parallel

disconformidad   discordancia en la cual las capas rocosas son paralelas

disruptive selection   a type of natural selection where selective pressures on a species favor extremes at both ends of the phenotypic range of traits

selección disruptiva   tipo de selección natural en la que las presiones selectivas sobre una especie favorece ambos extremos del rango fenotípico de los rasgos

divergent boundary   a tectonic plate boundary at which two tectonic plates move away from each other

límite divergente   límite de una placa tectónica en el cual dos placas tectónicas se mueven separándose una de otra

DNA   deoxyribonucleic acid; a molecule found in cells that carries genetic information to be passed from parents to offspring during reproduction

ADN   ácido desoxirribonucleico; molécula que se encuentra en las células que contienen información genética que puede pasar de progenitores a descendientes durante la reproducción

dominant allele   an allele that is fully expressed in the phenotype of a heterozygote

alelo dominante   alelo que está plenamente expresado en el fenotipo de un heterocigoto

double helix   the shape of a DNA molecule; two spiral strands wrapped around each other

hélice doble   forma de una molécula de ADN; dos hebras espirales enrolladas una alrededor de la otra

E

Earth   the third planet from the sun; the planet on which humans and other organisms live

Tierra   tercer planeta a partir del Sol; planeta en el cual vivimos los seres humanos y otros organismos

ecosystem   all the living and nonliving things in an area that interact with each other

ecosistema   todos los seres vivos y los elementos no vivos en un área que interaccionan entre sí

El Niño   1. a short period of abnormally warm temperatures across the globe caused by a band of warm ocean water that occasionally develops off the western coast of South America 2. the ocean current responsible for El Niño events

El Niño   1. periodo corto de temperaturas anormalmente cálidas en todo el planeta causadas por una banda de aguas oceánicas cálidas que se desarrolla de vez en cuando en la costa oeste de América del Sur 2. corriente oceánica responsable de El Niño

electron   a negatively charged subatomic particle that exists in various energy levels outside the nucleus of an atom

electrón   partícula subatómica con carga negativa que existe en varios niveles de energía alrededor del núcleo de un átomo

electron transport chain   a series of proteins in the mitochondrial membrane which transfer electrons to oxygen in a step-wise process which produces ATP

cadena de transporte de electrones   serie de proteínas en la membrana mitocondrial la cual transfiere electrones al oxígeno en un paso del proceso de producción de ATP

elevation   the vertical distance above sea level of a point on Earth's surface

elevación   distancia vertical sobre el nivel del mar desde un punto de la superficie terrestre

endergonic reaction   a chemical reaction in which energy is absorbed because the standard change in free energy is positive

reacción endergónica   reacción química en la cual la energía es absorbida debido a que la carga estándar en la energía libre es positiva

endocrine system   an internal system composed of several glands that secrete hormones directly into the blood that are related to growth, emotional responses, and sleep cycles among other things

sistema endocrino   sistema interno compuesto por varias glándulas que segregan hormonas directamente en la sangre; las hormonas están relacionadas con el crecimiento, las repuestas emocionales y los ciclos del sueño, entre otras cosas

endocytosis   a process in which cells take in materials by wrapping a section of plasma membrane around those materials and bringing them into the cell

endocitosis   proceso en el cual las células toman materiales envolviendo una parte de la membrana plasmática alrededor de estos materiales e introduciéndolos en la célula

endothermic   a reaction that absorbs heat from the surrounding area

endotérmico   reacción que absorbe calor de su entorno

energy   the ability to do work or cause change; can be stored in chemicals found in food and released to the organism to do work

energía   capacidad de realizar trabajo o producir un cambio; puede almacenarse en sustancias químicas que se encuentran en los alimentos y liberarse al organismo para realizar trabajo

energy pyramid   a model that shows the available amount of energy in each trophic layer in an ecosystem

pirámide de energía   modelo que muestra la cantidad disponible de energía en cada nivel trófico de un ecosistema

enzyme   proteins that catalyze specific chemical reactions in organisms by lowering the activation energy of the reaction

enzima   proteína que cataliza reacciones químicas específicas en los organismos al disminuir la energía de activación de la reacción

episodic speciation   the evolution of many new species in a relatively short period of time

especiación episódica   evolución de muchas especies nuevas en un periodo de tiempo relativamente corto

erosion   the process by which wind, water, ice, gravity, or other natural forces move sediment over Earth's surface

erosión   proceso en el cual el viento, el agua, el hielo, la gravedad u otras fuerzas naturales desplazan sedimentos sobre la superficie de la Tierra

eukaryotic cell   a type of cell with a nucleus enclosed by a membrane as well as membrane-enclosed organelles

célula eucariota   tipo de célula que tiene un núcleo dentro de una membrana y orgánulos, también dentro de membranas

eustatic (change)   alteration of global sea levels

austático (cambio)   alteración del nivel del mar global

evaporation   the process in which matter changes from a liquid to a gas

evaporación   proceso en el cual la materia cambia de estado líquido a gaseoso

evolutionary tree diagram   a diagram that depicts the evolutionary relationships between organisms

árbol filogenético   diagrama que muestra las relaciones evolutivas entre los organismos

exergonic reaction   a chemical reaction in which energy is released in the form of heat because the change in free energy is negative

reacción exergónica   reacción química en la cual la energía es liberada en forma de calor debido a que la carga estándar en la energía libre es negativa

exfoliation   a mechanical weathering process in which thin layers of rock on the outer surfaces of outcrops or other rock features break off, often creating dome-shaped patterns

exfoliación   proceso de desintegración mecánica en el cual se desprenden finas capas de roca de las superficies más exteriores de afloramientos o desintegración de otras estructuras rocosas, para crear patrones con forma de domo

exocytosis   a process in which cells expel materials within a vesicle by fusing the vesicle to the plasma membrane

exocitosis   proceso en el cual las células expulsan materiales del interior de una vesícula fusionando esta con la membrana plasmática

exotic species   a species either deliberately or accidentally introduced to a range that it is not native to

especie exótica   especie que es introducida de manera deliberada o por accidente en un entorno en el que no es nativa

exponential growth   growth of biological organisms which goes on unhindered when resources are unlimited

crecimiento exponencial   crecimiento de organismos biológicos sin obstáculos cuando los recursos son ilimitados

extinction   the permanent loss of a population or species

extinción   pérdida permanente de una población o especie

extinction rate   a measure of the frequency at which organisms become extinct

tasa de extinción   medida de la frecuencia a la que se extinguen los organismos

F

facilitated diffusion   a process in which chemicals that are unable to cross the membrane directly diffuse across the membrane through transport proteins. These proteins facilitate (or "help") the process of diffusion.

difusión facilitada   proceso en el cual las sustancias químicas que no son capaces de cruzar directamente la membrana se difunden a través de la membrana mediante proteínas transportadoras. Estas proteínas facilitan (o "ayudan") el proceso de difusión.

fat   a triester of triglycerol and fatty acids

grasa   triéster de triglicerol y ácidos grasos

feedback mechanism   the process in which part of the output of a system is returned to the input to regulate further output

mecanismo de retroalimentación   proceso en el que parte del producto de un sistema regresa al sistema para regular más productos

fermentation   conversion of carbohydrates into alcohols

fermentación   conversión de hidratos de carbono en alcoholes

fertilization   the process in which two gametes, such as an egg and sperm, unite to form a new organism, or zygote

fertilización   proceso en el cual dos gametos, como un óvulo y un espermatozoide, se unen para formar un nuevo organismo, o cigoto

food chain   a model that shows one set of feeding relationships among living things

cadena alimentaria   modelo que muestra un conjunto de relaciones alimentarias entre seres vivos

food web   a model that shows many different feeding relationships among living things in a given area

red alimentaria   modelo que muestra relaciones alimentarias muy variadas entre los seres vivos de un área determinada

fossil   the preserved remains of an organism, or traces of an organism such as a mark or print left by an animal

fósil   restos conservados de un organismo o de huellas de un organismo como marcas o huellas dejadas por un animal

fossil fuel a nonrenewable resource formed from organic carbon due to the compression and partial decomposition of organisms

combustible fósil recurso no renovable formado a partir del carbono orgánico originado por la compresión y la descomposición parcial de organismos

founder effect the loss of genetic diversity that occurs when a small number of individuals from a large population of a species establish a new population

efecto fundador pérdida de diversidad genética que ocurre cuando un pequeño número de individuos de una gran población de una especie establece una nueva población

fresh water water with a low salt concentration—usually 1% or less

agua dulce agua con una concentración baja de sal; por lo general, de menos del 1%

freshwater biome a major ecological community defined by freshwater regions that contain low salt content and experience average precipitation

bioma de agua dulce gran comunidad ecológica definida por regiones de agua dulce que contiene poca cantidad de sal y recibe precipitaciones promedio

fructose a naturally occurring monosaccharide

fructosa monosacárido natural

G

gabbro a black, mafic, coarse-grained intrusive igneous rock; the intrusive equivalent of basalt

gabro roca ígnea, intrusiva, máfica, de grano grueso y color negro; roca intrusiva equivalente del basalto

gene expression the result of coding information determined by DNA

expresión génica resultado de la codificación de información determinada por el ADN

gene therapy the introduction of cloned genes into living cells to replace an abnormal, disease-causing gene

terapia génica introducción de genes clonados en células vivas para sustituir un gen anormal causante de una enfermedad

genetic disorder an illness caused by abnormalities in genes or chromosomes

trastorno genético enfermedad producida por anormalidades en genes o cromosomas

genetic drift a random change in the allele frequency of a population over successive generations

deriva genética cambio aleatorio en la frecuencia de los alelos de una población en generaciones sucesivas

genetic testing tests that are used to predict whether a person is at risk of developing or is susceptible to a particular disease

examen genético examen que se realiza para predecir si una persona es susceptible a cierta enfermedad o si tiene riesgo de desarrollarla

genetic variation range of differences in DNA within a population or species organisms

variación genética rango de diferencias en el ADN dentro de una población o especie de organismos

genome   total of all DNA sequences in a cell or organism

genotype   the genetic code passed down from parents to offspring that determines all physical and physiological traits, also called phenotypes

geologic time   time measured on the scale of Earth's 4.56-billion-year history, as determined by the rock and fossil records

geology   the study of Earth through the study of rocks, minerals, water, and other Earth materials, as well as through seismic waves and other natural phenomena

geosphere   the combination of Earth's inner and outer core, mantle, and crust

geothermal energy   a natural, renewable energy resource produced by Earth's naturally occurring heat, steam, and hot water

glacial varve   alternating light- and dark-colored layers of sediment, deposited periodically in a glacial lake, that can be used to date annual, cyclical, or seasonal changes

glacier   a large mass of ice resting on, or overlapping, a land surface

global warming   the slow increase of Earth's average global atmospheric temperature due to climatic change

glucose   a carbohydrate; produced by photosynthesis; primary source of energy for some plant and animal cells

glycolysis   the breakdown of glucose through a series of biochemical reactions produces two molecules each of ATP, pyruvate, and NADH

genoma   total de todas las secuencias de ADN en una célula u organismo

genotipo   código genético que se transmite de los progenitores a su descendencia y que determina todos los rasgos físicos y psicológicos, también denominados fenotipos

tiempo geológico   tiempo medido en la escala de la historia de la Tierra de 4.56 mil millones de años, determinada por el estudio de rocas y registros fósiles

geología   estudio de la Tierra a través del estudio de las rocas, minerales, aguas y otros materiales terrestres y mediante el estudio de ondas sísmicas y otros fenómenos naturales

geosfera   combinación de los núcleos interno y externo de la Tierra, el manto y la corteza

energía geotérmica   recurso energético renovable producido de manera natural por la Tierra, presente en forma de calor, vapor y agua caliente

varva glacial   capas alternas de sedimentos, en colores claros y oscuros, que se depositan periódicamente en un lago glaciar, pueden usarse para datar cambios anuales, cíclicos o estacionales

glaciar   masa grande de hielo que se encuentra sobre una superficie de tierra o se superpone a ella

calentamiento global   lento aumento de la temperatura atmosférica promedio de la Tierra debido al cambio climático

glucosa   hidrato de carbono; producido por fotosíntesis; fuente primaria de energía para algunas células de animales y plantas

glicólisis   desintegración de la glucosa mediante una serie de reacciones bioquímicas produce dos moléculas de ATP, piruvato y NADH

grassland biome   a major ecological community characterized by extensive areas grasses, flowers, and herbs and an erratic precipitation that is enough to support such vegetation, but very few trees

bioma de pradera   gran comunidad ecológica caracterizada por extensas áreas de pasto, flores y hierbas; recibe precipitaciones variables suficientes para sostener la vida de este tipo de vegetación, pero muy pocos árboles

---

gravity   a force that exists between any two objects that have mass and that pulls the objects together. The greater the mass of an object, the greater its gravitational pull.

gravedad   fuerza entre dos objetos cualesquiera que tienen masa y que atrae uno hacia el otro. Cuanto mayor es la masa de un objeto, mayor es la atracción gravitacional.

---

greenhouse gas   a gas, usually carbon-based, that contributes to global warming through the greenhouse effect, which prevents the escape of radiant heat from Earth's atmosphere

gas invernadero   gas, por lo general a base de carbono, que contribuye al calentamiento global mediante el efecto invernadero, el cual impide que el calor radiante salga de la atmósfera terrestre

---

Gregor Mendel   (1822–1884) Austrian scientist and monk who is considered the founder of the science of genetics. His quantitative analysis of the inheritance of certain traits in pea plants allowed him to deduce two fundamental principles known as the laws of Mendelian

Gregor Mendel   (1822–1884) Científico y monje austriaco considerado el fundador de la ciencia de la genética. Sus análisis cuantitativos sobre la herencia de ciertos rasgos en plantas de arvejas le permitieron deducir dos principios fundamentales conocidos como leyes de Mendel

---

groundwater   water stored below Earth's surface in soil and rock layers

agua subterránea   agua almacenada bajo la superficie de la Tierra en capas de suelo y roca

---

guanine   one of the four nitrogenous bases contained in a DNA molecule; guanine is complementary to cytosine

guanina   una de las cuatro bases nitrogenadas que forman parte de una molécula de ADN; la guanina es complementaria a la citosina

H

haploid cell   a cell that contains one complete set of chromosomes and is designated as 1n

célula haploide   célula que tiene un grupo completo de cromosomas y se designa como 1n

---

Hardy-Weinberg equation $p^2 + 2pq + q^2 = 1$; The frequencies of two alleles, p and q, in a population will remain stable if no selective pressures are acting on a sufficiently large population.

ecuación de Hardy-Weinberg $p^2 + 2pq + q^2 = 1$; Las frecuencias de dos alelos, p y q, en una población permanecerán estables si no actúan presiones selectivas en una población suficientemente grande.

heart   the muscular organ of an animal that pumps blood throughout the body

corazón   órgano muscular de un animal que bombea sangre a través del cuerpo

heat energy   a form of energy that transfers between particles in a substance or system through kinetic energy transfer

energía calorífica   forma de energía que se transfiere entre partículas en una sustancia o en un sistema por medio de transferencia de energía cinética

herbivore   an animal that consumes only plants

herbívoro   animal que se alimenta solo de plantas

heterotroph   an organism that cannot synthesize its own food from simple substances

heterótrofo   organismo que no puede sintetizar su propio alimento a partir de sustancias simples

heterozygous   an organism that has two different alleles for a trait

heterocigótico   organismo que tiene dos alelos diferentes para un rasgo

homeostasis   the ability of the internal systems of an organism to maintain normal chemical balance, despite changing external conditions

homeostasis   capacidad de los sistemas internos de un organismo para mantener un equilibrio químico normal a pesar de los cambios en las condiciones externas

homology   shared ancestry of biological structures or molecules

homología   ascendencia compartida de estructuras o moléculas biológicas

homozygous   an organism that has a pair of identical alleles for a trait

homocigótico   organismo que tiene un par de alelos idénticos para un rasgo

hormone   signaling molecule produced by glands and targeting organs to maintain homeostasis

hormona   molécula de señalización producida por una glándula que se dirige hacia los órganos para mantener la homeostasis

hydroelectric energy   electricity generated by moving water flowing over a turbine

energía hidroeléctrica   electricidad generada por agua que discurre rápidamente sobre una turbina

hydrogen bond   a weak type of chemical link between a negatively charged atom and a hydrogen atom that is bonded to another negatively charged atom

enlace de hidrógeno   tipo de enlace químico débil entre un átomo con carga negativa y un átomo de hidrógeno que está enlazado con otro átomo con carga negativa

hydrolysis   a chemical weathering process resulting from the reaction between the ions of water (H^+ and OH^-) and the ions of a mineral

hidrólisis   proceso de meteorización química que es el resultado de la reacción entre los iones de agua (H^+ y OH^-) y los iones de un mineral

hydrosphere   all of the water on, under, and above Earth

hidrosfera   todo el agua existente en la Tierra, bajo ella o sobre ella

I

ice cap glaciated areas centered around geographic poles

casquete de hielo áreas glaciales que rodean a los polos geográficos

ice core a sample of ice taken by a hollow tube from a glacier or other large ice body

núcleo de hielo muestra de hielo que se toma de un glaciar o de otro gran cuerpo de hielo mediante un tubo hueco

ice wedging a type of mechanical weathering in which water gets into cracks or joints in a rock, then freezes and expands, pushing the rock apart

cuña de hielo tipo de meteorización mecánica en la cual el agua penetra en grietas o juntas en una roca, luego se congela y expande separando trozos de la roca

immune system the body's natural defense against infection and illness

sistema inmunitario defensas naturales del cuerpo contra infecciones y enfermedades

incomplete dominance a form of inheritance in which the phenotype of a heterozygote is intermediate between the phenotypes of individuals who are homozygous for each allele

dominancia incompleta forma de herencia en la cual el fenotipo de un heterocigoto es intermedio entre los fenotipos de individuos que son homocigotos para cada alelo

induced mutation changes in DNA caused by mutagens such as chemicals or radiation

mutación inducida cambios en el ADN originados por mutágenos como sustancias químicas y radiaciones

Industrial Revolution period in Western history characterized by rapid advances of technology and production

Revolución Industrial período de la historia occidental que se caracteriza por adelantos rápidos de la tecnología y la producción

inner core the solid, inner portion of Earth's core, composed of an alloy of iron, nickel, and other heavy elements; rotates within the liquid outer core

núcleo interno parte interna y sólida de la Tierra, compuesta por una aleación de hierro, níquel y otros elementos pesados; rota dentro del núcleo externo líquido

inorganic molecule any molecule that is not considered to be of a biological origin

molécula inorgánica cualquier molécula que no se considera de origen biológico

integumentary system a body system consisting of the skin, feathers, and other outer coverings of an animal that help protect the animal from external damage

sistema tegumentario sistema corporal que consiste en la piel, plumas y otras cubiertas exteriores de los animales que ayudan a proteger al animal de los daños del exterior

invertebrate an animal that does not have a backbone

invertebrado animal que no tiene columna vertebral

ion channel   regulates the flow of ions across the membrane in all cells; the flow of ions through an ion channel does not require energy

canal iónico   regula el flujo de iones a través de la membrana en todas las células; el flujo de iones a través de un canal iónico no requiere energía

ion pump   also known as an ion transporter; consumes energy to move ions across cellular membranes

bomba de iones   también conocida como transportador de iones; consume energía para mover los iones a través de membranas celulares

K

karst   limestone formation with caverns and ravines

karst   formación de piedra caliza con cavernas y barrancos

keystone species   within the ecological community, this species has a critical role in maintaining the structure of the community

especies clave   dentro de la comunidad ecológica, estas especies tienen un papel crucial en el mantenimiento de la estructura de la comunidad

kinetic energy   the energy an object has due to its motion

energía cinética   energía que tiene un objeto debido a su movimiento

L

lactose   a disaccharide formed from glucose and galactose

lactosa   disacárido formado por glucosa y galactosa

latitude   angular distance north and south of the equator

latitud   distancia angular al norte y sur del ecuador

Law of Independent Assortment   one of Mendel's laws that states each pair of alleles segregates independently of one another during the formation of gametes

ley de la recombinación independiente   una de las leyes de Mendel que establece que cada par de alelos se segregan independientemente uno del otro durante la formación de gametos

Law of Segregation   one of Mendel's laws that states that two copies of a gene will segregate so that each gamete receives only one copy

ley de la segregación   una de las leyes de Mendel que establece que dos copias de un gen se segregan para que cada gameto reciba una sola copia

lipid   a group of organic compounds that are not soluble in water, but can be dissolved by other nonpolar solvents

lípidos   grupo de compuestos orgánicos que no son solubles en agua, pero que pueden disolverse en otros solventes no polares

liquid   a state of matter with a defined volume but no defined shape and whose molecules roll past each other

líquido   estado de la materia con un volumen definido pero no forma definida y cuyas moléculas se deslizan unas sobre otras

lithosphere   the part of Earth which is composed mostly of rocks; the crust and outer mantle

litosfera   parte de la Tierra compuesta principalmente por rocas; corteza y manto exterior

logarithmic   a scale in which the logarithm of a number with a given base value is the exponent that the base must be raised to in order to obtain the number

logarítmica   escala en la cual el logaritmo de un número con una base dada es el exponente al cual hay que elevar la base para obtener el número

logistic growth   growth of biological organisms which slows as resources are depleted

crecimiento logístico   crecimiento de organismos biológicos que se desacelera cuando los recursos se agotan

lungs   organs of the respiratory system that bring oxygen-rich air into the body and send oxygen-poor air out of the body

pulmones   órganos del sistema respiratorio que traen aire rico en oxígeno al cuerpo y expulsan aire pobre en oxígeno fuera del cuerpo

M

macroevolution   large-scale evolutionary change above the species level that leads to the development or loss of many new species over time

macroevolución   cambio evolutivo a larga escala por encima del nivel de especie que conduce al desarrollo o pérdida de muchas especies nuevas con el paso del tiempo

magnetic field   a set of lines that defines the motion of charged particles near a magnet

campo magnético   conjunto de líneas que definen el movimiento de partículas cargadas cerca de un imán

mantle   the layer of solid rock between Earth's crust and core

manto   capa de roca sólida entre la corteza y el centro de la Tierra

marine biome   a major ecological community defined by abundant water, coral reefs, and estuaries which supply most of the worlds oxygen supply

bioma marino   gran comunidad ecológica definida por abundancia de agua, arrecifes de coral y estuarios; estos biomas proporcionan la mayor parte del oxígeno del mundo.

mass extinction   the loss of many species throughout the world in a short period of time

extinción masiva   pérdida de muchas especies en todo el mundo en un periodo de tiempo corto

meiosis   a form of cell division that takes place in organisms that undergo sexual reproduction. Meiosis specifically results in the formation of four haploid reproductive cells (gametes).

meiosis   forma de división celular que ocurre en organismos con reproducción sexual. La meiosis da como resultado específico la formación de cuatro células reproductivas haploides (gametos).

methane   molecule comprising one carbon atom and four hydrogen atoms

metano   molécula que tiene un átomo de carbono y cuatro átomos de hidrógeno

mid-ocean ridge   an oceanic rift zone that consists of long mountain chains with a central rift valley; divergent boundary

dorsales centro-oceánicas   zona dorsal centro-oceánica que consta de largas cadenas montañosas con una fosa tectónica central; límite divergente

Milankovitch cycle   periodic changes in Earth's climate-warming, followed by the onset of ice ages, followed by warming again; caused by irregularities in Earth's rotation and orbit

ciclo de Milankovitch   cambios periódicos en el calentamiento del clima de la Tierra seguido por un comienzo de edades de hielo, seguidas por un nuevo calentamiento; producido por irregularidades en la rotación y en la órbita de la Tierra

mineral   a naturally occurring, inorganic solid with a definite chemical composition and characteristic crystalline structure

mineral   sólido inorgánico natural con una composición química definida y una estructura cristalina característica

mitochondria   an organelle in eukaryotic cells that is the site of cellular respiration and generates most of the cell's ATP

mitocondria   orgánulo de las células eucariotas donde tiene lugar la respiración celular y donde se genera la mayor parte del ATP de la célula

mitosis   the process of cell division where one cell splits into two identical cells

mitosis   proceso de división celular en el cual la célula se divide en dos células idénticas

molecular sequences   the identity of the sequence of monomers in a polymer; the sequence of units that make up a larger molecule

secuencias moleculares   identidad de la secuencia de monómeros en un polímero; secuencia de unidades que constituye una molécula más grande

monohybrid cross   a cross between two organisms that differ with respect to a single trait

cruce monohíbrido   cruce entre dos organismos que son diferentes respecto a un solo rasgo

monosomy   the condition of having a single copy of a given chromosome

monosomía   condición de tener una sola copia de un cromosoma dado

mRNA   messenger RNA; RNA transcribed from a protein coding gene that travels to the ribosome and is translated into a protein

ARNm   ARN mensajero; ARN transcrito del código genético de una proteína que viaja al ribosoma y es traducido a proteína

multiple allele   a gene that exists in three or more alleles in a population

alelo múltiple   gen que existe en tres o más alelos en una población

muscle   an organ of the muscular system: Muscles can be either voluntary, such as a biceps, or involuntary, such as heart muscle. (related word: muscular)

músculo   órgano del sistema muscular: los músculos pueden ser voluntarios, como por ejemplo los bíceps, o involuntarios, como por ejemplo el músculo cardíaco (palabra relacionada: muscular)

---

muscular system   the body system that permits movement and locomotion in animals

sistema muscular   sistema corporal que permite el movimiento y la locomoción de los animales

---

mutation   a change in the nucleotide sequence of an organism's genome; also a change in the amino acid sequence of a protein as a result of a mutation in the gene; natural selection can act upon a mutation that results in a change in phenotype

mutación   cambio en la secuencia nucleotídica del genoma de un organismo; también un cambio en la secuencia del aminoácido de una proteína como resultado de una mutación en el gen; la selección natural puede actuar sobre una mutación que da como resultado un cambio en el fenotipo

---

mutualism   a relationship between two species of a plant, animal, or fungus in which one lives off the other and both organisms benefit

mutualismo   relación entre dos especies de una planta, animal u hongos en la cual uno vive a expensas del otro y ambos organismos obtienen beneficio

N

natural gas   a nonrenewable fossil fuel that exists in the form of a gas; like all fossil fuels, natural gas formed over many millions of years as ancient, dead organisms were gradually compressed and heated deep beneath Earth's surface

gas natural   combustible fósil no renovable que existe en forma de gas; al igual que todos los combustibles fósiles, el gas natural se formó a lo largo de muchos millones de años a partir de restos de antiguos organismos muertos que fueron sometidos a presión y calor en las profundidades de la Tierra

---

natural resource   a mineral, organic material, or fuel deposit that is currently or may become available for human use

recurso natural   depósito de mineral, materia orgánica o combustible que está disponible para el ser humano o puede estar disponible

---

natural selection   the process by which traits or alleles become more or less frequent in a population, depending on the advantage or disadvantage they confer on the survival and reproduction of the organism

selección natural   proceso mediante el cual los rasgos o alelos se hacen más o menos frecuentes en una población, dependiendo de las ventajas o desventajas que aporten para la supervivencia y la reproducción de los organismos

---

nerve   a cell of the nervous system that carries signals to the body from the brain, and from the body to the brain and/or spinal cord

nervio   célula del sistema nervioso que lleva señales al cuerpo desde el cerebro, y desde el cuerpo al cerebro y/o médula espinal

nervous system the system of the body that carries information to all parts of the body: The nervous system relies on nerve cells to move electrical signals to the body from the brain, and from the body to the brain and/or spinal cord.

neuron a cell in the nervous system responsible for sending neural messages

niche the unique physical environment occupied, and functions performed by, a species

nitrogen cycle a process in which nitrogen in the atmosphere enters the soil and becomes part of living organisms then eventually returns to the atmosphere

nonconformity an unconformity in which sedimentary rock layers overlie an erosion surface cut into igneous or metamorphic rocks

nondisjunction an error in meiosis in which a pair of chromosomes does not separate correctly during meiosis I or meiosis II

non-point source origin of pollution that is not from a single location

nonrenewable resource a natural resource of which a finite amount exists, or one which cannot be replaced with currently available technologies

nucleic acid a complex organic substance present in all living cells composed of a sugar, a base compound, and a phosphate group; includes both DNA and RNA

nucleus (cell) an organelle in eukaryotic cells that contains the cell's chromosomes

nutrients an element or compound that an organism must consume or synthesize in order to survive

sistema nervioso sistema del cuerpo que transporta información a todas las partes del cuerpo: El sistema nervioso depende de las células nerviosas para transportar señales eléctricas al cuerpo desde el cerebro y desde el cuerpo al cerebro y/o la médula espinal

neurona célula del sistema nervioso encargada de enviar los mensajes neuronales

nicho medio ambiente físico particular que ocupa y las funciones que realiza una especie

ciclo del nitrógeno proceso en el cual el nitrógeno de la atmósfera penetra en el suelo y se convierte en parte de los organismos vivos, luego, con el tiempo, regresa a la atmósfera

inconformidad discordancia en la cual las capas de rocas sedimentaria están sobre una superficie de erosión cortada en rocas ígneas o metamórficas

no disyunción error en la meiosis en el cual un par de cromosomas no se separa correctamente durante la meiosis I o la meiosis II

fuente no puntual origen de contaminación que no surge de un solo lugar

recurso no renovable recurso natural del cual existe una cantidad finita, o uno que no puede remplazarse con las tecnologías actualmente disponibles

ácido nucleico sustancia orgánica compleja que está presente en todas las células vivas, compuesta por azúcar, un compuesto base y un grupo fosfato; en ellos se incluye el ADN y el ARN

núcleo (de la célula) orgánulo en las células eucariotas que contiene los cromosomas de la célula

nutriente elemento o compuesto que un organismo debe consumir o sintetizar para sobrevivir

O

oceanic crust the portion of Earth's crust that makes up the ocean floor and is generally denser and thinner than continental crust

corteza oceánica parte de la corteza terrestre que conforma el fondo del océano y que por lo general es más densa y más fina que la corteza continental

oil a liquid fossil fuel composed primarily of carbon that forms from decomposed plant materials or algae

petróleo combustible fósil líquido compuesto principalmente por carbono que se forma a partir de materia vegetal o algas descompuestas

omnivore an animal that eats plants as well as other animals

omnívoro animal que se alimenta de plantas y de otros animales

oogenesis the process that results in the production of female gametes (eggs, or ova)

oogénesis proceso que da como resultado la producción de gametos femeninos (óvulos); también se denomina ovogénesis

organelle one of many membrane-enclosed structures that are found in the cytosol of eukaryotic cells, each with its own specific function

orgánulo una o varias estructuras encerradas en una membrana que se hallan en el citosol de las células eucariotas, cada uno de los cuales tiene una función específica

organic molecule a molecule found in or produced by living systems which contains carbon

molécula orgánica molécula que se halla en los sistemas vivos o que es producida por ellos y que contiene carbono

orogeny process of mountain formation by folding of Earth's crust

orogénesis proceso de formación de las montañas por plegamiento de la corteza de la Tierra

osmosis the diffusion of water through a selectively permeable membrane towards the side of the membrane with a higher solute concentration

ósmosis difusión de agua de manera selectiva a través de una membrana permeable hasta el otro lado de la membrana con una concentración de soluto más elevada

outer core the liquid outer portion of Earth's core, composed primarily of iron and nickel

núcleo externo parte exterior, líquida, del núcleo de la Tierra, compuesto principalmente por hierro y níquel

oxidation a chemical reaction resulting in the loss of electrons by a metal; for example, when iron rusts

oxidación reacción química que resulta de la pérdida de electrones por parte de un metal; por ejemplo, cuando el hierro se oxida

oxidizing agent the reactant that accepts electrons during an oxidation-reduction (redox) reaction

oxidante (agente oxidante) reactante que acepta electrones durante una reacción de reducción-oxidación (reacción redox)

ozone a molecule composed of three oxygen atoms (O^3)

ozono molécula compuesta por tres átomos de oxígeno (O^3)

P

paleontology the study of fossils and the fossil record

paleontología estudio de los fósiles y los registros fósiles

Pangaea the large supercontinent at the end of the Paleozoic Era consisting of all the land on Earth, including all seven continents and other landmasses

Pangea gran supercontinente al final de la Era Paleozoica que abarcaba toda la tierra de la Tierra, es decir, todos los siete continentes y las demás masas de tierra

parapatric speciation the evolution of an single population into more than one species as a result of individuals mating with their geographic neighbors rather than randomly within the population as a whole

especiación parapátrica evolución de una sola población en más de una especie como resultado de emparejamientos de los individuos con sus vecinos geográficos más bien que dentro de la misma población como un todo

parasitism a certain type of non-mutual relationship found between two different species in which one organism known as the parasite benefits at the expense of the other organism

parasitismo cierto tipo de relación no mutua que se produce entre dos especies diferentes en la que un organismo, conocido como parásito, se beneficia a expensas del otro organismo

passive transport movement of ions or molecules across a membrane down a concentration gradient ; it does not require the input of energy

transporte pasivo movimiento de iones o moléculas a través de una membrana hasta un gradiente de concentración; no requiere energía

per capita by individual persons or each individual

per cápita por persona o cada individuo

petroleum any form of naturally occurring hydrocarbons

petróleo hidrocarburo que se encuentra en la naturaleza en forma líquida

phenotype the observable traits of an individual, which are passed on from parent to offspring

fenotipo rasgo observable de un individuo que se pasa de un progenitor a su descendencia

phloem living tissue that transports nutrients to all parts of a plant

floema tejido vivo que transporta nutrientes a todas las partes de una planta

phospholipid bilayer (phospholipid membrane) a thin membrane made of two layers of phospholipids with the fatty acid chains in each layer facing towards the center of the membrane

bicapa fosfolipídica fina membrana compuesta por dos capas de fosfolípidos con las cadenas de ácidos grasos en cada capa mirando hacia el centro de la membrana

phosphorous cycle the transfer of phosphorous between the biosphere, lithosphere, and hydrosphere

ciclo del fósforo transferencia del fósforo entre la biosfera, litosfera e hidrosfera

photosynthesis   the biological process by which most plants, some algae, and some bacteria produce organic compounds for their food from water and carbon dioxide using solar energy

fotosíntesis   proceso biológico por el cual la mayoría de las plantas, algunas algas y algunas bacterias producen compuestos orgánicos que les sirven de alimento; estos compuestos los producen a partir de agua y dióxido de carbono usando la energía solar

---

phylogenetics   the study of evolutionary relationships between species and other taxonomic groups

filogenética   estudio de las relaciones evolutivas entre las especies y otros grupos taxonómicos

---

phylum   a taxonomic category between class and kingdom

filo   categoría taxonómica entre la clase y el reino

---

pioneer species   species which colonize and inhabit land which has not yet been settled; typically leads to ecological succession

especie pionera   especie que coloniza y ocupa una tierra que todavía no ha sido ocupada por otras; comúnmente conduce a una sucesión ecológica

---

plankton   small organisms that drift through bodies of water; include animals, plants, and bacteria

plancton   pequeños organismos que van a la deriva a través de los cuerpos de agua; incluye animales, plantas y bacterias

---

plant cell   a form of a eukaryotic cell that is distinct from animal cells in that it possesses a rigid cell wall, large vacuole, and chloroplasts

célula vegetal   tipo de célula eucariota que se diferencia de las células animales en que posee una pared celular rígida, una gran vacuola y cloroplastos

---

plate motion   the motion of tectonic plates, which occurs at a rate of a few centimeters per year

movimiento de placas   movimiento de las placas tectónicas que ocurre a un ritmo de pocos centímetros al año

---

plate tectonics   the theory that describes the movement and recycling of segments of Earth's crust, called tectonic plates

tectónica de placas   teoría que describe el movimiento y reciclaje de fragmentos de corteza terrestre, llamados placas tectónicas

---

point source   origin of pollution from a single location

fuente puntual   origen de la contaminación desde un solo lugar

---

polypeptide   a chain of amino acid molecules, such as a protein

polipéptido   cadena de moléculas de aminoácidos, como una proteína

---

population   the group of organisms of the same species living in the same area

población   grupo de organismos de la misma especie que viven en la misma área

---

population demographics   statistical characteristics of a population

demografía de una población   características estadísticas de una población

population density   number of individuals per unit area

densidad poblacional   número de individuos por área unitaria

potential energy   the amount of energy that is stored in an object; energy that an object has because of its position relative to other objects

energía potencial   cantidad de energía almacenada en un objeto; energía que tiene un objeto por su posición respecto a otros objetos

precipitation (crystallization)   the settling of solid particles, such as crystals, to the bottom of an aqueous solution

precipitación (cristalización)   asentamiento de partículas sólidas, como cristales en el fondo de una disolución acuosa

precipitation (weather)   the falling of liquid or frozen water droplets from clouds

precipitación (meteorología)   caída de agua líquida o congelada de las nubes

predation   a certain type of relationship primarily found between two animal species in which one hunts, kills, and feeds off the other

depredación   cierto tipo de relación que se produce principalmente entre dos especies animales en la cual una caza, mata y come a la otra como alimento

predator   an organism, usually an animal, that kills another organism for food

depredador   organismo, por lo general un animal, que mata a otro organismo para alimentarse

prey   an organism that is hunted and eaten by another organism

presa   organismo al que caza y come otro organismo

primary consumer   organisms that consume producers for energy and nutrients

consumidor primario   organismo que consume productores para obtener energía y nutrientes

primary succession   one type of biological and ecological succession that involves the growth of plant life in a newly developed area defined by rock or other minerals and either no or very little soil

sucesión primaria   tipo de sucesión biológica y ecológica que involucra el crecimiento de vida vegetal en un área de desarrollo reciente definida por rocas u otros minerales y ningún o muy poco suelo

principle of inclusions   the scientific law stating that inclusions or fragments in a rock unit are older than the rock unit itself

principio de inclusiones   ley científica que establece que las inclusiones o fragmentos dentro de una unidad rocosa son más antiguos que la propia unidad rocosa

principle of lateral continuity   the scientific law stating that sedimentary layers extend horizontally outward in all directions until they terminate

principio de la continuidad lateral   ley científica que establece que las capas sedimentarias se extienden horizontalmente hacia el exterior en todas direcciones hasta que terminan

principle of superposition   the scientific law stating that, in undisturbed rock layers, each layer is younger than the layer beneath it, and older than the layer above it

principio de superposición   ley científica que estable que, en capas de roca inalteradas, cada capa es más joven que la capa bajo ella y más antigua que la capa sobre ella

prokaryotic cell   a type of cell that is simple in structure and lacks a membrane-enclosed nucleus and membrane-enclosed organelles; they have an outer cell wall that gives them shape

célula procariota   tipo de célula de estructura simple que carece de un núcleo dentro de una membrana y orgánulos dentro de una membrana; tiene una pared celular externa que le da forma

protein   an organic molecule composed primarily of amino acids joined by peptide bonds in one or more chains; proteins function as enzymes, signaling molecules, structural molecules, and as a source of energy, among other functions

proteína   molécula orgánica compuesta principalmente por aminoácidos unidos por enlaces peptídicos en una o más cadenas; las proteínas funcionan como enzimas, moléculas señalizadoras, moléculas estructurales y fuentes de energía, entre otras funciones

R

radioactive decay   a process by which an unstable atom loses energy by emitting ionized particles over a period of time

desintegración radiactiva   proceso por el cual un átomo inestable pierde energía al emitir partículas ionizadas durante un periodo de tiempo

radioactive isotope   an isotope with an unstable nucleus, which can spontaneously decay

isótopo radiactivo   isótopo con un núcleo inestable, el cual puede desintegrarse espontáneamente

radioactivity   the spontaneous emission of radiation, which is the process in which unstable atoms break down into smaller atoms, releasing energy

radiactividad   emisión de radiación espontánea, que es el proceso en el cual un átomo inestable se divide en átomos más pequeños y libera energía

recessive allele   a genetic trait that lacks the ability to manifest itself when a dominant gene is present

alelo recesivo   rasgo genético que no tiene la capacidad de manifestarse cuando está presente un gen dominante

redox reaction   a short-hand term for an oxidation-reduction reaction, a chemical reaction that involves the transfer of one or more electrons from one species to another

reacción redox   término abreviado para reacción de reducción-oxidación; reacción química que implica la transferencia de uno o más electrones de una especie a otra

reducing agent   the reactant that donates electrons during an oxidation-reduction (redox) reaction

agente reductor   reactante que dona electrones durante una reacción de reducción-oxidación (reacción redox)

reduction a decrease in the oxidation state of an atom or molecule due to the gain of electrons

reducción disminución en el estado de oxidación de un átomo o una molécula debido a la ganancia de electrones

renewable resource a natural resource that can be replaced

recurso renovable recurso natural que puede remplazarse

replication fork Y-shaped structure that forms during the process of DNA replication; the unseparated double stranded DNA represents the base of the Y; the separated single strands are the arms of the Y

horquilla de replicación estructuras en forma de Y que se forman durante el proceso de replicación del ADN; la doble hebra de ADN no separada representa la base de la Y; las hebras simples separadas forman los brazos de la Y

respiratory system the system of the body that brings oxygen into the body and releases carbon dioxide

sistema respiratorio sistema del cuerpo que lleva oxígeno al cuerpo y libera dióxido de carbono

ribosome molecular structure that facilitates DNA translation into protein

ribosoma estructura molecular que facilita la traducción del ADN en proteína

ridge push the sliding of oceanic lithosphere downward and away from a mid-ocean ridge due to the higher elevation of the mid-ocean ridge relative to a subduction zone

empuje de las dorsales deslizamiento de la litosfera oceánica hacia abajo y alejándose de una dorsal centro-oceánica debido a la mayor elevación de la dorsal centro-oceánica respecto a la zona de subducción

rift valley a tectonic valley that forms by extensional stress which causes fracturing and the formation of normal faults

fosa tectónica valle tectónico que se forma por tensión de extensión, la cual produce la fractura y la formación de fallas normales

rift zone a divergent boundary where the crust is pulled apart

zona de fractura límite divergente en el cual la corteza terrestre se separa

RNA ribonucleic acid (RNA): one of the macromolecules that determines protein synthesis in the cell

ARN ácido ribonucleico (ARN): una de las macromoléculas que determinan la síntesis de las proteínas en las células

RNA polymerase enzyme that transcribes RNA from a DNA template

ARN-polimerasa enzima que transcribe el ARN de un molde de ADN

rock cycle the process during which rocks are formed, change, wear down, and are formed again over long periods of time

ciclo de las rocas proceso durante el cual las rocas se forman, cambian, se desgastan y se vuelven a formar a lo largo de grandes periodos de tiempo

rRNA ribosomal RNA; the RNA component of ribosomes, the site of protein synthesis.

ARNr ARN ribosómico; el componente ARN de los ribosomas, lugar de la síntesis de las proteínas

S

saccharide   organic molecule including sugars, starch and cellulose

sacárido   molécula orgánica que incluye azúcares, almidón y celulosa

scavenger   organism that feeds on the remains of other organisms

carroñero   organismo que se alimenta de los restos de otros organismos

seafloor spreading   the process by which new oceanic lithosphere forms at mid-ocean ridges as tectonic plates pull away from each other

expansión del fondo oceánico   proceso por el cual se forma nueva litosfera oceánica en las dorsales centro-oceánicas a medida que las placas tectónicas se separan una de otra

secondary consumer   an animal which feeds on primary consumers in the food chain

consumidor secundario   animal que se alimenta de consumidores primarios en la cadena alimentaria

secondary succession   one type of biological and ecological succession that involves the growth of plant life in an area that previously saw growth, but was destroyed for any reason

sucesión secundaria   tipo de sucesión biológica y ecológica que involucra el crecimiento de vida vegetal en un área en la que creció con anterioridad pero donde fue destruida por cualquier razón

sediment   solid material, moved by wind, water, and other forces, that settles on the surface of land or the bottom of a body of water

sedimento   material sólido transportado por el viento, el agua y otras fuerzas, que se asienta en la superficie de la tierra o en el fondo de un cuerpo de agua

selective permeability   property of a membrane to allow passage of specific molecules

permeabilidad selectiva   propiedad de una membrana que permite el paso de moléculas específicas

sex-linked disorders   a disorder that is determined by an alteration in the number of the X or Y sex chromosomes or by a defective gene on a sex chromosome

enfermedades ligadas al sexo   enfermedad o trastorno determinado por una alteración del número de cromosomas sexuales X o Y o por un gen defectuoso en un cromosoma sexual

sexual reproduction   the production of offspring in which two parents give rise to offspring with combinations of genes inherited from both parents via union of the gametes

reproducción sexual   producción de descendencia en la cual dos progenitores dan lugar a su descendencia con combinaciones de genes heredados de ambos progenitores mediante la unión de gametos

sexual selection   a type of natural selection where selective pressures result from the selection of mates with particular characteristics

selección sexual   tipo de selección natural en la que las presiones selectivas son el resultado de la selección de parejas con características particulares

single-gene disorders   a disorder that is the result of a defect or mutation in one gene

trastornos de un solo gen   trastorno que es el resultado de un defecto o mutación en un solo gen

skeletal system   the network of solid materials that give an organism's body its structure

sistema esquelético   red de materiales sólidos que proporcionan al cuerpo de un organismo sus estructura

slab pull   the gravitational force on dense oceanic lithosphere that forces one plate to slide beneath another

fuerza de tracción de la placa (o slab pull)   fuerza gravitacional en la densa litosfera oceánica que hace que una placa se deslice bajo otra

soil   the fertile, outermost layer of Earth's crust; composed of bits of rocks and minerals mixed with decomposing plant and animal material

suelo   capa fértil y más exterior de la Tierra; compuesta por trozos de rocas y minerales mezclados con materia animal y vegetal en descomposición

solar energy   radiant energy that comes from the sun

energía solar   energía radiante que procede del Sol

solar wind   a continuous stream of charged particles emitted by the sun which flows outward into the solar system

viento solar   corriente continua de partículas cargadas que emite el Sol la cual fluye hacia afuera, dentro del sistema solar

somatic cell nuclear transfer   a laboratory technique for creating a clonal organism by combining an egg and a donor nucleus; can be used as the first step in the process of reproductive cloning

transferencia nuclear de células somáticas   técnica de laboratorio para clonar organismos combinando un huevo u óvulo y un núcleo de un donante; puede usarse como primer paso en el proceso de clonado reproductivo

species   a group of organisms that share similar characteristics and can mate with each other to produce offspring

especie   grupo de organismos que comparten características similares y que se pueden aparear para producir descendencia

spermatogenesis   the process that results in the production of male gametes (sperm)

espermatogénesis   proceso que da como resultado la producción de gametos masculinos (espermatozoides)

spontaneous mutation   a change in DNA sequence that occurs during the process of DNA replication; an error in DNA replication

mutación espontánea   cambio en la secuencia de ADN que tiene lugar durante el proceso de replicación del ADN; error en la replicación del ADN

stabilizing selection   a type of natural selection where selective pressures favor the middle of the phenotypic range of traits

selección estabilizadora   tipo de selección natural en la que las presiones selectivas favorecen una zona media del rango fenotípico de rasgos

starch   a long-chain carbohydrate formed from glucose units joined by glycosidic bonds

almidón   larga cadena de hidrato de carbono formada por unidades de glucosa unidas mediante enlaces glucosídicos

stem   the part of a plant that grows away from the roots; supports leaves and flowers

tallo   parte de un planta que crece en dirección contraria a las raíces; da soporte a hojas y flores

steroid   organic compound with a four ring core structure

esteroide   compuesto orgánico con una estructura nuclear de cuatro anillos

sterol   a type of steroid with a hydroxyl substituent

esterol   tipo de esteroide con un hidroxilo sustituyente

stroma   the fluid portion of the chloroplast that surrounds the grana

estroma   parte líquida del cloroplasto que rodea la grana

subduction   the sinking of an oceanic plate beneath a plate of lesser density at a convergent boundary

subducción   hundimiento de una placa oceánica bajo una placa de menor densidad en un límite convergente

subduction zone   a convergent boundary where oceanic lithosphere is forced down into the asthenosphere under the lithosphere that comprises another, less dense tectonic plate

zona de subducción   límite convergente donde la litosfera oceánica es obligada a descender al interior de la astenosfera, bajo la litosfera, que comprende otras placas tectónicas menos densas

substrate   substance involved in chemical reaction

sustrato   sustancia implicada en una reacción química

substrate (biochemistry)   molecule acted upon by an enzyme

sustrato (bioquímica)   molécula sobre la que actúa una enzima

succession   the sequence of communities that develop in an area.

sucesión   secuencia de comunidades que se desarrollan en un área

sucrose   a disaccharide composed of glucose and fructose

sacarosa   disacárido compuesto por glucosa y fructosa

sunspot   a cooler darker spot on the surface of the sun

mancha solar   mancha más oscura y fría sobre la superficie del Sol

superposition   the ordering of sedimentary layers of rock with the oldest on the bottom and the youngest on top

superposición   orden de las capas sedimentarias de roca, la más antigua se encuentra en el fondo y la más joven en la parte superior

survivorship curve   a grapheither Type I, II, or IIIthat depicts either the proportion or number of people surviving at each age for a specific group or species

curva de supervivencia   gráfica de tipo I, II o III que muestra la proporción o el número de personas que sobreviven a cada edad para un grupo específico de especies

---

suspension   a heterogeneous mixture in which moderate sized particles are suspended, not dissolved, in a liquid or gas where they are supported by buoyancy

suspensión   mezcla heterogénea en la cual unas finas partículas se encuentran en suspensión, no disueltas, en un líquido o un gas en el que son soportadas por la flotabilidad

---

sustainable   describes a material or resource that is able to meet the demands of current use and yet be maintained in usable quantities to meet indefinite future demands.

sostenible   describe un material o recurso que es capaz de satisfacer las demandas de uso actual y mantenerse en cantidades utilizables para satisfacer demandas futuras indefinidas

---

sympatric speciation   the evolution of a population into a new species when two populations of the same species favor different niches in an area but mate only within their niche

especiación simpátrica   evolución de una población en nuevas especies cuando dos poblaciones de la misma especie favorecen nichos diferentes en un área pero se emparejan solo dentro de su nicho

---

system   a related set of components that react with one another that may or may not interact with the surrounding area

sistema   conjunto de componentes relacionados que reaccionan unos con otros y que pueden o no interactuar con el entorno

T

taiga biome   an ecological community that is characterized by cold weather, coniferous trees, and few food sources in winter

bioma de taiga   comunidad ecológica que se caracteriza por un clima frío, coníferas y pocas fuentes de alimentación en el invierno

---

tar pit   an accumulation of a natural, black, highly viscous mixture of hydrocarbons (called bitumen) exposed at the land surface

pozo de brea   acumulación de una mezcla natural, negra y muy viscosa de hidrocarburos (llamada bitumen) expuesta en la superficie de la tierra

---

taxonomic level   one of eight levels used by scientists to classify organisms; each species, the lowest taxonomic level, can also be classified into one of the higher levels: genus, family, order, class, phylum kingdom, domain

nivel taxonómico   uno de los ocho niveles que usan los científicos para clasificar organismos; cada especie, el nivel taxonómico más bajo, puede clasificarse a su vez en uno de los niveles superiores: género, familia, orden, clase, filo, reino, dominio

taxonomic unit   a group of organisms that are evolutionarily related, having a common ancestor; a group of organisms that all belong to the same taxonomic level (the same phyla, genus, or other taxonomic group)

technology   the use of scientific knowledge to solve problems and the devices created by this process

temperate deciduous forest biome   an ecological community that is defined by five different zones, four distinct seasons, and a mixed climate with mixed precipitation

temperature   a measure of the average kinetic energy of the atoms in a system, used to express thermal energy in degrees

tertiary consumer   a third-level consumer that feeds only on secondary consumers

The Theory of Evolution   A theory that the various species of living organisms have their origin in common ancestors and that the distinguishable differences are due to heritable modifications in successive generations

thermal energy   Thermal energy is the movement of molecules that make up the object. The molecules move faster when heated

thermodynamics   the study of effects of changes in temperature, pressure, and volume using statistics to analyze the collective motion of their particles

thylakoids   flat membrane-enclosed structures inside chloroplasts that contain chlorophyll and other pigments; they are the site for the light dependent reactions of photosynthesis

unidad taxonómica   grupo de organismos con una relación evolutiva, que tiene un antepasado común; grupo de organismos que pertenecen al mismo nivel taxonómico (el mismo filo, género u otro grupo taxonómico)

tecnología   uso del conocimiento científico para resolver problemas y los dispositivos que se crean por ese proceso

bioma de bosque templado caducifolio   comunidad ecológica que se define por cinco zonas diferentes, cuatro estaciones distintas y climas mixtos con precipitaciones mixtas

temperatura   medida del porcentaje de energía cinética de los átomos de un sistema, se usa para expresar la energía térmica en grados

consumidor terciario   consumidor de tercer nivel que se alimenta solo de consumidores secundarios

teoría de la evolución   teoría que establece que varias especies de organismos vivos tienen su origen en antepasados comunes y que las diferencias que se distinguen se deben a modificaciones heredadas en generaciones sucesivas

energía térmica   La energía térmica es el movimiento de las moléculas que conforman un objeto. Las moléculas se mueven más rápido cuando se calientan.

termodinámica   estudio de los efectos de los cambios en temperatura, presión y volumen usando la estadística para analizar el movimiento colectivo de las partículas

tilacoide   membrana plana que forma parte de las estructuras internas de los cloroplastos que contiene clorofila y otros pigmentos; es el lugar donde se llevan a cabo las reacciones de fotosíntesis que dependen de la luz

thymine one of the four nitrogenous bases contained in a DNA molecule; thymine is complementary to adenine

timina una de las cuatro bases nitrogenadas que forman parte de una molécula de ADN; la timina es complementaria a la adenina

tidal energy a form of hydroelectric energy which converts the energy of ocean tides into electricity

energía mareomotriz forma de energía hidroeléctrica que convierte la energía de las mareas oceánicas en electricidad

topography the physical features which define the relief of a landscape, such as mountains, valleys, and the shapes of landforms

topografía características físicas que definen el relieve de un lugar, como montañas, valles y la forma de los accidentes geográficos

topsoil the organic-rich, dark-colored soil on the surface of an area, defined as the A horizon

mantillo suelo de color oscuro y rico en elementos orgánicos que se halla en la superficie de un área, definido como horizonte A

trace fossil fossilized evidence of plant existence or animal movements such as root channels, footprints, and burrows

traza fósil evidencia fosilizada de la existencia de plantas o movimientos de animales, como canales de raíces, huellas de pies y madrigueras

transcription the process of synthesizing RNA from a DNA template

transcripción proceso de síntesis del ARN de un molde de ADN

transform boundary a tectonic plate boundary along which plates slide horizontally past one another in opposite directions

límite transformante límite de placas tectónicas a lo largo de la cual las placas se deslizan horizontalmente una junto a otra en direcciones opuestas

translation the process of building a protein based on a RNA template

traducción proceso por el cual se construye una proteína basada en un molde de ARN

transport the movement of materials

trasporte movimiento de materiales

tree ring a concentric layer of wood that a tree adds to its trunk and branches in one year; each successive ring represents a year of the tree's life

anillo de árbol capa de madera concéntrica que un árbol añade a su tronco y a sus ramas en un año; cada anillo sucesivo representa un año de la vida del árbol

trisomy a type of aneuploidy in which there are three copies of a particular chromosome

trisomía tipo de aneuploidía en la cual hay tres copias de un cromosoma particular

tRNA   transfer ribonucleic acid; tRNA transfers amino acids to a growing protein chain during protein synthesis; different tRNA molecules have different anticodons and carry amino acids specific to their anticodon

ARNt   ácido ribonucleico de transferencia; el ARNt transfiere aminoácidos a una cadena de proteínas en crecimiento durante la síntesis de proteínas; diferentes moléculas de ARNt tienen diferentes anticodones y llevan aminoácidos específicos a su anticodón

trophic level   the position an organism occupies at each level of the food chain

nivel trófico   posición que ocupa un organismo en cada nivel de la cadena alimentaria

tropical biome   an ecological community that is defined by year-round warmth and significant rainfall

bioma tropical   comunidad ecológica definida por temperaturas cálidas y lluvias significativas a lo largo de todo el año

tundra biome   an ecological community that is defined by stark, treeless land, and very cold temperatures

bioma de tundra   comunidad ecológica definida por tierras inhóspitas y sin árboles y temperaturas muy frías

U

unconformity   a gap (or break) in the rock record where younger rocks are separated from older rocks with intervening periods of deposition completely missing

discordancia   interrupción en el registro de la roca en la cual las rocas más jóvenes están separadas de las más antiguas con periodos intermedios de deposición completamente perdidos

uracil   a nitrogenous (nitrogen containing) base found in RNA

uracilo   base nitrogenada (que contiene nitrógeno) que se halla en el ARN

V

vein   a blood vessel that moves blood towards the heart

vena   vaso sanguíneo que transporta la sangre hacia el corazón

vertebrate   an animal with a backbone

vertebrado   animal con columna vertebral

W

water   a molecule that contains two hydrogen atoms and one oxygen atom; often called "the universal solvent"

agua   molécula que contiene dos átomos de hidrógeno y un átomo de oxígeno; con frecuencia se le llama "el solvente universal"

water cycle   the continual movement of water between the land, ocean, and the air through predictable physical processes

ciclo del agua   movimiento continuo del agua entre la tierra, el océano y el aire mediante procesos físicos predecibles

weathering   the physical or chemical breakdown of rocks and minerals into smaller pieces or aqueous solutions on Earth's surface

meteorización   desintegración física o química de rocas y minerales en trozos más pequeños o en soluciones acuosas en la superficie de la Tierra

weathering (physical)   the breaking down of rock into smaller pieces by the action of wind, rain, and temperature change

meteorización (física)   desintegración de las rocas en pequeños trozos por la acción del viento, de la lluvia y del cambio de temperatura

wind energy   electricity generated by turbines rotated by wind

energía eólica   electricidad generada por turbinas que hace girar el viento

X

xylem   plant tissue that transports water upwards from the roots and also transports some nutrients

xilema   tejido vegetal que transporta agua hacia arriba, desde las raíces, también transporta algunos nutrientes

INDEX